Apollo 7

The NASA Mission Reports

Compiled from the NASA archives & Edited
by Robert Godwin

All rights reserved under article two of the Berne Copyright Convention (1971).
We acknowledge the financial support of the Government of Canada through the
Book Publishing Industry Development Program for our publishing activities.
Published by Apogee Books an imprint of Collector's Guide Publishing Inc., Box 62034, Burlington, Ontario, Canada, L7R 4K2
Printed and bound in Canada by Webcom Ltd of Toronto
Apollo 7 - The NASA Mission Reports
by Robert Godwin
ISBN 1-896522-64-5
©2000
All photos courtesy of NASA

Introduction

As the first successful test of America's lunar spacecraft, the importance of the flight of Apollo 7 is undeniable.

On January 27th 1967 a catastrophic failure of the Apollo command module during a routine training exercise claimed the lives of the Apollo 1 prime crew. Gus Grissom, Ed White and Roger Chaffee didn't stand a chance when the over-pressurized pure oxygen atmosphere inside the spacecraft played catalyst to an explosive fire. The blaze swept through the vehicle in 15 seconds.

The resulting investigation revealed not only a myriad of problems in the design of Apollo, but also highlighted the fact that even a routine test could be fatal.

More than 1800 changes to the Command Module were subsequently recommended and over 1300 were implemented.

The crew of Apollo 7 were Commander Wally Schirra, Command Module Pilot Donn Eisele and Lunar Module Pilot Walt Cunningham, they had been selected to get America's space program back on track. In the process they had to learn how to fly the revamped (and so-called) "Block 2" spacecraft.

Wally Schirra would be the first man to fly three times in space, he would also become the only man to fly Mercury, Gemini and Apollo. Schirra was known for his gregarious and outgoing character but he was also known to be cautious. When it came time to fly the completely overhauled Apollo spacecraft, Schirra was not one for taking chances. He would make certain that the new spacecraft and booster "rang true" before risking his crew.

Another achievement which could be chalked up to Apollo 7 was the first successful manned launch of von Braun's Saturn IB rocket. The latest in the Saturn series, the S-IB had been successfully flown unmanned, but a new spacecraft on top of a new rocket presented a host of new obstacles to surmount. As with the entire Saturn family, the heavy-lifter performed flawlessly for Apollo 7, beginning a five-for-five success record which culminated in 1975 with the joint US-Soviet Apollo-Soyuz mission. The Saturn IB would ultimately be used for almost every manned Apollo flight that did not require a Lunar Module.

The mission objectives of Apollo 7 seem deceptively simple. In essence, the flight plan required that the vehicle remain in space for the amount of time it would take to get to the moon. Meanwhile the crew would analyse every single system to see how they reacted in space.

As with any first test flight, the crew are expected to look for hardware and procedural errors and then report back recommendations. This may seem relatively simple but it is worth considering that in 1968 Apollo was the most complex piece of machinery constructed anywhere in the world. Flight testing an Apollo could easily shape up to be not only an arduous task but also a hazardous one.

As you will see in the pages of this book, every single circuit and system was scrutinized and its performance documented. Schirra, Eisele and Cunningham were obliged to understand, operate and diagnose every facet of the vehicle.

The crew of Apollo 7 would perform a whole string of firsts. They were the first to feel the sudden explosive thrust of the Service Module's hypergolic-propelled motor and to flight test its restart capability. The engine had to survive what was known as "cold soak" and then still be called upon to restart reliably, ultimately propelling later Apollos in and out of lunar orbit.

Schirra, Eisele and Cunningham had to work with everything from cranky cameras to hydrogenated drinking water, from fuzzy navigational instruments to doing the first "live" tests of the Apollo parachute system. They also had to deal with experimental cuisine, while simultaneously fighting off colds, *and* hosting the first live TV broadcast from space.

Another test objective was to determine whether the Apollo Command and Service Module could be successfully flown to a rendezvous with the Saturn IV-B. On future Apollo flights the Lunar Module would be stowed inside the S-IVB and it would have to be retrieved if a lunar landing was to be achieved. It was up to the crew of Apollo 7 to be the first to attempt this difficult and potentially dangerous maneuver.

For Eisele and Cunningham, Apollo 7 would be their first and last trip into space. For the veteran Schirra, commanding the first successful flight of Apollo was a fitting final feather in his astronaut cap.

When the three men completed their ten day voyage by splashing down in the Atlantic ocean only one mile from the designated landing area, they had wrung every last drop of information out of the machine. Their success persuasively paid tribute to the sacrifice made by the crew of Apollo 1 and restored confidence in the NASA team to push on towards their ultimate goal.

Robert Godwin
(Editor)

(Editor's note: Many of the illustrations included in the Apollo 7 Press Kit are repeated in the Pre-flight Mission Operation Report. In the interests of avoiding redundancy I have reproduced them in their appropriate positions but have reduced some of them significantly in size.)

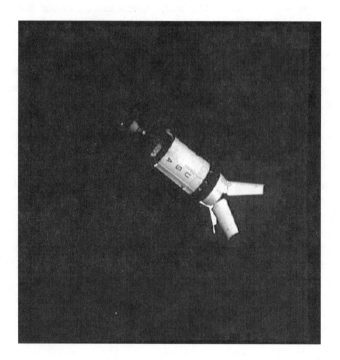

Apollo 7

The NASA Mission Reports

(from the archives of the National Aeronautics and Space Administration)

CONTENTS

Apollo 7 Press Kit Index

FIRST MANNED APOLLO	10
MISSION OBJECTIVES	11
MISSION DESCRIPTION	12
FLIGHT PLAN	18
ALTERNATE MISSIONS	19
EXPERIMENTS	22
ABORT MODES	22
SPACECRAFT STRUCTURE SYSTEMS	23
THE SATURN IB LAUNCH VEHICLE	30
FLIGHT SEQUENCE	32
LAUNCH PREPARATIONS	33
LAUNCH COMPLEX 34	35
MISSION CONTROL CENTER HOUSTON	37
MANNED SPACE FLIGHT NETWORK	38
PHOTOGRAPHIC EQUIPMENT	42
CREW BIOGRAPHIES	50
APOLLO 7 TEST PROGRAM	53
APOLLO CONTRACTORS	56
APOLLO PROGRAM OFFICIALS	57

Pre Launch Mission Operation Report

General	61
Program Development	61
The Apollo 7 Mission	62
NASA Mission Objectives for Apollo 7	64
Primary Objectives	64
Detailed Test Objectives	64
Launch Vehicle	64
Spacecraft	64
Secondary Objectives	66
Launch Vehicle	66
Spacecraft	66
Safety Planning	66
General	66
Pre-Launch Procedures	67
Range Safety	67
Launch Countdown and Turnaround Capability AS-205	67
Scrub Turnaround	67
Turnaround Conditions vs Time	67
Post LV Cryo Load (SC Cryo Reservicing)	67
Post LV Cryo Load (No SC Cryo Reservicing)	67
Pre LV Cryo Load (SC Cryo Reservicing)	68
Pre LV Cryo Load (No SC Reservicing)	68
Detailed Flight Mission Description	68
Nominal Mission	68
Pre-Launch	68
Launch and Parking Orbit	68
S-IVB/CSM Separation	69
CSM/S-IVB Rendezvous	69
Terminal Phase Initiation	70
CSM Operations	70
De-Orbit Maneuver	71
Re-Entry and Landing	71
Contingency Operations	71
Aborts	72
Alternate Missions	76
Space Vehicle Description	77
Launch Vehicle Description	78
First Stage (S-IB)	78
Second Stage (S-IVB)	78
Instrument Unit (IU)	79
Spacecraft Description	80
Safety Considerations	80
Launch Escape Assembly	80
Command Module (CM)	81
Service Module (SM)	85
Command/Service Module Systems	85
Spacecraft Lunar Module Adapter (SLA)	87
Significant Configuration Changes from Block I Spacecraft	87
Human System Provisions	88
AS-205 Space Suits Major Changes Subsequent to AS-204 Fire	88
Flight Apparel and Related Equipment	88
Bio-Instrumentation System	90

Medical Activities	91
Medical Kit	91
Crew Personal Hygiene	91
Body Cleanliness	91
Waste Management	91
Crew Meals	91
Oxygen Masks	92
Post Landing Ventilation Ducts	92
Survival Equipment	92
Launch Complex	92
Mission Support	94
Launch Control Center	94
Mission Control Center	94
Communications, Command & Telemetry System	95
Real-Time Computer Complex (RTCC)	95
Voice Communication System	96
Display Control System	96
Mission Operations Control Room	96
Staff Support Rooms (SSR)	97
Recovery Control Room	97
Manned Space Flight Network (MSFN)	97
MSFN Interfaces	97
Recovery Operations	99
Apollo 7 Recovery	101
Launch Site Area	101
Launch Abort Areas	101
Primary Landing Area	101
Secondary Landing Area	101
Contingency Landing Area	101
Flight Crew	101
General	101
Flight Crew Assignments	107
Prime Crew Biographical Data	108
Backup Crew Biographical Data	110
Mission Management Responsibility	111
Program Management	112
List of Abbreviations	112

LIST OF FIGURES

Figure	Title	
1	Apollo Space Vehicle	62
2	Nominal Mission Profile-Apollo 7	63
3	CSM/S-IVB Rendezvous Relative Positions	70
4	Apollo 7 Summary Flight Plan	73
5	Orbital Events Ground Track	74
6	AS-205 Space Vehicle	78
7	Saturn IB 1st Stage (S-IB)	79
8	Saturn IB 2nd Stage (S-IVB)	79
9	Instrument Unit (IU)	79
10	Apollo 7 Spacecraft Configuration	80
11	Launch Escape Assembly (LEA)	81
12	Block II Command Module	82
13	CSM-101 Couch Installation	82
14	Crew Couch Positions	83
15	CM Side Access Hatch	84
16	Service Module (Block II)	86
17	Space Suits	89
18	Apollo Survival Kit and Components	92
19	Launch Complex 34	93
20	Space Vehicle and Umbilical Tower	93
21	MCC Functional Configuration	95
22	Apollo Launch/Orbital NASCOM Network	100
23	Apollo 7 Recovery Zones, Contingency Areas and Aircraft Staging Bases	102
24	Launch Site Area and Force Deployment	104
25	Apollo 7 Launch Abort Areas and Force Deployment	105
26	Primary Landing Area and Recommended Force Deployment	106
27	Prime Flight Crew	107
28	Backup Flight Crew	108

LIST OF TABLES

Table	Title	
1	Launch Countdown Sequence of Events	68
2	Apollo 7 Mission Sequence of Events Launch Phase	69
3	Apollo 7 Mission Sequence of Events	

	Insertion to Splashdown	71
4	DTO Accomplishment for the Apollo 7	
	Alternate Missions	76
5	AS-205 Space Vehicle Weight Summary	78
6	Network Configuration for the Apollo 7 Mission	98
7	MSFN Mobile Facilities	99
8	Formal Flight Crew Training Time Apollo 7	106

Post Launch Mission Operation Report

GENERAL	115
PRIMARY OBJECTIVES	116
RESULTS OF APOLLO 7 MISSION	116
COUNTDOWN	116
FLIGHT SUMMARY	116
LAUNCH VEHICLE	118
1ST STAGE	118
2ND STAGE	118
INSTRUMENT UNIT & OTHER SYSTEMS	118
SPACECRAFT	118
STRUCTURES	118
PROPULSION	118
ELECTRICAL POWER SYSTEM	120
THERMAL CONTROL	121
CRYOGENICS	121
COMMUNICATIONS	121
ENVIRONMENTAL CONTROL SYSTEM	121
EARTH LANDING SYSTEM	122
INSTRUMENTATION	122
FLIGHT CREW	122
CREW PROVISIONS	122
CREW PERFORMANCE	123
MISSION SUPPORT	123
FLIGHT CONTROL	123
NETWORK	123
RECOVERY	123
LAUNCH COMPLEX	124

Tables

1 Summary Of Mission Events	117
2 Orbital Maneuvers	119

Technical Debriefing

PART ONE

PRE-INGRESS	126
1.0 COUNTDOWN	127
1.2 Prime Ingress and Status Check	127
1.2.1 SECS Pyro	127
1.2.2 Suit Connections	127
1.2.3 Comm Verification	127
1.2.4 PGA Circuit Check	127
1.2.5 Cabin Closeout	127
1.2.6 EDS	128
1.2.7 The RCS Check	128
1.2.8 G & C Verification	128
1.2.9 Launch Preparation	128
1.2.10 Systems Prep	131
1.2.11 Crew Comfort	131
1.2.12 Crew Station Controls and Displays	131
1.2.13 Distinction of Sounds Countdown to Lift Off	131
1.2.14 Vehicle Sway Prior to Ignition	131
2.0 POWERED FLIGHT	132
2.1 S-IB Ignition	132
2.2 Lift-Off	132
2.3 L/V Lights	132
2.4 Roll Program	132
2.5 Pitch Program	132
2.6 Roll Complete	132
2.7 Rate Change	132
2.8 Effect at Mach 1 Transient	132
2.9 Max Q	132
2.10 EDS Manual	·134
2.11 GO/NO-GO for Staging	134
2.12 Inboard Cut-Off	134
2.13 Outboard Cut-Off	134
2.14 S-IB/S-IVB Sep	134

2.15 S-IVB Engine Ignition	134
2.16 S-IVB Plume	134
2.17 Scale Change	135
2.18 Distinction of Sounds	135
2.19 Trajectory GO/NO-GO	135
2.20 LET and BPC Jettison	135
2.21 Guidance - Initiate	136
3.1.8 CSM Systems Checkout	136
3.1.9 SXT Calibration Test	138
3.1.10 COAS Calibration	140
3.1.11 S-IVB Ventilation	140
3.2 Rendezvous	140
3.2.1 IMU Orientation and Alignment	140
3.2.2 AUTO Maneuver-To-Burn Attitude	140
3.2.3 SPS Burn 1	140
3.2.4 SPS Burn 2	142
3.2.5 TPI Burn (RCS)	142
3.2.6 Thrust Monitor (LOS Control)	143
3.3 Post-rendezvous Through Deorbit Burn	145
3.3.1 S-IVB Post-rendezvous Tracking at 80, 160, and 320 NM	145
3.3.2 SCT Star Count Test	145
3.3.3 S005, S006 Photography	147
4.0 REENTRY	153
4.1 CM/SM Separation	153
4.2 Reentry Parameters	153
4.4 Attitude Control Mode	158
4.5 Guidance	161
4.6 Visual Sighting and Oscillation	162
4.7 Drogue Chute Deployment	165
4.8 Main Chute Deployment	166
4.9 Communications	167
4.10 ECS	167
5.0 LANDING AND RECOVERY	167
5.1 Impact on Touchdown	167
5.2 Postlanding Checklist	167
5.4 Spacecraft Status	168
5.5 Battery Power	170
6.5 Electrical Power	171
6.5.1 Fuel Cells	171

PART TWO

2.24 SECO 1	
2.25 Orbital GO/NO-GO	176
2.26 Communications	176
2.27 Control and Displays	176
2.28 Crew Comfort	176
3.0 Orbital Operations	177
3.1 Insertion Through COAS Calibration	177
3.1.1 CSM/S-IVB Orbital Operations	177
3.1.2 S-IVB Safing	177
3.1.3 S-IVB Take-Over Demonstration	178
3.1.4 Return to S-IVB Auto Control	178
3.1.5 Separation Transposition and Simulated Docking	178
3.1.6 SLA Photography	178
3.1.7 RCS Phasing	180
3.1.8 CSM Systems Checkout	180
3.1.9 Sextant Calibration Test	180
3.1.11 S-IVB Ventilation	180
3.2 Rendezvous	180
3.2.7 Braking	180
3.2.8 Rendezvous Navigation	181
3.2.9 Formation	181
3.2.10 Final Separation Burn	181
3.2.11 S-IVB Activity	182
3.3 Post-rendezvous Through Deorbit	182
3.3.5 Sextant Tracking	182
3.3.6 SPS Burn Number 3	182
3.3.7 Slosh Damping Test	182
3.3.8 ECS Radiator Test	182
3.3.9 Midcourse Navigation	183
3.3.10 Cryogenic Stratification Test	184
3.3.11 SPS Burn Number 4	184
3.3.12 SPS Cold Soak	184
3.3.13 SPS Burn Number 5	185
3.3.14 Passive Thermal Control Test	186
3.3.15 Window Photography	186
3.3.16 ECS Secondary Coolant Loop Test	187
3.3.17 SCS Backup Align	187

3.3.18	SPS Burns Numbers 6 and 7	188
3.3.20	SXT Calibration	188
3.3.21	PIPA Bias and EMS Bias Test	188
3.4.17	SPS Propellant Thermal Control	188
3.4.18	Auxiliary Propellant Gauging System	188
3.4.26	SCS Backup Alignment Procedure	189
3.4.29	Launch Vehicle Propellant Pressure Displays	189
3.4.30	Window Deposits	189
3.4.31	Manual Retro Attitude Orientation	189
3.4.33	CSM ARIA Communications	189
3.4.34	CSM Structural Performance	189
3.4.35	Crew Activities	190
5.0	Landing and Recovery	190
5.1	Impact on Touchdown	190
5.2	Postlanding Checklist	192
5.3	Communications	194
5.4	Spacecraft Status	195
5.5	Battery Power	195
5.6	Postlanding ECS System	195
5.7	Ventilation	195
5.8	Internal Temperature	195
5.9	Spacecraft Attitude	195
5.10	Couch Position	196
5.11	Internal Pressure	196
5.12	Recovery Operations	196
5.13	Grappling Hook Deployment	196
5.14	Egress	197
5.16	Crew Pickup	198
6.0	Systems Operation	198
6.1	Guidance and Navigation	198
6.1.1	ISS Modes	198
6.1.2	Optical Subsystems	199
6.1.3	Computer Subsystem	199
6.1.4	Rendezvous Radar Modes and Programs	201
6.1.5	G&N Controls and Displays	202
6.1.6	Procedural Data	203
6.2	Stabilization and Control	203
6.2.1	Control	204
6.3	Service Propulsion	204
6.3.1	DELTA-V Thrust Switches	204
6.3.2	Engine Thrust Vector Alignment	204
6.3.3	DELTA-V Remaining Counter and Thumbwheel	204
6.3.4	SPS Thrust Direct Arm Switch	204
6.3.5	Direct Ullage Button	204
6.3.6	Thrust On Button	204
6.3.7	SPS PC Indicator	204
6.4	Reactor Control	204
6.4.1	SM/RCS	204
6.4.2	CM/RCS	204
6.5	Electrical Power	204
6.5.2	Battery Charger Switch	206
6.5.3	DC Monitor or Group	207
6.5.4	AC Monitor or Group	207
6.5.5	AC Inverters	208
6.5.6	Main Bus Tie Switches	208
6.5.7	NON ESS Bus Switch	208
6.5.9	G&N Power System	209
6.5.11	Cryogenic System	209
6.6	Environmental Control	213
6.6.1	Oxygen Subsystem	213
6.6.2	Water Supply System	217
6.6.3	Water-Glycol System	219
6.6.4	Suit Circuit	221
6.6.5	Gauging System	223
6.6.6	Waste Management System	223
	Dew-Point Hygrometer	226
6.7	Telecommunications	226
6.7.1	Monitoring	226
6.7.2	Audio Center Controls	227
6.7.3	VHF	228
6.7.6	S-band	229
6.7.8	Power Switches	230
6.7.9	Telemetry Switches	230
6.7.10	Flight Quality Recorder	230
6.7.11	Voice Record Indicator	230
6.7.12	PTT Switches	230
6.7.13	VOX Circuitry	230
6.7.14	The USB Emergency Keying	230
6.7.15	ISE Storage	230
6.8	Miscellaneous Systems and GFE	231
6.8.1	Cabin Lighting System and Controls	231
6.8.2	Clocks	232
6.8.3	Event Timers and Controls	233
6.8.4	Accelerometer Indicator	233
6.8.5	Electrical Cables and Adapters	233
6.8.6	Crew Compartment Configuration	235
6.8.7	Mirrors	236
6.8.8	COAS	237
6.8.9	Clothing	239
6.8.10	PGA Connecting Equipment	243
6.8.11	Crew Couches	244
6.8.12	Restraints	244
6.8.13	Flight Data Files	246
6.8.14	Inflight Tool Set and Worksheet	247
6.8.15	Food	247
6.8.16	Personal Hygiene Equipment	249
7.3	Visual Sightings in Orbit	251
8.0	EXPERIMENTS	251
8.2	Synoptic Weather Photography	252
8.5	Lower Body Negative Pressure	252
9.0	PREMISSION PLANNING	253
9.4	Mission Rules	253
10.0	MISSION CONTROL	255
10.1	GO/NO-GO's	256
10.2	PTP and ATP Updates	256
10.3	Consumables	256
10.4	Flight Plan Changes	257
10.5	Real Time Scheduling	259
11.0	TRAINING	259
11.1	CMS	259
11.2	The DCPS	260
11.3	CMPS	260
11.4	North American Evaluator	261
11.5	Egress Training	261
11.6	Planetarium	262
11.7	MIT	262
11.8	Systems Briefing	263
11.9	Experiments	265
11.10	Spacecraft Systems test	265
11.11	Launch Simulations	266
11.12	Reentry Simulations	266
11.13	Sim Net Sim	266
11.14	Mockups	267
11.16	Sextant training equipment	267
11.16	Planning of Training	267

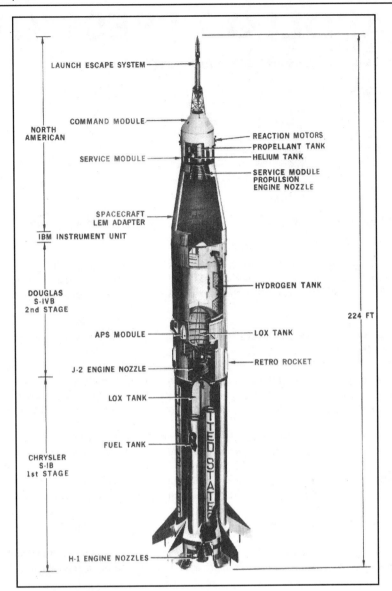

- LAUNCH ESCAPE SYSTEM
- COMMAND MODULE
- REACTION MOTORS
- PROPELLANT TANK
- SERVICE MODULE
- HELIUM TANK
- SERVICE MODULE PROPULSION ENGINE NOZZLE
- NORTH AMERICAN
- SPACECRAFT LEM ADAPTER
- IBM INSTRUMENT UNIT
- HYDROGEN TANK
- DOUGLAS S-IVB 2nd STAGE
- APS MODULE
- LOX TANK
- J-2 ENGINE NOZZLE
- RETRO ROCKET
- LOX TANK
- FUEL TANK
- CHRYSLER S-IB 1st STAGE
- H-1 ENGINE NOZZLES

224 FT

UNITED STATES

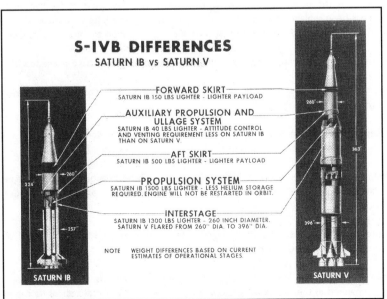

S-IVB DIFFERENCES
SATURN IB vs SATURN V

FORWARD SKIRT
SATURN IB 150 LBS LIGHTER - LIGHTER PAYLOAD

AUXILIARY PROPULSION AND ULLAGE SYSTEM
SATURN IB 40 LBS LIGHTER - ATTITUDE CONTROL AND VENTING REQUIREMENT LESS ON SATURN IB THAN ON SATURN V.

AFT SKIRT
SATURN IB 500 LBS LIGHTER - LIGHTER PAYLOAD

PROPULSION SYSTEM
SATURN IB 1500 LBS LIGHTER - LESS HELIUM STORAGE REQUIRED. ENGINE WILL NOT BE RESTARTED IN ORBIT.

INTERSTAGE
SATURN IB 1300 LBS LIGHTER - 260 INCH DIAMETER. SATURN V FLARED FROM 260" DIA. TO 396" DIA.

NOTE   WEIGHT DIFFERENCES BASED ON CURRENT ESTIMATES OF OPERATIONAL STAGES.

SATURN IB   224'   260"   257"

SATURN V   260"   363'   396"

APOLLO 7 PRESS KIT

NATIONAL AERONAUTICS AND SPACE ADMINISTRATION
WASHINGTON, D.C. 20546
TELS. WO 2-4155 WO 3-6925

NEWS
FOR RELEASE: SUNDAY
October 6, 1968
RELEASE N0: 68-168

FIRST MANNED APOLLO

Apollo 7, the first manned flight in the lunar landing program, will be launched into an Earth orbit Oct. 11 at Cape Kennedy, Fla.

Apollo 7 is an engineering test flight with crewmen Walter M. Schirra, Jr., commander; Donn F. Eisele, command module pilot; and Walter Cunningham, lunar module pilot. (The LM will not be flown on Apollo 7.) Launch will be made on a Saturn IB rocket from Launch Complex 34 at the National Aeronautics and Space Administration's Kennedy Space Center.

A TV camera will be carried on Apollo 7 and live TV pictures will be transmitted to two U.S. ground stations at various times during the mission.

An open-ended mission up to 11 days is planned, but success can be achieved with less than a full-duration flight. Mission sequences are planned to gather the most important data early in the flight. In addition, spacecraft instrumentation is designed to identify systems problems so that they can be analyzed and, if necessary, fixed before subsequent flights.

Combined operation of the Saturn IB launch vehicle, the Apollo command and service modules, and the Manned Space Flight Network during a manned orbital mission will be examined. Unmanned operation in space has been demonstrated.

The Apollo program's forerunners, Mercury and Gemini, provided invaluable operational experience, especially development of rendezvous techniques and knowledge of human and spacecraft performance in space up to two weeks.

Apollo is much more complex than its predecessor Gemini, and is capable of operating at lunar distance.

Apollo 7 is the first of several manned flights aimed at qualifying the spacecraft for the half-million-mile round trip to the Moon. Earlier flights have yielded all the spacecraft information possible without a crew aboard.

The Apollo 7 spacecraft is the product of extensive redesign in the past year and a half. For example, the original two-piece side hatch has been replaced by a quick-opening, one-piece hatch. Extensive materials substitution has reduced flammability within the command module, and systems redundancy has been expanded to reduce single failure points.

This Saturn IB launch vehicle is different from the four unmanned rockets that have preceded it:

* The amount of telemetry and instrumentation equipment has been reduced. This lowers vehicle weight and increases its payload capability;

* New propellant lines to the augmented spark igniter (ASI) on the J-2 engine of the second stage have been installed to prevent early shutdown as occurred on Apollo 6;

* One important event scheduled for the flight is the launch vehicle propellant dump that begins about 1 hour 34 minutes after launch. Dumping all remaining propellants will make the stage safe for rendezvous with the Apollo command service module later in the mission.

About 2.5 hours after launch, the astronauts will begin a 25-minute period of manual control of the vehicle from the spacecraft. Then the spacecraft will be separated from the second stage.

The flight of Apollo 7 is the culmination of exacting structural and systems testing on the ground and in space. A spacecraft is flown unmanned in the first few development missions, but the real test of its capability comes when it is checked out in space with men at the controls — the condition for which it was designed and built.

Apollo 7 will be inserted into a 123-by-153 nautical mile (142 by 176 statute miles, 228 by 284 kilometers) orbit by the launch vehicle's second stage (S-IVB). Spacecraft systems checkout will be the principal activity in the first two revolutions.

Near the end of the second revolution, the crew will separate the spacecraft from the second stage and perform a simulated transposition and docking maneuver, using the spacecraft lunar module adapter attached to the second stage as a target.

Extensive operational checkouts of the environmental control, guidance and navigation, and service propulsion systems will occupy the crew for the next several revolutions. Included will be one of the mission's secondary objectives, rendezvous with the S-IVB approximately 30 hours after liftoff.

Crew activities, systems performance, and ground support facilities will be evaluated in the remainder of the mission. Five additional burns of the service propulsion system are scheduled in that period to further evaluate the service propulsion system and spacecraft guidance modes.

Ten days 21 hours after liftoff, the crew will fire the service propulsion system to deorbit the spacecraft, using the command module guidance and navigation system for control. They will control the spacecraft manually during entry after separation from the service module, using the guidance system as a reference.

Landing is planned in the Atlantic Ocean about 200 nautical miles (230 statute miles, 3,70 kilometers) south-southwest of Bermuda at the end of the 164th revolution. The aircraft carrier U.S.S. Essex will be the prime recovery ship.

MISSION OBJECTIVES

Most of the critical tests of spacecraft systems necessary for "wringing out" a new generation of spacecraft take place early in the Apollo 7 flight. The mission has been designed to gather much of the vital data early, in case of premature termination.

Onboard and telemetered data on spacecraft systems performance will pinpoint problems to permit fixes before the next manned Apollo flies.

In addition to checking performance of the crew, prime and backup spacecraft systems and mission support facilities in Earth orbit, the objectives of Apollo 7 are:

* Collect data on forward command module heat-shield in entry conditions

* Measure change of environmental control system radiator coating in space environment

* Perform transposition and simulated docking maneuver with S-IVB stage

* Test guidance system's inertial measurement unit in flight

* Conduct navigational exercises using landmarks and stars

* Optically track a target vehicle (S-IVB stage)

* Measure performance of spacecraft propulsion systems

* Measure accuracy of propellant gauging system

* Gather data on spacecraft systems thermal balance

* Evaluate general crew activity in operating command module

* Evaluate command module crew displays and controls

* Gather data on post-maneuver propellant sloshing

* Evaluate quality of air-to-ground voice communications

* Control S-IVB attitude manually prior to separation

* Evaluate opened spacecraft-lunar module adapter panels

* Conduct visual out-the-window horizon attitude reference for de-orbit maneuver

* Evaluate procedures for stabilizing spacecraft systems thermal balance during the Earth-return portion of a lunar mission

* Rendezvous with S-IVB stage.

MISSION DESCRIPTION

(Times given are ground elapse time and are for a nominal mission. Late changes may be made before launch or while the mission is in progress.)

Launch Phase

Apollo 7 will lift off Eastern Test Range Launch Complex 34 at 11 a.m. EDT, and roll to an azimuth of 72 degrees. The launch window will remain open until about 3 p.m. EDT. Lighting conditions both for launch and recovery are considered in establishing the window.

At insertion, the spacecraft and S-IVB stage will be in a 123-by-153-nautical miles (142 x 176 statute miles, 228 x 284 kilometers) orbit at an inclination of 31.59 degrees to the Equator.

Orbital Phase

The vehicle will maintain an orbital pitch rate to keep the spacecraft longitudinal axis parallel with the local horizontal until just prior to separation from the S-IVB late in the second revolution.

Remaining S-IVB propellants and cold gases will be dumped through the J-2 engine near the end of the first revolution, and the added velocity from propellant dumping will be about 30 feet-per-second, raising apogee to 171 nm (197 statute miles, 316 kilometers).

If the propellant dump cannot be accomplished, the Apollo 7 spacecraft will separate from the launch vehicle immediately and maneuver to a safe distance. There will be a small amount of residual propellants remaining in the tanks and it is highly improbable that a tank overpressure will exist. However, this remote situation must be considered in the mission planning to ensure the maximum safety for the crew.

At 2 hr. 55 min. GET, the spacecraft will separate from the S-IVB stage with a one-foot-per-second velocity from firing of the service module reaction control thrusters.

At a distance of 50 feet the differential velocity between the spacecraft and the S-IVB will be reduced to 0.5 feet-per-second while the crew pitches the spacecraft 180 degrees. The remaining .5 feet-per-second velocity will then be damped out and the spacecraft will station keep with the S-IVB while the crew photographs the opened spacecraft/LM adapter panels.

A phasing maneuver of 7.6 feet-per-second retrograde to set up rendezvous with the S-IVB stage at 29 hours (GET) will be made over the Antigua-station at 3 hr. 20 min. GET. The maneuver will compensate for the greater drag of the S-IVB, and at the time of the first service propulsion system burn at 26-hr. 25 min. GET, the spacecraft will be an estimated 72 nm (83 sm, 133 km) ahead of the S-IVB.

The first corrective combination service propulsion system burn at 26 hr. 24 min. GET will be a 209 feet-per-second burn with a 72-degree pitch-down attitude. This is the first of two maneuvers to set up a phase angle of 1.32 degrees and a distance of 8.0 nm (9.2 sm, 14.8 km) below the S-IVB in a co-elliptic orbit.

A corrective maneuver to cancel out cumulative errors may be performed over Ascension Island, depending on tracking data gathered since the first SPS burn. If the corrective maneuver is less than 15 feet-per-second, the service module reaction control system thrusters will be used.

The second service propulsion system burn, co-elliptic maneuver, nominally will be made at 28 hr. 00 min. GET when the spacecraft is 82 nm (94 sm, 152 km) behind and 8.0 nm below the S-IVB stage. The burn will be 186 feet-per-second retrograde with a 59-degree pitch-up attitude. The Apollo 7 crew will then begin optical tracking of the S-IVB stage to compute terminal phase burns. Maneuvers performed up to this time will be based on ground computed data.

When the line-of-sight angle to the S-IVB reaches 27.45 degrees, a 17 feet-per-second terminal phase initiation burn will be made. The maneuver nominally will be made over Ascension Island at 29 hr. 22 min. GET at a range of about 15 nm (17.3 sm, 27.8 km). The burn will be made with the service module reaction control system thrusters at a pitch-up attitude of 32 degrees.

Two small mid-course corrections three feet per second and 0.3 feet-per-second will be made in a radially upward direction at 14 min. and 21 min. after terminal phase initiation. These small burns will be calculated in real time to compensate for cumulative errors in onboard guidance targeting for terminal phase initiation.

The braking approach should begin about 29 hr. 36 min. when the spacecraft is about one mile (1.9 km) from the S-IVB, using the service module RCS thrusters. Velocity match (about 18 feet-per-second) and station-keeping at 100 to 200 feet range will continue until revolution 19 state-side pass, when at 30 hr. 20 min. GET, a small service module RCS posigrade burn will break off the rendezvous.

The service propulsion system will not be fired again until revolution 58 over Carnarvon, Australia at three days 19 hr. 43 min. GET. The 116 feet-per-second third SPS burn will be made with a spacecraft attitude of 17.7 degrees pitch up and 122 degrees yaw right, and will lower perigee to 96 nm, (110 sm 178 km) raise apogee to 155 nm (178 sm, 287 km), provide orbital lifetime to complete the mission, and provide the capability of de-orbit with the RCS thrusters.

In the 77th revolution at a ground elapsed time of five days 00 hr. 52 min., the first of two minimum-impulse SPS burns will be performed. The fourth SPS burn will be in-plane posigrade with a velocity of 15 feet-per-second.

The fifth SPS burn, primarily a test of SPS performance and the propellant utilization and gauging system, will take place at six days 21 hr. 08 min. in the 105th revolution. The 1469-feet-per-second burn will begin under guidance and navigation control system direction, and after 30 seconds will switch over to manual thrust vector control. Spacecraft attitudes during the burn will be set up to target for a 97 by 242 nm orbit (112 x 277 sm, 180 x 406 km).

The second minimum-impulse burn SPS burn no. 6 will nominally take place during the 132nd revolution at eight days 19 hr. 42 min. GET, under guidance and navigation control system, and will impart a velocity of 17 feet-per-second in-plane retrograde.

SPS burn no. 7 at nine days 21 hr. 25 min. in the 150th revolution, will "tune up" the orbit to adjust the location of perigee and to assure landing in the primary recovery zone in the Atlantic at 67 degrees W. longitude. The burn will be controlled by the stabilization and control system and will be calculated to maintain a 91 by 225 nm (105 x 255 sm, 169 x 407 km) orbit through the end of the mission.

The eighth and final SPS burn will be a 279 feet-per-second retrograde de-orbit maneuver at 10 days 21 hr. 08 min. GET in revolution 163. The spacecraft will be pitched down 49.3 degrees during the de-orbit burn to permit the flight crew to verify de-orbit attitude visually and to take over manual control if the guidance and navigation system malfunctions.

Entry Phase

Approximately 90 seconds after SPS shutdown, the command module will be separated from the service module and placed into entry attitude. Entry will take place about 14 minutes after SPS de-orbit burn at 31.03 degrees N. latitude by 98.83 degrees W. longitude at 400,000 feet.

Spacecraft splashdown should take place about 200 nm (230 sm, 370 km) south-southwest of Bermuda at 10 days 21 hr. 40 min. GET at 29.80 degrees N. latitude by 67.00 degrees W. longitude.

Recovery Operations

The primary recovery zone for Apollo 7 is in the West Atlantic, centered at 28 degrees N. latitude by 63 degrees W. longitude, where the primary recovery vessel, the aircraft carrier USS Essex will be on station. Expected splashdown for a full 10-day 164-revolution mission will be at 29.8 degrees N. latitude by 67.0 degrees W. longitude, about 200 nm (230 sm, 370 km) south-southwest of Bermuda and 600 nm (690 sm. 1,112 km) east of Cape Kennedy.

Other planned recovery zones and their center coordinates are east Atlantic (23 degrees N. by 27 de degrees W), west Pacific (28 degrees N. by 137.5 degrees E), and mid-Pacific (28 degrees N. by 162 degrees W.).

In addition to the Essex, three other vessels will be stationed in the launch abort area. After launch the LSD Rushmore will take up station in the southern part of the west Atlantic recovery zone, while the minesweeper countermeasure ship Ozark will move into the east Atlantic zone. The tracking ship USNS Vanguard will not be committed to recovering Apollo 7 unless a landing should occur in its vicinity following a launch abort.

The USS Essex will be on station in the northern sector of the west Atlantic zone at splashdown.

In addition to surface vessels deployed in the four recovery zones 18 HC-130 aircraft will be on standby at nine staging bases around the Earth: Perth, Australia; Tachikawa, Japan; Pago Pago, Samoa; Hawaii; Lima, Peru; Bermuda; Lajes, Azores; Ascension Island and Mauritius.

Apollo 7 recovery operations will be directed from the Recovery Operations Control Room in Mission Control Center, Houston, and will be supported by the Atlantic Recovery Control Center, Norfolk, Va.; Pacific Recovery Control Center, Kunia, Hawaii; and control centers at Ramstein, Germany, and Albrook AFB, Canal Zone.

The Apollo 7 crew will be flown from the primary recovery vessel to Kennedy Space Center after recovery. The spacecraft will receive a preliminary examination, safing and power-down aboard the Essex prior to offloading at Mayport, Fla., where the spacecraft will undergo a more complete deactivation. It is anticipated that the spacecraft will be flown from Mayport to Long Beach, Calif., within 24 hours, thence trucked to the North American Rockwell Plant in Downey, Calif., for postflight analysis.

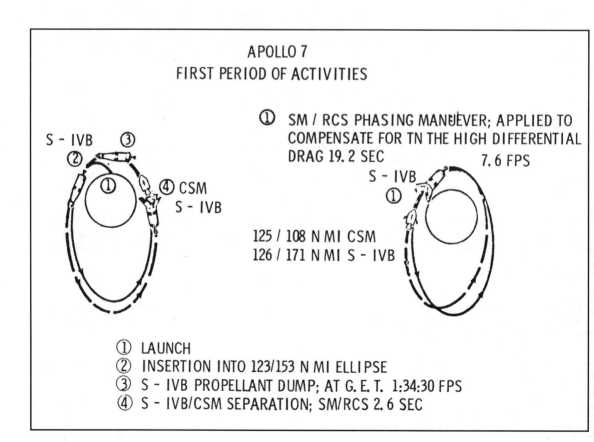

APOLLO 7
FIRST PERIOD OF ACTIVITIES

① SM / RCS PHASING MANEUVER; APPLIED TO COMPENSATE FOR TN THE HIGH DIFFERENTIAL DRAG 19.2 SEC   7.6 FPS

S - IVB

125 / 108 N MI CSM
126 / 171 N MI S - IVB

S - IVB

④ CSM
S - IVB

① LAUNCH
② INSERTION INTO 123/153 N MI ELLIPSE
③ S - IVB PROPELLANT DUMP; AT G. E. T. 1:34:30 FPS
④ S - IVB/CSM SEPARATION; SM/RCS 2.6 SEC

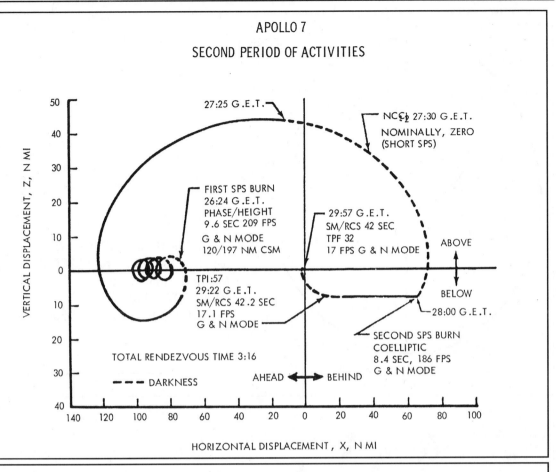

APOLLO 7

SECOND PERIOD OF ACTIVITIES

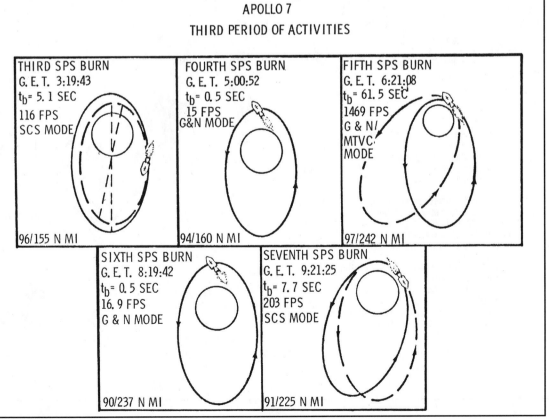

APOLLO 7

THIRD PERIOD OF ACTIVITIES

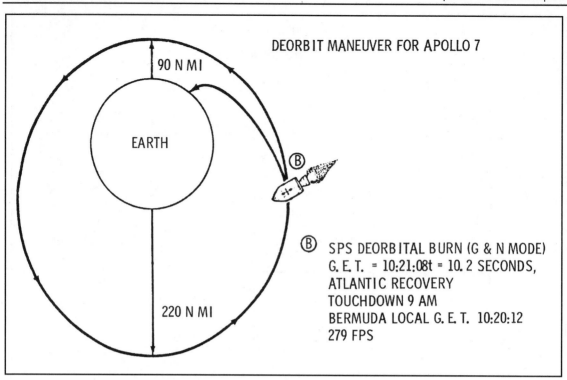

DEORBIT MANEUVER FOR APOLLO 7

90 N MI

EARTH

220 N MI

Ⓑ SPS DEORBITAL BURN (G & N MODE)
G. E. T. = 10:21:08t = 10. 2 SECONDS,
ATLANTIC RECOVERY
TOUCHDOWN 9 AM
BERMUDA LOCAL G. E. T. 10:20:12
279 FPS

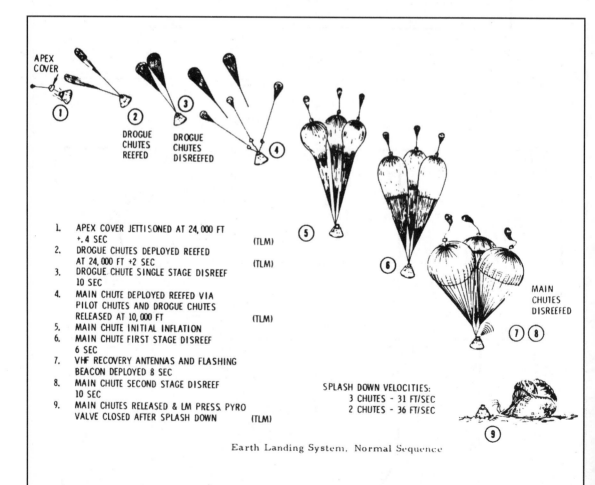

APEX COVER

DROGUE CHUTES REEFED

DROGUE CHUTES DISREEFED

1. APEX COVER JETTISONED AT 24,000 FT
    +.4 SEC   (TLM)
2. DROGUE CHUTES DEPLOYED REEFED
    AT 24,000 FT +2 SEC   (TLM)
3. DROGUE CHUTE SINGLE STAGE DISREEF
    10 SEC
4. MAIN CHUTE DEPLOYED REEFED VIA
    PILOT CHUTES AND DROGUE CHUTES
    RELEASED AT 10,000 FT   (TLM)
5. MAIN CHUTE INITIAL INFLATION
6. MAIN CHUTE FIRST STAGE DISREEF
    6 SEC
7. VHF RECOVERY ANTENNAS AND FLASHING
    BEACON DEPLOYED 8 SEC
8. MAIN CHUTE SECOND STAGE DISREEF
    10 SEC
9. MAIN CHUTES RELEASED & LM PRESS. PYRO
    VALVE CLOSED AFTER SPLASH DOWN   (TLM)

MAIN CHUTES DISREEFED

SPLASH DOWN VELOCITIES:
3 CHUTES - 31 FT/SEC
2 CHUTES - 36 FT/SEC

Earth Landing System, Normal Sequence

APOLLO 7 MISSION EVENTS

Event	Ground Elapsed Time day: hr: min	Velocity ft/sec	Purpose
Orbital insertion	0:00:10	——	Insertion into 123x153 nm orbit (140 x 176 sm, 228x284 km)
CSM/S-IVB separation	0:02:55	1	
SM RCS phasing burn	0:03:20	-7.5	Set up rendezvous phasing
First SPS burn	1:02:24	209	Corrective combination maneuver
Second SPS burn	1:04:00	185.6	Concentric maneuver
Terminal Phase Initiate	1:05:23	17.1	Final approach for S-IVB rendezvous
Post-rendezvous separation	1:06:20	2	Assure no CSM/S-IVB recontact
Third SPS burn	3:19:43	116	Tune up orbit; set up for fuel gauge test
Fourth SPS burn	5:00:52	15	First minimum-impulse test
Fifth SPS burn	6:21:08	1469	Tune up orbit for life time, deorbit position; test of fuel gauging system
Sixth SPS burn	8:19:42	-17	Second minimum-impulse test
Seventh SPS burn	9:21:25	203	Adjust orbit for proper location of deorbit burn, landing
Eighth SPS burn	10:21:08	-278.9	De-orbit

Apollo 7 Rendezvous

While Earth orbit rendezvous of a spacecraft with a target vehicle was accomplished many times in the Gemini program, the Apollo 7 rendezvous with the S-IVB stage has further implications for future lunar landing missions. The main purpose of Apollo 7 rendezvous is to demonstrate the capability to rendezvous with and rescue a lunar module after an aborted lunar landing, or after the lunar module has staged from the lunar surface into lunar orbit.

The rendezvous trajectory techniques are essentially the same as those developed in Gemini phasing, corrective combination and co-elliptic maneuvers followed by the terminal phase maneuver when the spacecraft is 15 nm (17.3 sm, 27.8 km) behind and at a constant differential height of about 8 nm (9.2 sm, 14.8 km) below the target.

Also significant is the fact that during a LM rescue the CSM must be flown by one crewman a situation that requires ground control to bring the CSM up to the terminal phase while the crewman performs the rest of the rendezvous using onboard computer and line-of-sight control to the LM.

Apollo 7 Guidance Techniques

Many of the Apollo 7 principal test mission objectives are concerned with a thorough checkout of navigation and guidance equipment for this third generation of manned spacecraft.

Primary guidance is obtained by a combination of computer programs and inertial platform and optics inputs. Backup control, in case of primary guidance failure, is furnished by the stabilization and control system which uses body-mounted attitude gyros.

As a precursor to navigation in a trans-Earth trajectory in later lunar landing flights, the Apollo 7 crew will conduct mid-course navigation sextant sightings using combinations of stars and Earth horizon. Later missions will use the star-lunar landmark-horizon technique.

The S-IVB stage will serve as a sextant tracking target during the rendezvous phase. Optical tracking and rendezvous navigation techniques will be emphasized to gain experience and confidence in these systems. In the Gemini flights, the primary target tracking mode was with rendezvous radar.

Inputs from the Inertial Measurement Unit (IMU) and the optical navigation devices are processed by the command module computer.

FLIGHT PLAN

The Apollo 7 flight plan calls for at least one crew member to be awake at all times. The normal cycle will be 16 hours of work followed by eight hours of rest. The command pilot and lunar module pilot sleep periods are scheduled simultaneously.

Early in the flight, the crew may doff pressure suits and don the inflight coveralls.

Two full night passes are needed to orient the inertial measurement unit (IMU) and to ready other systems before any crew activity involving the guidance and navigation system. When the IMU orientation is known but is determined to be inaccurate, the flight plan calls for one full night pass for realignment of the IMU platform.

Crew work-rest cycles have been planned so that all three crewmen are awake for at least a half-hour before IMU orientations that precede a maneuver using the service propulsion system.

The flight plan schedules an hour for each meal period with all three crewmen eating together whenever possible. Other mission activities, such as experiments, status reports and maneuvers will be kept to a minimum during meal periods.

Spacecraft systems checkouts will be scheduled periodically by the crew to coincide with planned check list procedures. Lithium hydroxide canisters for removal of carbon dioxide from the cabin atmosphere will be changed each 12 hours, with the first canister removed 10 hours after lift-off.

Air-to-ground voice communications will be on the VHF frequency, although the unified S-band equipment will be powered throughout the mission for testing and as a VHF backup.

During a state-side pass once each day, the crew will report to Mission Control Center such information as times of accomplishing flight plan tasks, film type and quantity used and lithium hydroxide canister changes.

The spacecraft communicator in Mission Control Center in turn will provide flight plan updates on a daily basis.

Following is a brief summary of tasks to be accomplished in Apollo 7 on a day-to-day schedule. The tasks are subject to changes to suit opportunity or other factors.

Launch day (0-24 hours):

Spacecraft-S-IVB orbital operations prior to separation
* S-IVB safing and fuel jettison
* Demonstrate S-IVB takeover
* Transposition and simulate docking with spacecraft-LM adapter
* Photograph deployed spacecraft-LM adapter panels
* Phasing maneuver using service module reaction control system
* Checkout spacecraft systems
* Cryogenic stratification test No. 1
* Calibrate sextant and crew optical alignment sight (COAS)

Second day (24-48 hours):

*Service propulsion systems burns Nos. 1 and 2
*Rendezvous with S-IVB
*Track S-IVB post-rendezvous at 80 and 160 nm (92 x 184 sm 148 x 296 km) ranges

Third day (48-72 hours):

* Track S-IVB at 320 nm range (368 sm, 593 km)
* Daylight star visibility test No. 1
* S005, S006 photographic experiments

Fourth day (72-96 hours):

* Lunar module rendezvous radar test No. 1 over White Sands, N.M., Test Facility
* Landmark tracking
* Daylight star visibility test No. 2
* S005, S006 photographic experiments
* Service propulsion system burn No. 3
* Slosh damping test No. 1
* Environmental control system radiator test

Fifth day (96-120 hours):

* Mid-course navigation exercise
* Cryogenic stratification test No. 2

Sixth day (120-144 hours):

* Service propulsion system burn No. 4
* Slosh damping test No. 2
* Daylight star visibility test. No. 3
* Service propulsion system cold soak
* Landmark tracking

Seventh day (144-168 hours):

* Service propulsion system burn No. 5
* Service propulsion system cold soak
* Passive thermal control test No. 1
* Mid-course navigation exercise
* photograph rendezvous window coating

Eighth day (168-192 hours):

* S005, 5006 photographic experiments
* Test environmental control system secondary coolant loop

Ninth day (192-216 hours):

* Lunar module rendezvous radar test No. 2 over White Sands Test Facility
* Daylight star visibility test No. 1
* Perform backup alignment of stabilization control system
* Service propulsion system burn No. 6
* Passive thermal control tests Nos. 2 and 3

Tenth day (216-240 hours)

* Service propulsion system burn No. 7
* Calibrate sextant
* Determine bias of pulse integrating pendulous accelerometer (PIPA) and entry monitor system (EMS)
* S005, S006 photographic experiments

Eleventh day (240 hours-de-orbit):

* Photograph rendezvous window coating
* Cryogenic stratification test No. 3
* De-orbit burn

ALTERNATE MISSIONS

The preceding mission description is for a nominal or prime mission. Plans may be altered at any time to meet changing conditions.

In general, three alternate missions (one-day, two-day and three-day) are ready if necessary. Each of these, in turn, has variations depending on whether the S-IVB stage is available, what spacecraft system problems are encountered and the amount of service propulsion system propellants available. In addition, alternate rendezvous plan, if a one-day delay occurs, has been prepared. Alternate missions greater than three days will be planned in real time.

One-Day Mission Plans

Four plans are being considered for one-day alternate missions. The first two, called 1a and 1b, terminate with a landing in the middle Pacific Recovery Zone in the sixth revolution. Alternates 1c and 1d terminate in the West Atlantic near the end of the first day. In the alternate one-day missions the service propulsion system will be used only for the de-orbit burn except if needed to place the command and service module in orbit. Alternates 1b and 1d follow the prime mission's first day flight plan.

Two-Day Mission Plans

Three two-day mission plans, alternates 2a, 2b, 2c, are being considered. Two days do not permit all test objectives to be met. The mission can have a rendezvous and two additional Service Propulsion System (SPS) maneuvers (one for de-orbit) or no rendezvous and four maneuvers (one for de-orbit).

Alternate 2a. - Alternate 2a assumes the S-IVB is in an acceptable orbit and has been made safe. In this case, the rendezvous will occur as in the prime mission, the de-orbit will be under Guidance, Navigation and Control System control, and the other maneuver will be used to evaluate Stabilization and Control System control.

The latter burn would occur over Carnarvon in revolution 28. The de-orbit burn of the former would occur over Hawaii in revolution 31, with landing in the west Atlantic in revolution 32.

If the Stabilization and Control System burn were extended to approximately 70 seconds, the system performance and gauging tests could be accomplished.

Alternate 2b.- Alternate 2b assumes a burn of the Stabilization and Control System for Contingency Orbit Insertion of less than 31 seconds. The first maneuver will be a Guidance and Navigation Control System burn in revolution 16 over Carnarvon to adjust the propellant level for the gauging system test. If the Contingency Orbit Insertion burn did not satisfy the test requirement for the Stabilization System, this first maneuver would be under control of that System. If the Insertion burn were between 28 and 31 seconds, this maneuver could be a minimum-impulse test.

A 57-second burn for test of the Service Propulsion System (SPS) performance, gauging and Guidance and Navigation Control System Manual Thrust Vector Control will occur over Cape Kennedy in revolution 19. A minimum impulse test will be performed over Carnarvon in revolution 29 and the Guidance System de-orbit burn over Hawaii occurs in revolution 32 for a west Atlantic landing in revolution 33.

Because the CSM-active rendezvous objective can be traded for tests of the minimum-impulse, gauging system, and manual takeover, this plan may be preferable to the 2a plan when possible.

Alternate 2c.- The third two-day plan assumes that the S-IVB is not available and that a Contingency Orbit Insertion burn of more than 31 seconds has occurred. Such a burn would suffice for test of the Stabilization Control System.

The first scheduled maneuver would be performed over Cape Kennedy in revolution 17. The burn objective will be a minimum impulse test. The second maneuver would occur two revolutions later over Cape Kennedy. Burn objectives depend on the exact propellant level. The most desirable objective would be a Guidance and Navigation System-Manual Thrust Vector Control maneuver. This requires a minimum maneuver time of 35 seconds.

If this time is unavailable, the maneuver will be a Guidance System-controlled, orbit-shaping maneuver that uses available propellants. The third maneuver will be a second minimum-impulse test over Carnarvon in revolution 29. The de-orbit maneuver would be over Hawaii in revolution 32, landing in the west Atlantic in revolution 33.

Three-Day Mission Plans

There are three three-day missions which would allow all mission objectives to be scheduled.

Alternate 3a.- Assuming the S-IVB is available, the rendezvous will occur as in the prime mission. In revolution 28 a Stabilization Control System burn over Carnarvon would adjust the level for the test of the Service Propulsion System performance and gauging system. These tests would be performed over Cape Kennedy in revolution 32. A minimum-impulse test would be performed shortly before the Guidance and Navigation Control System in revolution 45 over Hawaii. Landing will be in revolution 46 in the west Atlantic.

Alternate 3b.- With the S-IVB unavailable and a Contingency Orbit Insertion burn of less than 31 seconds, the first maneuver would be controlled by the Guidance and Navigation System in revolution 17 over Cape Kennedy to adjust the propellant level for Service Propulsion System (SPS) performance and gauging system tests. If the Insertion burn did not provide a satisfactory test of the Stabilization Control System, this maneuver will be under control of that System. The second maneuver will be a minimum-impulse test over Cape Kennedy two revolutions later. The SPS performance and gauging system tests will occur over Cape Kennedy in revolution 32. A second minimum-impulse test will be performed shortly prior to the Guidance System de-orbit, in revolution 47 over Hawaii.

Alternate 3c.- The third three-day plan considers that the S-IVB is unavailable and that a Contingency Orbit Insertion burn of more than 31 seconds has occurred. That burn would suffice for test of the Stabilization Control System. The first maneuver would be a minimum-impulse test over Cape Kennedy in revolution 17. The objector of the second maneuver, over Cape Kennedy two revolutions later, will be determined by the propellant level as on alternate 2c. The second minimum-impulse test would be over Cape Kennedy in revolution 32. The Guidance and Navigation System de-orbit burn will occur over Hawaii in revolution 46 with a landing in the west Atlantic in revolution 47.

Alternate Rendezvous Plan

The only alternate rendezvous plan being considered is a one-day delay. Alternate rendezvous plans with a delay of one revolution are ruled out because of the loss of good coverage by the tracking network. A rendezvous delay of more than one day is not planned because of the drag uncertainties of the S-IVB. A one-day delay in the rendezvous allows approximately the same maneuver plan, the same station coverage and the same lighting.

The plan involves deleting the phasing maneuver at 26 hours 25 minutes GET and making, instead, a maneuver with the Service Module Reaction Control System to reestablish the near nominal phasing (CSM leading by about 75 nautical miles (86 statute miles, 139 kilometers) one day later. The burn of about 12 feet-per-second of that system has been scheduled over Ascension Island in revolution 18 about 27 hours 30 minutes GET. The phasing and concentricity maneuvers necessary for rendezvous will delay about one day and the terminal phase will follow essentially the same plan as that of the nominal. The remainder of the mission follows the nominal operational trajectory.

APOLLO 7 ALTERNATE MISSIONS OBJECTIVES

MISSION PRIORITY	1	5	6	7	11	12	13	14	18	38	
DTO#	7.19	3.15	3.14	1.13	2.5	20.13	1.10	20.8	2.6	57.21	
ALTERNATE MISSION	RADIATOR TEST	SPS PERFORMANCE	SPS MINIMUM IMPULSE	GNCS ΔV CONTROL	SCS ΔV CONTROL	CSM-ACTIVE RENDEZVOUS	SEXTANT TRACKING	TRANSPOSITION AND DOCKING	GNCS/MTVC ΔV TAKE OVER	SLA DEPLOYMENT	COMMENTS
1A				◐	●						
1B				◐				●		●	
1C	○			◐	●						
1D	○			◐				●		●	
2A	●			●	●	●	●	●		●	
2B	●	●	◐	●	●		○	○	●		S-IVB RELATED TEST OBJECTIVES SATISFIED IF COI=0
2C	●		●	●	●				○		MANUAL TAKE OVER BURN MUST BE AT LEAST 35 SECONDS LONG
3A	●	●	◐	●	●	●	●	●	●	●	
3B	●								●		
3C	●		●	●	●				○		MANUAL TAKE OVER BURN MUST BE AT LEAST 35 SECONDS LONG
ALTERNATE RENDEZVOUS	●	●	●	●	●	●	●	●	●	●	

DETAILED TEST OBJECTIVE ACCOMPLISHMENT
FOR THE APOLLO 7 ALTERNATE MISSIONS

● FULFILLED

◐ PARTIALLY FULFILLED

EXPERIMENTS

Five experiments will be carried out in the Apollo 7 mission. They are:

* S005-synoptic terrain photography — The Apollo 7 crew will photograph land and ocean areas for geologic, geographic and oceanographic study and for evaluation of various film types.

* S006-synoptic weather photography — Global as well as local weather systems will be photographed by the crew for use by scientists in improving techniques of interpretation of orbital altitude weather photographs.

Both photography experiments may require service module reaction control system propellants for attitude control. Selections of areas and weather systems to be photographed will be made by the crew as the opportunities arise.

* M006-bone demineralization — Pre- and post-flight X-ray studies of selected bones of crew members is aimed toward establishing occurrence and degree of bone demineralization during long space flights.

* M011-blood studies — Pre- and post-flight crew blood samples are compared to determine if the space environment fosters any cellular changes in human blood.

* M023-lower body negative pressure — Pre- and postflight medical examinations will measure change in lower body negative pressure as evidence of cardiovascular deconditioning resulting from prolonged weightlessness.

All three medical experiments require no in-flight crew activity nor use of any spacecraft consumables.

ABORT MODES

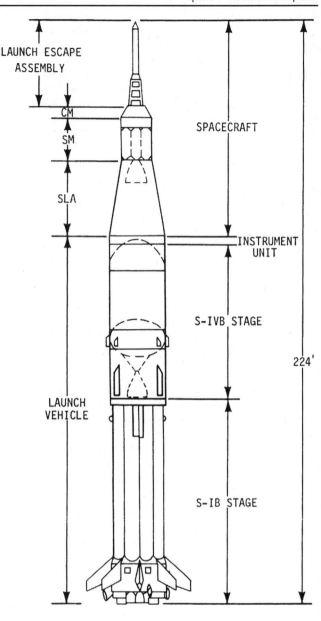

APOLLO 7 SPACE VEHICLE

From Apollo 7 liftoff until orbital insertion, there are four periods (modes) in which the mission may be aborted either by the emergency detection system or by the crew.

They are:

Mode I — Liftoff to launch escape tower jettison, 2 min. 44 sec. GET; Launch escape system initiated automatically or by crew command when two launch vehicle engines fail or excessive rates build up. Drogue and main parachutes deploy after tower jettison and command module lands up to 400 nm (460 sm., 741 km) downrange.

Mode II — 2 min. 44 sec. to 9 min. 33 sec., GET: Separation of Command Service Module from S-IVB, 20-second service module Reaction Control System, separation of Command and Service Modules and full-lift entry, and landing from 400 to 3,200 nm (460 to 3,680 sm, 741 to 5,930 km) downrange.

Mode III — 9 min. 33 sec., GET to insertion (9 min. 53 sec. GET): Separation sequence same as Mode II, but service propulsion system burn retrograde. Command module flown in open-loop entry to recovery area at 3,200 nm (3,680 sm, 5,930 km).

Mode IV — 9 min. 27 sec., GET to insertion: Service propulsion system used to insert spacecraft into orbit, leaving enough Service Propulsion System fuel for de-orbit burn.

SPACECRAFT STRUCTURE SYSTEMS

Apollo spacecraft No. 101 for the Apollo 7 mission is comprised of a launch escape system, command module, service module and a spacecraft-lunar module adapter. The latter serves as a mating structure to the instrument unit atop the S-IVB stage of the Saturn IB. For this mission, it does not contain a lunar module.

Launch Escape System - Propels command module to safety in an aborted launch. It is made up of an open-frame tower structure mounted to the command module by four frangible bolts, and three solid-propellant rocket motors: a 155,000   pound-thrust-launch escape system motor, a 33,000 pound-thrust tower jettison motor, and a jettison 3,000-pound-thrust pitch control motor that bends the command module trajectory away from the launch vehicle and pad area. Two canard vanes near the top deploy to turn the command module aerodynamically to an attitude with the heat-shield forward. Attached to the base of the Escape System is a boost protective cover composed of glass, cloth and honeycomb, that protects the command module from rocket exhaust gases from the main and the jettison motor. The system is 33 feet tall, four feet in diameter at the base and weighs 8,900 pounds.

Command Module Structure - The basic structure of the command module is a pressure vessel encased in heat-shields, cone-shaped 12 feet high, base diameter of 12 feet 10 inches, and launch weight 12,659 pounds.

The command module consists of the forward compartment which contains two negative pitch reaction control engines and components of the Earth landing system; the crew compartment, or inner pressure vessel, containing crew accommodations, controls and displays, and spacecraft systems; and the aft compartment housing ten reaction control engines and fuel tankage.

Heat-shields around the three compartments are made of brazed stainless steel honeycomb filled with phenolic epoxy resin as an ablative material.   Heat-shield thickness, varying according to heat loads, ranges from 0.7 inches to 2.7 inches on the aft side.

The spacecraft inner structure is of aluminum alloy sheet-aluminum honeycomb bonded sandwich ranging in thickness from 0.25 inches thick at forward access tunnel to 1.5 inches thick at base.

Service Module Structure - The service module is a cylinder 12 feet 10 inches in diameter by 22 feet long.

For the Apollo 7 mission, it will weigh 19,730 pounds at launch. Aluminum honeycomb panels one inch thick form the outer skin, and milled aluminum radial beams separate the interior into six sections containing service propulsion system and reaction control fuel-oxidizer tankage, fuel cells and onboard consumables.

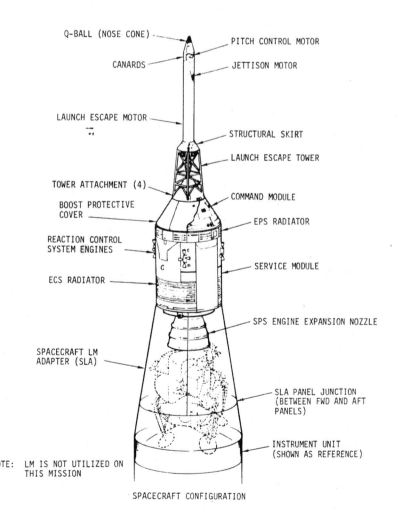

Q-BALL (NOSE CONE)
PITCH CONTROL MOTOR
CANARDS
JETTISON MOTOR
LAUNCH ESCAPE MOTOR
STRUCTURAL SKIRT
LAUNCH ESCAPE TOWER
TOWER ATTACHMENT (4)
COMMAND MODULE
BOOST PROTECTIVE COVER
EPS RADIATOR
REACTION CONTROL SYSTEM ENGINES
SERVICE MODULE
ECS RADIATOR
SPS ENGINE EXPANSION NOZZLE
SPACECRAFT LM ADAPTER (SLA)
SLA PANEL JUNCTION (BETWEEN FWD AND AFT PANELS)
INSTRUMENT UNIT (SHOWN AS REFERENCE)
NOTE: LM IS NOT UTILIZED ON THIS MISSION

SPACECRAFT CONFIGURATION

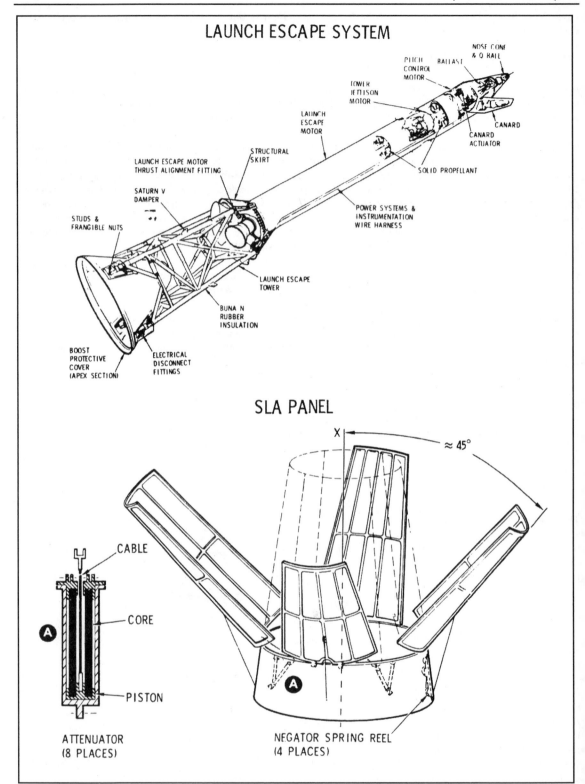

LAUNCH ESCAPE SYSTEM

SLA PANEL

ATTENUATOR
(8 PLACES)

NEGATOR SPRING REEL
(4 PLACES)

Spacecraft-LM Adapter Structure - The spacecraft-LM adapter is a truncated cone 2 feet long tapering from 260 inches diameter at the base to 154 inches at the forward end at the service module mating line. Aluminum honeycomb 1.75 inches thick is the stressed-skin structure for the spacecraft adapter, which will house the Lunar Module on Saturn V flights. On Apollo 7, the adapter serves as a structural inter-stage between the instrument unit atop the S-IVB stage and the service module. It weighs 3,800 pounds.

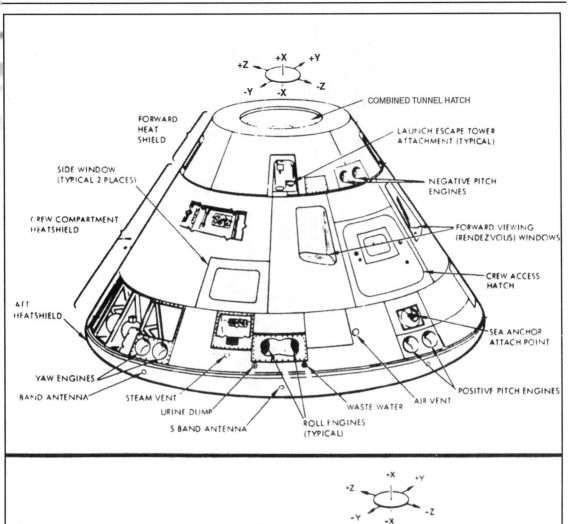

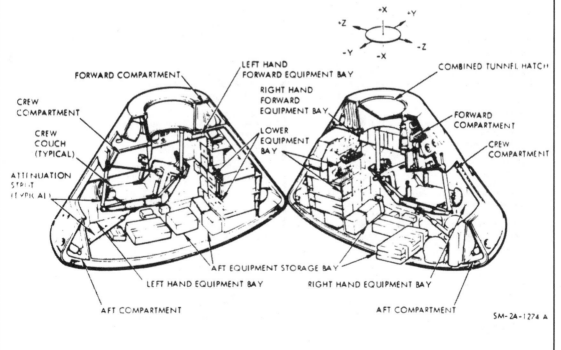

SM-2A-1274 A

APOLLO COMMAND MODULE

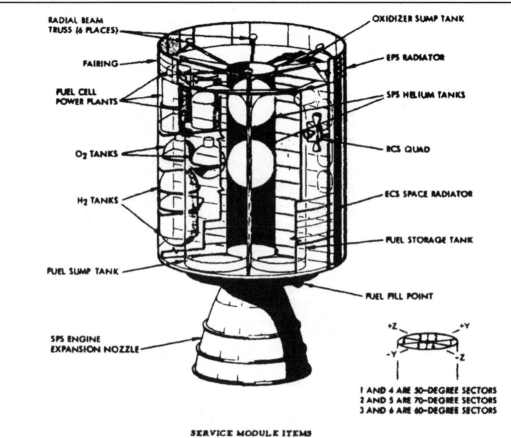

RADIAL BEAM TRUSS (6 PLACES)

FAIRING

FUEL CELL POWER PLANTS

O₂ TANKS

H₂ TANKS

FUEL SUMP TANK

SPS ENGINE EXPANSION NOZZLE

OXIDIZER SUMP TANK

EPS RADIATOR

SPS HELIUM TANKS

RCS QUAD

ECS SPACE RADIATOR

FUEL STORAGE TANK

FUEL FILL POINT

+Z   +Y
-Y   -Z

1 AND 4 ARE 50-DEGREE SECTORS
2 AND 5 ARE 70-DEGREE SECTORS
3 AND 6 ARE 60-DEGREE SECTORS

SERVICE MODULE ITEMS

Sector I
   Empty NASA equipment

Sector II
   Environmental system space radiator
   Service propulsion system
   Reaction control system package (+Y-axis)
   Service propulsion system oxidiser sump tank

Sector III
   Service propulsion system
   Reaction control system package (+Z-axis)
   Environmental system space radiator
   Service propulsion system oxidiser storage tank

Sector IV
   Fuel cell power plant (three)
   Helium servicing panel
   Super-critical oxygen tank (two)
   Super-critical hydrogen tank (two)
   Reaction control system control unit
   Electrical power system power control relay box
   Service module jettison controller sequencer (two)

Sector V
   Environmental control system space radiator
   Service propulsion system fuel sump tank
   Reaction control system package (-Y axis)

Sector VI
   Environmental control system space radiator
   Reaction control system package (-Z axis)
   Service propulsion system fuel storage tank

Center Section
   Service propulsion system helium tank (two)
   Service propulsion system engine

Fairing
   Electrical power system space radiator's (eight)

SM-2A-1278

BLOCK II SERVICE MODULE

Spacecraft Systems

<u>Guidance, Navigation and Control System</u> — Measures and controls spacecraft attitude and velocity, calculates trajectory, controls Spacecraft Propulsion System thrust vector and displays abort data. The Guidance System consists of three subsystems: inertial, made up of inertial measuring unit and associated power and data components; computer, consisting of display and keyboard panels and digital computer which processes information to or from other components; and optic, including scanning telescope, sextant for celestial and/or landmark spacecraft navigation.

Stabilization and Control System — Controls spacecraft rotation, translation and thrust vector and provides displays for crew-initiated maneuvers; backs up the guidance system. It has three subsystems; attitude reference, attitude control and thrust vector control.

Service Propulsion System — Provides thrust for large spacecraft velocity changes and de-orbit burn through a gimbal-mounted 20,500-pound-thrust hypergolic engine using nitrogen tetroxide oxidizer and a 50-50 mixture of unsymmetrical dimethyl hydrazine and hydrazine fuel. Tankage of this system is in the service module. The system responds to automatic firing commands from the guidance and navigation system or to manual commands from the crew. The engine provides a constant thrust rate. The stabilization and control system gimbals the engine to fire through the spacecraft center of gravity.

Reaction Control System — This includes two independent systems for the command module and the service module. The service module reaction controls have four identical quads of four 100-pound thrust hypergolic engines mounted, near the top of the Service Module, 90 degrees apart to provide redundant spacecraft attitude control through cross-coupling logic inputs from the Stabilization and Guidance Systems. Small velocity change maneuvers can also be made with the Service Module reaction controls. The Command Module Reaction Control System consists of two independent six-engine subsystems of 94 pounds thrust each. One is activated after separation from the Service Module, and is used for spacecraft attitude control during entry. The other is maintained in a sealed condition as a backup. Propellants for both systems are monomethyl hydrazine fuel and nitrogen tetroxide oxidizer with helium pressurization. These propellants are hypergolic, i.e.: they burn spontaneously on contact without need for an igniter.

Electrical Power System — Consists of three 31-cell Bacon-type hydrogen-oxygen fuel cell power plants in the Service Module which supply 28-volt DC power, three 28-volt DC zinc-silver oxide main storage batteries in the Command Module lower equipment bay, two pyrotechnic batteries in the Command Module lower equipment bay, and three 115-200-volt 400-cycle three-phase AC inverters powered by the main 28-volt DC bus. The inverters are also located in the lower equipment bay. Supercritical cryogenic hydrogen and oxygen react in the fuel cell stacks to-provide electrical power, potable water and heat. The Command Module main batteries can be switched to fire pyrotechnics in an emergency. A battery charger builds the batteries to full strength as required.

Environmental Control System — Controls spacecraft atmosphere, pressure and temperature and manages water. In addition to regulating cabin and suit gas pressure, temperature and humidity, the system removes carbon dioxide, odors and particles, and ventilates the cabin after landing. It collects and stores fuel cell potable water for crew use, supplies water to the glycol evaporators for cooling, and dumps surplus water overboard through the urine dump valve. Excess heat generated by spacecraft equipment and crew is routed by this system to the cabin heat exchangers, to the space radiators, to the glycol evaporators, or it vents the heat to space.

Telecommunication System — Consists of pulse code modulated telemetry for relaying to Manned Space Flight Network stations data on spacecraft systems and crew condition, VHF/AM and unified S-Band tracking transponder, air-to-ground voice communications, onboard television, and a VHF recovery beacon. Network stations can transmit to the spacecraft such items as updates to the Apollo guidance computer and central timing equipment, and real-time commands for certain onboard functions.

Sequential System — Interfaces with other spacecraft systems and subsystems to initiate critical functions during launch, docking maneuvers, pre-orbital aborts and entry portions of a mission. The system also controls routine spacecraft sequencing such as Service Module separation and deployment of the Earth landing system.

Emergency Detection System — Detects and displays to the crew launch vehicle emergency conditions, such as excessive pitch rates or two engines out, and automatically or manually shuts down the booster and activates the launch escape system; functions until the spacecraft is in orbit.

Earth Landing System — Includes the drogue and main parachute system as well as post-landing recovery aids. In a normal entry descent, the Command Module apex cover is jettisoned at 24,000 feet, followed by two mortar-deployed reefed 16.5-feet diameter drogue parachutes for orienting and decelerating the spacecraft. After drogue release, three pilot chutes pull out the three main 83.3-feet diameter parachutes with two-stage reefing to provide gradual inflation in three steps. Two main parachutes out of three will provide a safe landing. Recovery aids include the uprighting system, swimmer interphone connections, sea dye marker, flashing beacon, VHF recovery beacon and VHF transceiver. The uprighting system consists of three compressor-inflated bags to turn the spacecraft upright if it should land in the water apex down (Stable II position).

Caution and Warning System — Monitors spacecraft systems for out-of-tolerance conditions and alerts crew by visual and audible alarms so that crewmen may trouble-shoot the problem.

Controls and Displays — Provide readouts and control functions of all other spacecraft systems in the command and service modules. All controls are designed to be operated by crewmen in pressurized suits. Displays are grouped according to the frequency the crew refers to them.

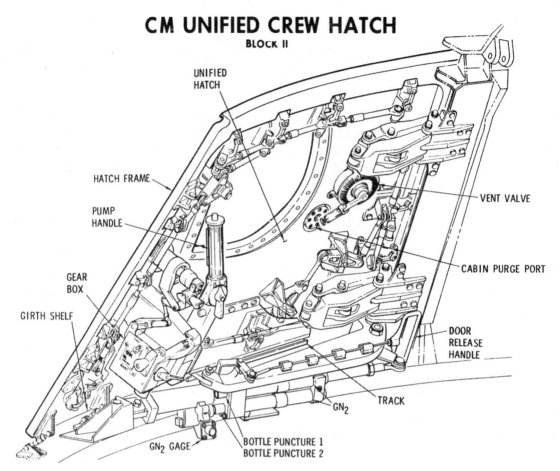

CM UNIFIED CREW HATCH
BLOCK II

Spacecraft Design Changes, Materials Substitution

Numerous hardware and operational procedures changes in the Apollo spacecraft have been made in the 18 months since the Apollo 204 fire which killed the prime crew of the first programmed manned Apollo mission.

A single quick-operating, outward opening crew hatch has replaced the earlier two-piece hatch. The new aluminum and fiberglass hatch can be opened from inside in seven seconds and by a pad safety crew in 10 seconds. Ease of opening is enhanced by a gas-powered counterbalance mechanism.

In order to reduce support of any combustion, launch pad spacecraft cabin atmosphere for pre-launch testing is now a mixture of 60 per cent oxygen and 40 per cent nitrogen instead of the 100 per cent oxygen. The "enriched air;" supplied by ground equipment, involved no hardware changes in the spacecraft. The crew suit loops, however, still carry 100 per cent oxygen. After launch, the 60-40 oxygen-nitrogen mix is gradually replaced with pure oxygen until cabin atmosphere reaches 100 per cent oxygen at 5 psi. The enriched air mix was selected after extensive flammability tests in various percentages of oxygen at varying pressures.

Other Apollo spacecraft changes:

*Substituting stainless steel for aluminum in high-pressure oxygen tubing.

*Armor plating water-glycol liquid line solder joints.

*Protective covers over wiring bundles.

*Stowage boxes built of aluminum.

*Replacement of materials to minimize flammability.

*Installation of fireproof storage containers for flammable materials.

*Mechanical fasteners substituted for gripper cloth patches.

*Flameproof coating on wire connections.

*Replacement of plastic switches with metal ones.

*Installation of an emergency oxygen system to isolate the crew from toxic fumes.

*Inclusion of portable fire extinguisher and fire-isolating panels in the cabin.

APOLLO . . . A COMPARISON

	Mercury	Gemini	Apollo
Length	9 ft. 6 in.	19 ft.	34 ft. 9 in. (CSM only)
Base diameter	6 ft. 6 in.	10 ft.	12 ft. 10 in.
Habitable volume	50 cu. ft.	80 cu. ft.	210 cu. ft.
Launch weight	3,649 pounds	8,360 pounds	41,358 pounds
Docking	None	Index bar, latches for Agena collar	Probe, docking ring for missions with lunar module
Abort system	Launch escape rocket, malfunction detection system	Pilot ejection seats, malfunction detection system	Launch escape rocket, emergency detection system
Propulsion system	Hydrogen peroxide attitude jets, retro rocket motors	Hypergolic orbit attitude maneuvering system, retro rockets	Restartable 20,500 lb. thrust service propulsion engine, separate reaction control system on command and service modules
Available velocity change (V)	None	750 fps	3,374 fps (Apollo 7)
Electrical power	Storage batteries	Two fuel cells storage batteries	Three large fuel cells rechargeable storage batteries
Communications	Voice, telemetry, radar transponders	Voice, telemetry, rendezvous radar, radar tracking transponders	Voice, telemetry, S-Band for deep space
Parachutes	Drogue, main, reserve	Drogue, pilot, main	2 drogue, 3 pilot, 3 main

THE   SATURN   IB   LAUNCH   VEHICLE

The fifth Saturn IB is the 15th in the Saturn I series of launch vehicles. Ten Saturn I and four IB rockets have been launched successfully.

The Saturn IB consists of two propulsive stages and an instrument unit. The first stage is essentially the same as that of Saturn I. For Saturn IB the stage was lightened, strengthened and modified to accept the S-IVB stage, which is larger-than the second stage of Saturn I, and the H-1 engines of the first stage were uprated. The IB second stage, identical to Saturn V third stage, is an outgrowth of the Saturn I second stage. The instrument units are almost identical on Saturn IB and V.

A "hybrid" vehicle, Saturn IB is capable of delivering about 40,000 pounds of payload to low Earth orbit. In addition to its role as Apollo carrier, it is expected to be used for other manned and unmanned space flights.

The Saturn IB launch vehicle for Apollo 7 will have several innovations. A reduction in the amount of telemetry and instrumentation equipment has reduced vehicle weight and increased the payload capability. (See Telemetry On AS-205 Launch Vehicle page). New propellant lines to the augmented spark igniter (ASI) on the J-2 engine of the second stage have been installed.

One important event scheduled for the flight is the launch vehicle propellant dump. This exercise will begin at about 1 hour 34 minutes after liftoff. Propellants remaining in the second stage (S-IVB) after insertion into orbit will be dumped overboard through the J-2 engine. This will prevent any buildup of pressure inside the tanks due to boil-off — the changing of the cryogenic liquids to gases, with the accompanying expansion. This "orbital safing" of the stage will avert a possible rupture of the tanks while the stage is attached to the Apollo command service module, or while it is close to the CSM following rendezvous with the stage later in the flight. The rendezvous is one of the primary objectives of the flight.

The astronauts, about 2.5 hours after liftoff, will begin manual control of the vehicle from their stations inside the spacecraft. After 25 minutes, control will be returned to the launch vehicle instrument unit. The spacecraft will be separated from the second stage about two hours 55 minutes after launch.

FIRST STAGE

The Saturn IB booster (S-IB) is 80.2 feet long and 21.5 feet in diameter. Dry weight of the redesigned booster is 84,401 pounds, about 10 tons lighter than the Saturn I booster (S-I).

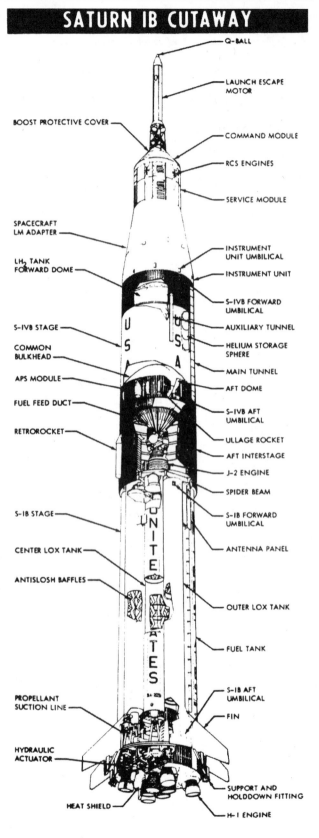

SATURN IB CUTAWAY

- Q-BALL
- LAUNCH ESCAPE MOTOR
- BOOST PROTECTIVE COVER
- COMMAND MODULE
- RCS ENGINES
- SERVICE MODULE
- SPACECRAFT LM ADAPTER
- INSTRUMENT UNIT UMBILICAL
- LH₂ TANK FORWARD DOME
- INSTRUMENT UNIT
- S-IVB FORWARD UMBILICAL
- S-IVB STAGE
- AUXILIARY TUNNEL
- COMMON BULKHEAD
- HELIUM STORAGE SPHERE
- MAIN TUNNEL
- APS MODULE
- AFT DOME
- FUEL FEED DUCT
- S-IVB AFT UMBILICAL
- RETROROCKET
- ULLAGE ROCKET
- AFT INTERSTAGE
- J-2 ENGINE
- SPIDER BEAM
- S-IB STAGE
- S-IB FORWARD UMBILICAL
- CENTER LOX TANK
- ANTENNA PANEL
- ANTISLOSH BAFFLES
- OUTER LOX TANK
- FUEL TANK
- S-IB AFT UMBILICAL
- PROPELLANT SUCTION LINE
- FIN
- HYDRAULIC ACTUATOR
- SUPPORT AND HOLDDOWN FITTING
- HEAT SHIELD
- H-1 ENGINE

The stage has eight 70 in. diameter tanks clustered around a center tank 105 inches in diameter. Four of the outer tanks and the center tank contain liquid oxygen. The other four tanks, alternating with the LOX tanks, contain kerosene (RP-1) fuel. Eight Rocketdyne H-1 engines provide a total thrust of 1.6 million pounds.

The engines are mounted on the thrust structure. The four outboard engines are equipped with independent, closed-loop hydraulic systems which gimbal the engines as much as eight degrees for vehicle flight direction control.

In about 2.5 minutes of operation, the stage burns about 42,000 gallons (277,000 pounds of fuel and 67,000 gallons (631,000 pounds) of oxidizer to reach an altitude of about 33 nm (38 sm, 61 km) at engine cutoff.

The stage has eight fins equally spaced around the tail unit assembly to increase aerodynamic stability in the lower atmosphere. The fins also support the vehicle on the launch pad and provide tie-down points for restraint momentarily after ignition.

Equipment on the S-IB stage includes the propulsion system, the hydraulic system, a control pressure system, purge systems, a fire detection and water quench system, a flight termination or "destruct" system, electrical power, instrumentation, and telemetry systems.

Chrysler assembles S-IB stages at NASA's Michoud Assembly Facility, New Orleans and tests them at the NASA's Marshall Space Flight Center, Huntsville, Ala.

SECOND STAGE

The S-IVB stage is 58.4 feet long and 21.7 feet in diameter. One Rocketdyne J-2 engine powers the stage. Empty weight of the stage is 21,909 pounds.

The cylindrical stage has a liquid hydrogen tank and a liquid oxygen tank. The tanks are separated by a common bulkhead which isolates the hydrogen about minus 423 degrees F and oxygen about minus 297 degrees F. The common bulk head is of honeycomb construction for strength and insulation.

The J-2 engine produces thrust of 200,000 pounds for about 7.5 minutes of operation. It will burn some 64,000 gallons (37,000 pounds) of liquid hydrogen and some 20,000 gallons (193,000 pounds) of LOX.

One-piece, stronger propellant lines have replaced lines with flex joints that feed the augmented spark igniter inside the injector of the J-2 engine. Analysis of data on the second Saturn V flight indicated leaks in the igniter propellant lines of two J-2 engines — one on the second stage and one on the third. Extensive ground testing led to a redesign and "beefing up" of these lines. The redesigned line, thoroughly tested on the ground, is being flight tested for the first time in Apollo 7.

The stage is made up of propulsion and hydraulic systems, a control pressure system, a flight termination system, electrical power supply and distribution system, and an instrumentation and telemetry system.

The S-IVB stage is connected to the first stage by an aft interstage. The separation sequence starts immediately after first stage outboard engines cut off. The stages separate by simultaneous operations of an ordnance system which severs the separation joint; four retro motors which slow the first stage; and three ullage rockets, which impart a slight acceleration to the S-IVB stage and payload.

McDonnell Douglas Corp. builds the S-IVB at Huntington Beach, Calif., and tests it at the Sacramento Test Center.

INSTRUMENT UNIT

The 4,280-pound instrument unit is a cylinder three feet high and 260 inches in diameter. It contains electrical and mechanical equipment which guides, controls and monitors vehicle performance from liftoff until after insertion of the spacecraft into orbit. It controls first stage powered flight, stage separation, second stage powered flight and orbital flight until the spacecraft is separated.

Equipment includes guidance and control, electrical power supply and distribution, instrumentation, telemetry, radio frequency, command, environmental control, and emergency detection systems.

The instrument unit was designed by the Marshall Center. International Business Machines Corp., Federal Systems Division, is the contractor for fabrication, systems testing and integration and checkout with the launch vehicle. Major elements of the unit come from Bendix, IBM and Electronic Communications, Inc.

LAUNCH VEHICLE TELEMETRY

Instrument Unit

Total Measurements	200

Telemetry Systems:
1 PCM
1 FM/FM
Tracking System:
1 C Band
1 Azusa
Ground Command System (1)

S-IB Stage

Total Measurements	260

Telemetry Systems:
1 PCM
1 FM/FM
Tracking System:
1 ODOP
Range Safety Systems:
2 Secure Command Systems

S-IVB Stage

Total Measurements	260

Telemetry Systems:
1 PCM
Range Safety Systems:
2 Secure Command Systems

Total Vehicle Measurements	720

NOTE: The total of 720 measurements is in sharp contrast to the 1,225 taken on the fourth Saturn IB, due to the removal of research and development equipment, leaving only those items required for an operational vehicle. Tape recorders have been removed. Telemetry systems were reduced by two in the instrument unit, two in the first stage and four in the second stage. Tracking and secure command systems remain the same. Removal of equipment reduced the number of events to be monitored and reduced total vehicle weight, making possible an increase in payload capability.

FLIGHT SEQUENCE

HOURS	MINUTES	SECONDS	EVENT
00	00	00	Liftoff
00	00	10	Pitch and Roll maneuver initiated
00	00	38	Roll Terminated
00	01	15	Maximum dynamic pressure (altitude 7.6 miles, about 2.4 miles downrange, velocity 1,660 mph)
00	02	14	Pitch terminated
00	02	20	First stage inboard engines cutoff
00	02	23	First stage outboard engines cutoff (altitude 37.6 miles, 37 miles downrange, velocity 5,201 mph)
00	02	24	Second stage ullage rocket Ignition, separation signal
00	02	24	First Stage separates
00	02	26	J-2 engine start command
00	02	28	90 percent J-2 thrust level
00	02	43	Crew jettisons launch escape system

00	02	48	Initiate active guidance
00	10	15	Guidance signal cutoff, second stage engine cutoff (altitude 141.6 miles, 1,130.9 miles down range, velocity 17,405.4 mph)
00	10	25	Insertion into orbit (altitude 141.7 miles, 1,175.2 miles down range, velocity 17,420.4 mph)
01	34	6	Begin orbital safing of vehicle. Dump pressurant and propellants (Altitude 142 miles, 1,617.9 miles west of KSC, velocity 17,418.4 mph)
02	29	55	Begin manual crew control of vehicle from spacecraft (altitude 190.4 miles, 11,928.6 miles west of KSC, velocity 17,240.3 mph)
02	54	55	Spacecraft-launch vehicle separation (150.1 miles altitude, 5,436.3 miles west of KSC, velocity 17,403.2 mph)

LAUNCH PREPARATIONS

Pre-launch checkout and the countdown for Apollo 7 are conducted by a government-industry team headed by NASA's Kennedy Space Center. The Launch Control Center in the Complex 34 blockhouse will be manned by a crew of about 250 during the final countdown.

The two propulsion stages and the instrument unit of the Saturn IB launch vehicle were erected at Complex 34 in April. KSC crews conducted a series of preliminary tests with the individual stages prior to electrical mate and integrated systems tests of the overall vehicle.

The Apollo 7 Command and Service Modules arrived at KSC in May. Preliminary checkout of spacecraft systems was conducted at the Manned Spacecraft Operations Building. The two Modules were mated in the MSOB vacuum chamber for a series of unmanned and manned altitude runs. The prime crew and the backups each participated in one of the altitude runs before the spacecraft was mated to its adapter and taken to Complex 34. The spacecraft was mated to the launch vehicle at the pad in August. The initial mating was mechanical, followed by an electrical mating some three weeks later. When this was accomplished, overall tests of the space vehicle were ready to begin.

Tests of the integrated launch vehicle and spacecraft followed. The launch escape tower was mated and a series of simulated missions were performed. Several of the runs were conducted with the launch pad umbilicals connected. One major test was made with umbilicals disconnected in a complete launch mission on the ground — a "Plugs Out Test" — with the prime crew in the spacecraft with hatch open.

A Countdown Demonstration Test was conducted about four weeks prior to the scheduled launch date. This is a complete dress rehearsal of the countdown. It is divided into "wet" and a "dry" test. The "wet" test encompassed the entire countdown, including the fueling, but the astronauts did not board the spacecraft. The "dry" portion picked up the countdown shortly before propellant loading. This time the loading was simulated and the flight crew participated as it would on launch day.

About two weeks before the scheduled launch date a Flight Readiness Test is conducted to exercise the launch vehicle and spacecraft systems. The Mission Control Center, Houston, participates in this test with the KSC launch team.

Following a data review of the Flight Readiness Test, hypergolic propellants are loaded aboard the Apollo spacecraft and the Auxiliary Propulsion System propellants aboard the second stage (S-IVB), and the system is static fired. RP-1, the fuel for the first stage, is brought aboard prior to picking up the precount at about T-102 hours.

Automatic checkout, utilizing RCA-110A computers, plays a major role in checkout and countdown preparations for both the launch vehicle and spacecraft. Computer functions for the launch vehicle are located in the blockhouse and at the automatic ground control station at the launch pad. Spacecraft checkout, centralized at the KSC Manned Spacecraft Operations Building, is controlled by a computer complex known as Acceptance Checkout Equipment. The use of the computers enables the launch crews to receive rapid readouts on launch vehicle and spacecraft systems during the checkout and countdown.

The final countdown for Apollo 7 will begin at T-14 hours 15 minutes, when power is applied to the Saturn IB launch vehicle. A planned six-hour built-in hold is scheduled at T-6 hours, before final propellant loading. Liftoff is scheduled for 11 a.m. EDT.

A pre-count operation begins at T-five days to cover an extensive series of preparatory tasks with the spacecraft. These include checks of the environmental control system, stabilization control system, guidance and navigation system, and water servicing of the spacecraft. Pyrotechnic devices are installed and mechanical closeout of the spacecraft accomplished. Helium servicing is performed, followed by fuel cell activation at T-32:30 hours. Cryogenic loading (bringing aboard the liquid oxygen and liquid hydrogen) extends from T-27:30 to T-21:30 hours.

Launch vehicle preparations in the precount include radio frequency and telemetry checks, and installation of ordnance and the flight batteries.

Following are highlights of the final countdown:

T-14:15 hours	—	Power up launch vehicle
T-13:00	—	Mission Control Center Houston, launch vehicle command checks
T-10:55	—	Range Safety command checks
T-9:30	—	Launch vehicle ordnance operations
T-9:00	—	Backup command module pilot (John Young) and backup lunar module pilot (Eugene Cernan) enter spacecraft
T-6:50	—	Move service structure to park-site
T-6:00	—	Six hour built in hold
T-6:00	—	Pad area cleared. Resume count. Begin LOX loading, first and second stages.
T-4:30	—	Lox loading complete. Begin liquid hydrogen loading, second stage.
T-3:10	—	Liquid hydrogen loading complete
T-3:00	—	Closeout crew returns to spacecraft White Room Prime crew departs quarters at Manned Spacecraft Operations Building
T-2:25	—	Prime crew begins spacecraft ingress
T-1:50	—	Abort advisory system checks
T-1:25	—	Space vehicle emergency detection system test
T-1:10	—	Range Safety tracking checks
T-50 minutes	—	Begin terminal count phase
T-45	—	Activate launch vehicle radio frequency and telemetry
T-40	—	Clear pad area
T-39	—	Final Houston launch vehicle command checks
T-33	—	Retract Apollo access arm to standby position. Arm Launch Escape System
T-31	—	Launch vehicle power transfer test
T-28	—	Final launch vehicle Range Safety command checks
T-25	—	Pressurize spacecraft reaction control system (RCS)
T-20	—	Spacecraft RCS static fire
T-15	—	Spacecraft to internal power
T-6	—	Final Go-No Go status check
T-5	—	Apollo access arm to full retract position
T-2:43	—	Begin automatic launch sequence
T-28 sec.	—	Launch vehicle to internal power
T-3 secs	—	First stage ignition
T-0	—	Liftoff

Note: Times are subject to change prior to launch.

LAUNCH COMPLEX 34

Launch Complex 34 is located at the north end of Cape Kennedy and covers approximately 77 acres. Major features on the Complex include the launch pad and pedestal, an umbilical tower, a service structure mounted on rails which moves back to a parked position about 600 feet from the pad at launch, a launch control center (blockhouse), an automatic ground control station, propellant facilities, and an operations support building.

Construction at Complex 34 was completed in time for the first Saturn I launch, Oct. 27, 1961. The first four launches in the Saturn development program took place there, the fourth one on Mar. 28, 1963. The last six Saturn I's were launched at Complex 37, north of 34.

Since its final test at Complex 34, the pad was modified for launching the Saturn IB. In addition, hurricane gates have been installed on the service structure so that a launch vehicle could ride out hurricane force winds without being taken to a hangar area.

SAFETY CHANGES

Preparations were in progress for the first manned Apollo flight at Complex 34 when a fire in the spacecraft took the lives of Astronauts Virgil I. Grissom, Edward H. White, II and Roger B. Chaffee Jan. 27, 1967. The accident occurred in the "plugs out" test.

As a result of review board recommendations, a number of changes were made at Complex 34, including structural modifications to the white room for the new quick-opening spacecraft hatch, improved fire fighting equipment, emergency egress routes and emergency access to the spacecraft.

A number of other safety features have been added. All electrical equipment in the white room is now purged with nitrogen. A hand-held water hose is available for fire fighting and a large exhaust fan draws smoke and fumes from the white room. The room is covered with a fire-resistant paint. Certain structural members have been moved to provide easier access to the spacecraft and faster egress.

A water spray system was added which would cool the launch escape system positioned above the command module, in the event of fire. The launch escape system contains solid propellants which could be ignited by extreme heat. Additional water spray systems were installed along the egress route from the spacecraft to ground level.

The primary mode of emergency egress for astronauts and technicians during the final phase of the countdown is the high-speed elevator which is set to run nonstop from the 220-foot level of the umbilical tower to the ground. A slide-wire system provides an alternate means of quick exit; this would be used for immediate escape from the pad area. The 1,200-foot slide-wire, attached at the 220-foot level, takes only 30 seconds to carry a man to the edge of the launch complex.

Complex 34 Data

The launch pad is 430 feet in diameter. Part of the pad is covered with refractory brick that minimizes damage from the rocket exhaust. The surface is 16 feet above sea level.

The 42-foot-square, reinforced concrete launch pedestal, located in the center of the pad, provides a platform for the launch vehicle and certain ground support equipment. It is 27 feet high. Plate steel covers all surfaces exposed to rocket flame which is exhausted through an opening 25 feet in diameter to a deflector below. This opening also provides access to the first stage engines. Eight hold-down arm assemblies are bolted around this opening to anchor the launch vehicle to the top of the pedestal. The hold-down arms are released after full thrust for liftoff is reached by the first stage engines.

The launch team, instrumentation, and control equipment connected with launch activities are housed in the blockhouse, which also provides blast protection for personnel and equipment.

The blockhouse is a two-story, reinforced concrete igloo-type building located 1,000 feet from the launch pad. Its walls vary from 7 feet thick at the top of the dome to 30 feet at the base. The building contains 11,650 square feet of space and is designed to withstand blast pressures of 2,188 pounds per square inch.

The first floor houses one of the RCA-110A computers used for automatic checkout, and personnel involved in tracking, telemetry, closed-circuit television, communication, etc. Launch control and the various monitoring and recording consoles are located on the second floor.

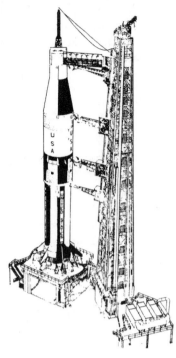

APOLLO 7 SPACE VEHICLE AND UMBILICAL TOWER

The service structure, a movable steel framework used during vehicle erection, assembly and checkout, provides work platforms for personnel, cranes for lifting rocket stages and spacecraft into place on the launch pedestal, and protection from the weather for both the space vehicle and launch personnel. The inverted U-shaped structure rises 310 feet above the launch pad, and its base measures 70 by 130 feet.

There are four elevators and seven fixed work platforms at various levels within the structure legs. Eight enclosed platforms can be extended to the vehicle from the tower. The launch escape system for the Apollo spacecraft is reached from two additional work platforms located near the top of the service structure.

The 3,552-ton service structure moves on four 12-wheel trucks along a special dual track railway within the complex. At the launch pad, support points remove the service structure from the trucks and anchor it to the ground. Before the rocket is launched, the service structure is moved to its parking position some 600 feet away from the pedestal. A 500-kva diesel electric generator, enclosed in the base, powers the 100-horsepower traction motors in each truck.

The 240-foot umbilical tower at Complex 34 is a steel-trussed structure with four swing arms attached to the space vehicle from the joints. Each swing arm carries links between the space vehicle and tower which lead to ground-based power, air conditioning, hydraulic, pneumatic, fuel, measuring, and command systems.

LAUNCH COMPLEX 34

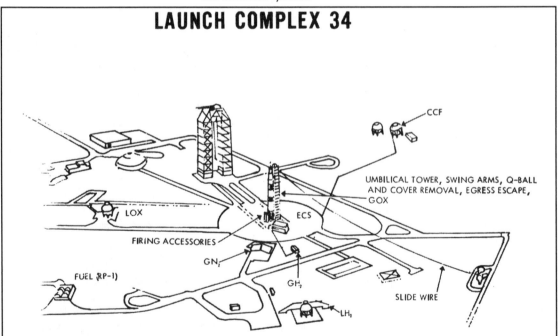

At the 220-foot level is the Apollo spacecraft access arm. Astronauts go to and from the spacecraft through this access arm, which is connected to the white room. The umbilical elevator, which can move 450 feet-per-minute, is the astronauts' prime emergency escape.

Service facilities store and transfer RP-1 fuel to the launch vehicle's first stage under remote control of the automatic-semi-automatic system. The two cylindrical RP-1 storage tanks, measuring 41 feet long, 11 feet in diameter, have a total capacity of 60,000 gallons-per-minute and a slow-fill rate of 200 gallons-per-minute. The system has facilities for filtration and water separation.

Liquid hydrogen fuel to the second stage of the Saturn 1B is stored and transferred at minus 423 degrees F. The remotely-controlled facility, also automatic-semi-automatic, has a 125,000-gallon storage capacity in a double-walled, vacuum-insulated spherical tank 38 feet in diameter. It is insulated by perlite, a glassy volcanic rock. The system has a transfer capability of 3,000 gallons-per-minute, a replenish rate of 0 to 200 gallons, and a fine-fill rate of 500 gallons. One hydrogen burn pond, located near the storage area, disposes of vented gas from the storage tank and part of the transfer line system. A second burn pond, located adjacent to the launch pads is used to dispose of hydrogen vented from the vehicle, the helium heat exchange, and the remainder of the transfer line.

Liquid oxygen is stored and transferred at minus-297 degrees F, for the Saturn's first and second stages. The main 125,000 gallon tank is a double-walled sphere with an outside diameter of 41.25 feet. A 4-foot separation between the inner and outer tanks is filled with expanded perlite and pressurized with gaseous nitrogen. The 11-foot diameter, cylindrical, perlite-insulated, replenishing tank holds 13,000 gallons. LOX is transferred by three pumps: a 2,500-gallon-per-minute pump for filling the first stage, a 1,000 gallon one for filling the second stage, and one of 1,000 gallons capacity for transferring LOX from the main tank into the replenish tank. The fast-fill, slow-fill, and replenish rates for servicing the first stage are 2,500, 500 and 0-50 gallons per minute, respectively.

For the second stage, the fast-fill, slow-fill rates are 1,000, 300, and 0-10 gallons respectively. Initiation and control of the tanking and replenishing operations are accomplished and monitored from the control center during launch operations.

MISSION CONTROL CENTER-HOUSTON

The Mission Control Center at the Manned Spacecraft Center, Houston, is the focal point for all Apollo flight control activities. The Center will receive tracking and telemetry data from the Manned Space Flight Network. These data will be processed through the Mission Control Center Real-Time Computer Complex and used to drive displays for the flight controllers and engineers in the Mission Operations Control Room and staff support rooms.

The Manned Space Flight Network tracking and data acquisition stations link the flight controllers at the Center to the spacecraft.
For Apollo 7, all stations will be remoted sites without flight control teams. All uplink commands and voice communications will originate from Houston, and telemetry data will be sent back to Houston at high speed (2,400 bits per second). They can be either real time or playback information.

Signal flow for voice circuits between Houston and the remote sites is via commercial carrier, usually satellite, wherever possible using leased lines which are part of the NASA Communications Network.

Commands are sent from Houston to NASA's Goddard Space Flight Center, Greenbelt, Md., lines which link computers at the two points. The Goddard computers provide automatic switching facilities and speed buffering for the command data. Data are transferred from Goddard to remote sites on high speed (2,400 bits per second) lines. Command loads also can be sent by teletype from Houston to the remote sites at 100 words per minute. Again, Goddard computers provide storage and switching functions.

Telemetry data at the remote site are received by the RF receivers, processed by the Pulse Code Modulation ground stations, and transferred to the 642B remote-site telemetry computer for storage. Depending on the format selected by the telemetry controller at Houston, the 642B will output the desired format through a 2010 data transmission unit which provides parallel to serial conversion, and drives a 2,400 bit-per-second modem. The data modem converts the digital serial data to phase shifted keyed tones which are fed to the high speed data lines of the Communications Network.

Telemetry summary messages can also be output by the 642B computer, but these messages are sent to Houston on 100-word-per-minute teletype lines rather than on the high speed lines.

Tracking data are output from the sites in a low speed 100 words) teletype format and a 240-bit block high speed (2400 bits) format, Data rates are 1 sample-6 seconds for teletype and 10 samples (frames) per second for high speed data.

All high speed data, whether tracking or telemetry, which originate at a remote site are sent to Goddard on high speed lines. Goddard reformats the data when necessary and sends them to Houston in 600-bit blocks at a 40,800 bits-per-second rate. Of the 600-bit block, 480 bits are reserved for data, the other 120 bits for address, sync, intercomputer instructions, and poly-nominal error encoding.

All wideband 40,800 bits-per-second data originating at Houston are converted to high speed (2,400 bits-per-second) data at Goddard before being transferred to the designated remoted site.

MANNED SPACE FLIGHT NETWORK

The Manned Space Flight Tracking Network for Apollo 7, consisting of 14 ground stations, four instrumented ships and five instrumented aircraft, is working its first manned flight. It is the global extension of the monitoring and control capability of the Mission Control Center in Houston. The network, developed by NASA through the Mercury and Gemini programs, now represents an investment of some $500 million and, during flight operations, has 4,000 persons on duty. In addition to NASA facilities, the network includes facilities of the Department of Defense and the Australian Department of Supply.

The network was developed by the Goddard Space Flight Center under the direction of NASA's Associate Administrator for Tracking and Data Acquisition.

Basically, manned flight stations provide one or more of the following functions for flight control:

1. Telemetry;
2. Tracking;
3. commanding, and
4. voice communications with the spacecraft.

Apollo missions require the network to obtain information simultaneously — instantly recognize it, decode it, and arrange it for computer processing and display in the Houston Control Center.

Apollo generates much more information than either Mercury or Gemini did, so data processing and display capability are needed. Apollo also requires network support at both Earth orbital and lunar distances. The Apollo Unified S-Band System (USB) provides this capability.

Network Support Team - Goddard

The 30-man network support team mans the various communications positions at the Manned Space Flight Operations Center. The team is comprised of technical and operational personnel required by the Network Director, Network Operations Manager and Network Controller to assist in operating the network around the clock and coordinating its activities.

The team coordinates network communications and provides the Network Operations Manager and Network Controller with the necessary technical assistance and monitoring capability. The Network Support Team also is responsible for communicating with non-NASA facilities for assistance not available in the network.

As in Apollo 6 the network stations, launch site, and control and communications centers will be connected through the two million miles of communications circuitry of the NASA Communications Network.

NASA Communications Network - Goddard

This network consists of several systems of diversely routed communications channels leased on communications satellites, common carrier systems and high frequency radio facilities where necessary to provide the access links.

The system consists of both narrow and wide-band channels, and some TV channels. Included are a variety of telegraph, voice and data systems (digital and analog) with a wide range of digital data rates. Wide-band and TV systems do not extend overseas. Alternate routes or redundancy are provided for added reliability in critical mission operations.

A primary switching center and intermediate switching and control points are established to provide centralized facility and technical control, and switching operations under direct NASA control. The primary switching center is at Goddard, and intermediate switching centers are located at Canberra, Australia; Madrid, Spain; London, England; Honolulu, Hawaii; Guam and Cape Kennedy, Fla.

For Apollo 7, Cape Kennedy is connected directly to the Mission Control Center, Houston, by the communication network's Apollo Launch Data System, a combination of data gathering and transmission systems designed to handle launch data exclusively.

After launch all network and tracking data are directed to the Mission Control Center, Houston, through Goddard. A high-speed data line (2,400 bits-per-second) connects Cape Kennedy to Goddard, where the transmission rate is

MANNED SPACE FLIGHT NETWORK (Apollo 7)

increased to 40,800 bits-per-second from there to Houston. Upon orbital insertion, tracking responsibility is transferred between the various stations as the spacecraft circles the Earth.

Two Intelsat communications satellites will be used for Apollo 7, one positioned over the Atlantic Ocean in an equatorial orbit varying about six degrees N. and S. latitude and six degrees W. longitude. The Atlantic satellite will service the Ascension Island USB station, the Atlantic Ocean ship and the Canary Island site.

Only two of these three stations will be transmitting information back to Goddard at any one time, but all four stations can receive at all times.

The second Apollo Intelsat communications satellite is located about 170 degrees E. longitude over the mid-Pacific near the Equator at the international dateline. It will service the Carnarvon, Australian USB site and the Pacific Ocean ships. All these stations will be able to transmit simultaneously through the satellite to Houston via Brewster Flat, Wash., and the Goddard Space Flight Center.

Network Computers

At fraction-of-a-second intervals, the network's digital data processing systems, with NASA's Manned Spacecraft Center as the focal point, "talk" to each other or to the astronauts in real time. High speed computers at the remote sites (tracking ships included) issue commands or "up" data on such matters as control of cabin pressure, orbital guidance commands, or "go-no-go" indications to perform certain functions.

In the case of information originating from Houston, the computers refer to their pre-programmed information for validity before transmitting the required data to the capsule.

Such "up" information is communications by ultra-high frequency radio about 1,000 bits-per-second. Communication between remote ground sites, via high-speed communications links, occurs about the same rate. Houston reads information from these ground sites at 2,000 bits-per-second, as well as from remote sites at 100 words-per-minute.

The computer systems perform many other functions, including:

   * Assuring the quality of the transmission lines by continually exercising data paths.
   * Verifying accuracy of the messages by repetitive operations.
   * Constantly updating the flight status

For "down" data, sensors built into the spacecraft continually sample cabin temperature, pressure, physical information on the astronauts such as heartbeat and respiration, among other items. These data are transmitted to the ground stations at 51.2 kilobits (12,800 binary digits) per second.

The computers then:

   * Detect and select changes or deviations, compare with their stored programs, and indicate the problem areas or pertinent data to the flight controllers.
   * Provide displays to mission personnel.
   * Assemble output data in proper formats.
   * Log data on magnetic tape for replay.
   * Provide storage for "on-call" display for the flight controllers.
   * Keep time.

Fourteen land stations are outfitted with computer systems to relay telemetry and command information between Houston and Apollo spacecraft: Canberra and Carnarvon, Australia; Guam; Kauai, Hawaii; Goldstone, Calif; Corpus Christi, Tex.; Cape Kennedy; Grand Bahama Island; Bermuda; Madrid; Grand Canary Island; Antigua; Ascension Island; and Guaymas, Mex.

Network Testing

Although the network operators and equipment are under regular testing exercises, approximately 14 days before a planned launch, each system and subsystem in the network undergoes nearly continuous testing and checking.

Each system and subsystem at each station has its own performance criteria. At Goddard these criteria are stored in a computer memory system. Each station reports its own system-by-system checks via high-speed digital circuits. By comparing these reports automatically with the stored values, any variation from the desired, the computer reports a "no-go" condition. If there is no variation from what is expected there is a "go". The process is repeated until the test conducted finds the entire network ready. Normally some 100 separate system checks are required for a checkout of the net. The procedure, known as Computer and Data Flow Integrated Subsystems Test, is repeated for each mission.

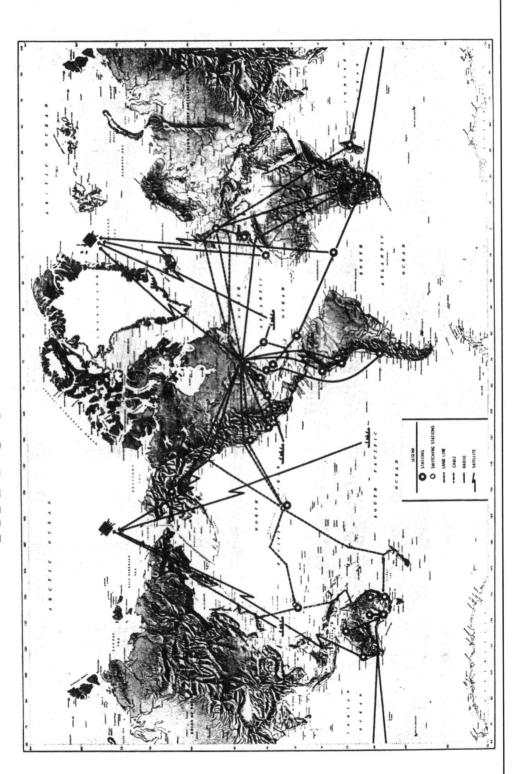

Network Configuration for Apollo 7

Unified S-Band Sites:

NASA 30-Ft. Antenna Sites	NASA 85-Ft. Antenna Sites
Antigua (ANG)	Canberra (CNB), Australia
Ascension Island (ACN).	(Prime)
Bermuda (BDA)	Goldstone (GDS), Calif.
Canary Island (CYI)	(Prime)
Carnarvon (CRO), Australia	Madrid (MAD), Spain (Prime)
Grand Bahama Island (GBM)	*Canberra (DSS-42-Apollo Wing)
Guam (GWM)	(Backup)
Guaymas (GYM), Mexico	*Goldstone (DSS-11-Apollo Wing)
Hawaii (HAW)	(Backup)
Merritt Island (MIL), Fla.	*Madrid (DSS-61-Apollo Wing)
Texas (TEX), Corpus Christi	(Backup)

Tananarive (TAN), Malagasy Republic (STADAN station in support role only.)

Wings have been added to JPL Deep Space Network site operations buildings. These wings contain additional Unified S-Band equipment as backup to the Prime sites.

The Apollo Ships

For this mission, four Apollo Instrumentation Ships will serve several purposes in the Manned Space Flight Network. They will support launch abort contingencies, fill gaps in ground station coverage and monitor the early part of the reentry phase.

The Vanguard will be positioned about 1,000 miles east of Bermuda (32.7° N – 48° W) and will assist that station in covering orbital insertion, and will supply data in case of an abort.

The ships, Redstone and Mercury, will serve as orbital gap fillers, with Redstone positioned about 3,600 miles south of Los Angeles (25° S – 118° W), and Mercury will be located some 90 miles east of Taiwan (25° N 125° E).

The Mercury will be able to support the alternate reentry area in the Pacific Ocean.

The primary tracking function of the Huntsville will be to cover the de-orbit burn phase of reentry. For other parts of the mission, Huntsville will be used for unified S-band telemetry receive and record and astronaut-ground voice remoting. This ship will be situated about 1,200 miles west of Los Angeles (25° N –136° W).

The ships are operated by civilian Military Sea Transport crews. The instrumentation is operated and maintained by civilian technical crews. These technical crews are trained to NASA specifications and standards, and operate in accordance with NASA-specified procedures in operation, calibration, checkout, maintenance, failure-reporting and modifications control.

Five Apollo Range Instrumentation Aircraft will take part in Apollo 7, two from Patrick Air Force Base, Fla., three from Australia. They are part of a group of eight EC-135A, four-engine jets supplementing land and ship stations in support of Apollo.

The range aircraft provide two-way voice relay between the spacecraft and Mission Control Center, receive and record telemetry signals from the spacecraft and transfer these data to ground stations for relay to mission control.

PHOTOGRAPHIC EQUIPMENT

Apollo 7 will carry a 70 mm Hasselblad still camera and two 16 mm Maurer sequence cameras. Film magazines for specific mission photographic objectives are carried for each camera.

The Hasselblad is fitted with an 80 mm f/2.8 standard lens and the Maurer has bayonet-mount 18 mm f/2 and 5 mm wide angle f/2 lenses.

Hasselblad shutter speeds are variable from 1 sec. to 1/500 sec., and sequence camera frame rates of 1, 6, 12 and 24 frames-per-second can be selected.

NETWORK CONFIGURATION FOR THE APOLLO 7

Facilities	C-band (high speed)	C-band (low speed)	ODOP	USB	Voice	Command	TLM	VHF Links	FM Remoting	Mag Tape Recording	Decoms	Displays	UHF Commanding	CMD Destruct	DRUL Remoting 642B	642B TLM	642B CMD	High Speed Data	Wideband Data	TTY	Voice (SCAMA)	Voice VHF A/G	Biometer	SPAN	Remarks
						TRACKING / USB		**TLM**					**CMD**			**Data Processing**		**Comm**					**Other**		
PAT	2	2											1												Launch Abort Contingency
CNV	1	2	1																						
MLA	2	2																							
TEL-IV																									
CIF																									
MIL				2	2	2	2	2	2	2	2		2	2		2	2	2		2	2	2			
GBI	2	2													1										
GBM				1	1	1	1	1	1	1	1		1		1	1	1	1		1	1	1			
ANT		3																							
ANG				3	3	3	3		3	3	3		3		1	3	3	3		3	3	3			
BDA	2	2		2	2	2	2	2	2	2	2	1	2	1		2	2	2		2	2	2			Launch Abort Contingency
CYI		3		3	3	3	3	3	3	3	3		3			3	3	3		3	3	3	3	3	
ASC		3																							
ACN				3	3	3	3	3	3	3						3	3			3	3	3			
PRE		3																							
TAN		3						3		3										3	3	3			
CRO	3	3		3	3	3	3	3	3	3	3		3			3	3	3		3	3	3	3	3	
WOM		3																		3	3				
GWM				3	3	3	3	3	3	3	3		3			3	3	3		3	3	3			
HAW		3		3	3	3	3	3	3	3	3		3			3	3	3		3	3	3			
CAL		3																		3	3				
GDS				3	3	3	3		3	3	3					3	3	3		3	3				
GYM				3	3	3	3	3	3	3	3					3	3	3		3	3	3			
WHS		3																		3	3				
TEX				3	3	3	3	3	3	3	3		3			3	3	3		3	3	3			Backup to BDA
GTK														1											
LIMA																				3			3		
HSK		3		3	3	3		3	3	3						3	3	3		3	3				
HSKX		3*		3*																					
KSC																									
MAD		3		3	3	3		3	3	3						3	3	3		3	3				
MADX		3*			3*																				
ARIA		3		3	3	3	3	3	3							3	3	3		3	3	3			Reentry Support
RED		3		3	3	3	3	3	3	3															
VAN		2		2	2	2	2	2	2	2			2			2	2	2		2	2	2			Insertion Ship
MER		3		3	3	3	3	3	3	3						3	3	3		3	3	3			Alt. Reentry
HTV		3		3	3	3		3	3	3										3	3	3			Reentry

LEGEND:
1 LAUNCH
2 LAUNCH AND ORBIT
3 ORBIT
4 LAUNCH ABORT
* - RECEIVE and RECORD ONLY

Film emulsions have been chosen for each specific mission photographic objective. For example, a medium-speed color reversal film will be used for synoptic terrain-weather experiments and rendezvous and spacecraft-LM adapter photography, and a high-speed color film for cabin interior photography. Additionally, a high resolution low-speed black and white film will be used for some phases of the synoptic terrain-weather photographic experiments.

Camera accessories carried aboard Apollo 7 include window mounting brackets, right-angle mirror attachments, ultraviolet filter, a ringsight common to both camera types, and a spotmeter for determining exposures.

Onboard Television

A television camera aboard the spacecraft will relay live TV pictures from Apollo 7 to the ground.

The 4.5-pound RCA camera is equipped with a 160 degree wide-angle lens and a 9 degree lens. A 12-foot power-video cable permits the camera to be hand-held at the command module rendezvous windows for out-the-window photography as well as mounted in other locations for interior photography.

Mission activities during the first 16 revolutions, such as S-IVB rendezvous, will not permit the crew to operate the camera. After revolution 16, one live TV transmission each day will be possible. Only the Corpus Christi and the Merritt Island Launch Area stations of the Manned Space Flight Network are equipped to receive and convert the spacecraft TV signal.

Among crew activities scheduled for television photography are meal periods, operation on the display keyboards, lithium hydroxide canister changes, Earth scan during photographic experiments and systems test operations.

The onboard system scans at 10 frames a second; ground equipment converts the scan rate to the industry standard 30 frames a second before relaying the picture to Mission Control Center-Houston.

The Corpus Christi and Cape Kennedy ground stations have to use large antennas and extremely sensitive unified S-band receivers to detect the very weak signals from the spacecraft.

In TV broadcast to homes, the average distance is only five miles between the transmitting station and the house receiver, while the station transmits an average of 50,000 watts of power. In contrast, the Apollo 7 spacecraft will be as much as 1,000 miles away from the ground and the power will be only 20 watts.

Because of the greater distance and lower power signals received by the ground antennas will be only 100,000,000th as strong as normally received at private homes. The NASA ground station's large antenna and sensitive receivers make up for most of this difference, but the Apollo pictures are not expected to be as high in quality as normal broadcast programs. The spacecraft TV may be fuzzy and low in contrast, but the home viewer should still be able to see the picture with reasonable clarity.

APOLLO 7 CREW

The crewmen of Apollo 7 have spent more than five hours of formal crew training for each hour of the mission's possible 10-day duration. Almost 1,200 hours of training were in the Apollo 7 crew training syllabus over and above the normal preparations for the mission — technical briefings and reviews, pilot meetings and study. The Apollo 7 crewmen have virtually lived with their spacecraft in its pre-flight checkouts at the North American Rockwell plant in Downey, Calif. and in pre-launch testing at NASA Kennedy Space Center. Taking part in factory and launch area testing has provided the crew with valuable operational knowledge of this complex vehicle.

Highlights of specialized Apollo 7 crew training topics:

* Detailed series of briefings on spacecraft systems, operation and modifications.

* Saturn launch vehicle briefings on countdown, range safety, flight dynamics, failure modes and abort conditions. The launch vehicle
briefings were updated periodically with a final briefing at T-30 days.

* Apollo Guidance and Navigation system briefings and simulations at the Massachusetts Institute of Technology Instrumentation Laboratory.

* Briefings and continuous training on mission photographic objectives and use of camera equipment.

* Training for the five Apollo 7 experiments. The two photographic experiments will be conducted in flight and the three medical experiments before and after flight.

* Extensive pilot participation in reviews of all flight procedures for normal as well as emergency situations.

* Stowage reviews and practice in training sessions in the spacecraft, mockups, and Command Module simulators allowed the crewmen to evaluate spacecraft stowage of crew-associated equipment.

* More than 160 hours of training per man in Command Module simulators at MSC and KSC, including closed-loop simulations with flight controllers in the Mission Control Center. Other Apollo simulators at various locations were used extensively for specialized crew training.

* Water egress training conducted in indoor tanks as well as in the Gulf of Mexico, included uprighting from the Stable II position (apex down) to the Stable I position (apex up), egress onto rafts and helicopter pickup.

* Launch pad egress training from mockups and from the actual spacecraft on the launch pad for possible emergencies such as fire, contaminants and power failures.

* The training covered use of Apollo spacecraft fire suppression equipment in the cockpit.

* Planetarium reviews at Morehead Planetarium, Chapel Hill, N. C., and at Griffith Planetarium, Los Angeles, Calif., of the celestial sphere with special emphasis on the 37 navigational stars used by the Apollo Guidance Computer.

Crew Training Summary Table

Activity	Hours
Briefings and Reviews:	
Command-Service Module Systems	140
Launch Vehicle	20
Guidance and navigation program	36
Photography	8
Experiments	8
Procedures:	
Operational Checkout Procedures and Test Checkout Procedures	60
Checklist and Apollo Operations Handbook	50
Emergency and abort	24
Stowage	30
Flight Plan	50
Mission Rules	16
Design and Acceptance	60
Flight Readiness	10
Training reviews	30
Team meetings	60
Pilot meetings	40
Rendezvous	20
Spacecraft test participation:	
Spacecraft cockpit Operational Checkout Procedures and Test Checkout Procedures	80
Simulator training:	
Command Module simulator	160
Command Module Procedures Simulator	60
Dynamic Crew Procedures Simulator	15
Contractor simulators	20
Simulator briefings	75
Special purpose training:	
Stowage	20
Egress	20
Planetarium	20
Spacecraft fire training	5
Intravehicular activity training	9
Total:	1,146

Apollo 7 Spacesuits

Apollo 7 crewmen, for the first hours of flight, and for the four hours prior to the de-orbit burn, will wear the A7L pressure garment assembly — a multi-layer spacesuit consisting of a helmet, torso and gloves which can be pressurized independently of the spacecraft.

The spacesuit outer layer is Teflon-coated Beta fabric woven of fiberglass strands with inner layers of aluminized Kapton-coated Beta fabric marquisette spacer for separating insulating layers, restraint layer, a pressure bladder and an inner high-temperature nylon liner.

Oxygen connections, communications and biomedical data lines attach to fittings on the front of the torso.

A one-piece constant wear garment, similar to "long johns," is worn as an undergarment for the spacesuit and for the in-flight coveralls provided for shirtsleeve operations. The constant wear garment is porous-knit cotton with a waist-to-neck zipper for donning. Attach points for the biomedical harness also are provided.

After doffing the spacesuits, the crew will wear Teflon fabric in-flight coveralls over the constant wear garment. The two-piece coveralls provide warmth in addition to pockets for personal items.

The crewmen will wear communications carriers inside the pressure helmet. The communications carriers provide redundancy in that each has two microphones and two earphones.

A lightweight headset is worn with the inflight coveralls.

APOLLO SPACE SUIT

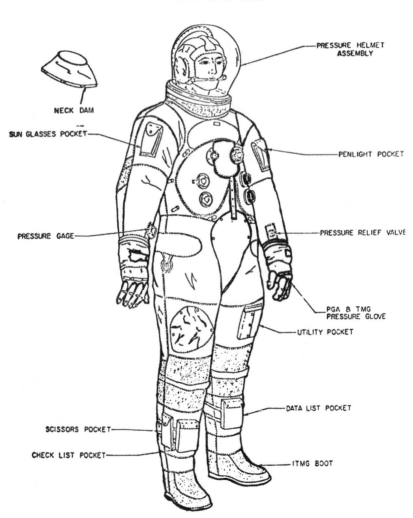

Apollo 7 Crew Meals

The Apollo 7 crew had a wide range of food items from which to select their daily mission space menu. More than 60 items comprise the selection list of freeze-dried bite-size rehydratable foods.

Average daily value of three meals will be 2,500 calories per man.

Unlike Gemini crewmen who prepared their meals with cold water, Apollo crewmen have running water for hot meals and cold drinks.

Water is obtained from three sources — a portable dispenser for drinking water and two water spigots at the food preparation station, one supplying water at about 155 degrees F., the other at about 55 degrees F. The portable water dispenser emits half ounce spurts with each squeeze and the food preparation spigots dispense water in one-ounce increments.

Spacecraft potable water is supplied from service module fuel cell by-product water.

The Menu.

The day-by-day, meal-by-meal Apollo 7 menu for each crewman is listed on the following pages.

Day 1, 5 and 9	Day 2, 6 and 10	Day 3, 7 and 11	Day 4 and 8
Meal A	**Meal A**	**Meal A**	**Meal A**
Peaches (R) Bacon Squares (8) Cinnamon Toasted Bread Cubes (8) Breakfast Drink (R)	Applesauce (R) Sausage Patties (R) Apricot Cereal Cubes (8) Breakfast Drink (R)	Fruit Cocktail (R) Bacon Squares (8) Cinnamon Toasted Bread Cubes (8) Cocoa (R) Breakfast Drink (R)	Canadian Bacon & Applesauce (R) Strawberry Cereal Cubes (8) Cinnamon Toasted Bread Cubes (8) Breakfast Drink (R)
(Calories 500)	(Calories 595)	(Calories 669)	(Calories 611)
Meal B	**Meal B**	**Meal B**	**Meal B**
Corn Chowder (R) Chicken Sandwiches (6) Beef Stew Bites (8) Sugar Cookies (8) Orange Drink (R) Breakfast Drink (R)	Spaghetti w/Meat Sauce (R) Beef Bites (8) Banana Pudding (R) Pineapple Fruitcake (6)	Beef Pot Roast (R) Sugar Cookies (8) Butterscotch Pudding (R) Breakfast Drink (R)	Pea Soup (R) Salmon Salad (R) Cheese Sandwiches (6) Grapefruit Drink (R) Breakfast Drink (R)
(Calories 809)	(Calories 915)	(Calories 665)	(Calories 756)
Meal C	**Meal C**	**Meal C**	**Meal C**
Beef and Gravy (R) Brownies (8) Chocolate Pudding (R) Grapefruit Drink (R)	Tuna Salad (R) Cinnamon Toasted Bread Cubes (8) Chocolate Pudding (R) Pineapple-Grapefruit Drink (R) Breakfast Drink (R)	Potato Soup (R) Chicken Salad (R) Barbecue Beef Bites (8) Gingerbread (8) Grapefruit Drink (R)	Shrimp Cocktail (R) Chicken and Gravy (R) Cinnamon Toasted Bread Cubes (8) Date Fruitcake (6) Pineapple-Grapefruit Drink (R)
Calories 917)	(Calories 895)	(Calories 975)	(Calories 965)
Total Calories 2,226	Total Calories 2,408	Total Calories 2,309	Total Calories 2,332

Day 1, 5 and 9	Day 2, 6 and 10	Day 3, 7 and 11	Day 4 and 8
* Meal A	Meal A	Meal A	Meal A
Peaches (R) Corn Flakes (R) Bacon Squares (8) Toasted Bread Cubes(8) Grapefruit Drink (R) Breakfast Drink (R)	Applesauce (R) Bacon squares (8) Cinnamon Toasted Bread Cubes (8) Orange Drink (R) Breakfast Drink (R)	Fruit Cocktail (R) Sausage Patties (R) Apricot Cereal Cubes(8) Cocoa (R) Breakfast Drink (R)	Canadian Bacon and Applesauce (R) Apricot Cereal Cubes (8) Pineapple-Grapefruit Drink (R) Breakfast Drink (R)
(Calories 813)	(Calories 700)	(Calories 710)	(Calories 660)
Meal B	Meal B	Meal B	Meal B
Cream of Chicken Soup (R) Chicken do Vegetables(R) Sugar Cookies (8) Chocolate Pudding (R) Orange-Grapefruit Drink (R)	Salmon Salad (R) Butterscotch Pudding (R) Vanilla Ice Cream (8) Grapefruit Drink (R)	Canadian Bacon and Applesauce (R) Beef Pot Roast (R) Sugar Cookies (8) Butterscotch Pudding (R) Cocoa (R)	Pea Soup (R) Salmon Salad (R) Turkey Bites (8) Cheese Sandwiches (6) Grapefruit Drink (R)
(Calories 913)	(Calories 963)	(Calories 967)	(Calories 852)
Meal C	Meal C	Meal C	Meal C
Chicken Salad (R) Beef and Gravy R Date Fruitcake (43 Cocoa (R)	Beef Hash (R) Chicken & Gravy (R) Cinnamon Toasted Bread Cubes (8) Pineapple Fruitcake(4) Grapefruit Drink (R)	Potato Soup (R) Beef and Gravy (R) Creamed Chicken Bites (8) Cinnamon Toasted Bread Cubes (8) Pineapple-Grapefruit Drink (R)	Sausage Patties (R) Cinnamon Toasted Bread Cubes (8) Date Fruitcake (6) Grapefruit Drink (R)
(Calories 788)	(Calories 892)	(Calories 832)	(Calories 991)
Total Calories 2,514	Total Calories 2,555	Total Calories 2,5	Total Calories 2,503

* Meal A, Day 1 omitted on launch day.

Day 1, 5 and 9	Day 2, 6 and 10	Day 3, 7 and 11	Day 4 and 8
* Meal A	Meal A	Meal A	Meal A
Peaches (R) Bacon Squares (8) Cinnamon Toasted Bread Cubes (8) Grapefruit Drink (R)	Applesauce (R) Beef Hash (R) Cinnamon Toast(8) Apricot Cereal Cubes (8) Grapefruit Drink (R)	Fruit Cocktail (R) Bacon Squares (8) Cinnamon Toast (4) Orange Drink (R)	Canadian Bacon and Applesauce·(R) Cinnamon Toast (8) Apricot Cereal Cubes (8) Pineapple-Grapefruit Drink (R)
(Calories 696)	(Calories 786)	(Calories 500)	(Calories 611)
Meal B	Meal B	Meal B	Meal B
Cream of Chicken Soup (R) Chicken Sandwiches(6) Beef Sandwiches (8)	Tuna Salad (R) Beef Sandwiches 8) Cinnamon Toast (8) Butterscotch Pudding (R)	Corn Chowder (R) Barbecued Beef Bites (8) Cinnamon Toasted	Salmon Salad (R) Beef Sandwiches (8) Cinnamon Toasted Bread Cubes (8)

Sugar Cookies (8) Chocolate Pudding (R) Pineapple-Grapefruit Drink (R)	Pineapple-Grapefruit Drink (R)	Bread Cubes (8) Chocolate Pudding(R) Orange-Grapefruit Drink (R)	Gingerbread (8) Cocoa (R)
(Calories 1,020)	(Calories 846)	(Calories 1,060)	(Calories 1,017)
Meal C	Meal C	Meal C	Meal C
Beef and Gravy (R Beef Stew Bites (8) Cinnamon Toast (8) Brownies (8) Orange-Grapefruit Drink (R)	Beef & Vegetables (R) Barbecued Beef Bites (8) Cinnamon Toasted Bread Cubes (8) Banana Pudding(R) Orange Drink (R)	Chicken Salad (R) Beef Sandwiches (8) Cinnamon Toast (8) pineapple Fruitcake(6) Orange-Grapefruit Drink (R)	Creamed Chicken Bites (8) Chicken and Gravy (R) Toasted Bread Cubes (8) Date Fruitcake (4) Orange Drink (R)
(Calories 788)	(Calories 897)	(Calories 912)	(Calories 837)
Total Calories 2,504	Total Calories 2,529	Total Calories 2,472	Total Calories 2,465

* Meal A, Day 1 omitted on launch day.

Personal Hygiene

Crew personal hygiene equipment aboard Apollo 7 includes body cleanliness items, the waste management system and a medical kit.

Packaged with the food is a toothbrush and a 2-ounce tube of toothpaste for each crewman. Each man-meal package contains 3.5 by 4-inch wet-wipe cleansing towel. Additionally, three packages of 12 by 12-inch dry towels are stowed beneath the Command Module pilot couch. Each package contains seven towels.

Also stowed under the Command Module pilot couch are six tissue dispensers containing 55 3-ply tissues each.

Solid body wastes are collected in Gemini-type plastic defecation bags which contain a germicide to prevent bacteria and gas formation. The bags are sealed after use and stowed in empty food containers for post-flight analysis.

Urine collection devices are provided for use either while wearing the pressure suit or in the flight coveralls. Both devices attach to the spacecraft urine dump valve.

A medical accessory kit 6 by 4.5 by 4-inches is stowed on the spacecraft back wall at the feet of the Command Module pilot.

Medical kit contents are three motion sickness injectors, three pain suppression injectors, one 2-oz. bottle first aid ointment, two 1-oz. bottles eye drops, two compress bandages, 12 adhesive bandages and one oral thermometer. Pills contained in the medical kit are 24 antibiotic, 24 nausea, 12 stimulant, 12 pain killer, 24 decongestant, 24 diarrhea and 72 aspirin.

Sleep-work Cycles

At least one crew member will be awake at all times. The normal cycle will be 16 hours of work followed by eight hours of rest. Simultaneous periods of sleep are scheduled for the command pilot and lunar module pilot.

Sleeping positions in the command module are under the left and right couches, with heads toward the crew hatch. Two lightweight Beta fabric sleeping bags are each supported by two longitudinal straps attaching to lithium hydroxide storage boxes at one end and to the inner structure at the other end.

The bags are 64 inches long and are fitted with torso zipper openings and seven-inch diameter neck openings.

Survival Gear

The survival kit is stowed in two rucksacks in the right-hand forward equipment bay above the LM pilot.

Contents of rucksack No. 1 are: two combination survival lights, one desalter kit, three pair sunglasses, one radio beacon, one spare radio beacon battery and spacecraft connector cable, one machete in sheath, three water containers and two containers of Sun lotion. Rucksack No. 2: one three-man life raft with CO2 inflater, one sea anchor, two sea dye markers, three sunbonnets, one mooring lanyard, three manlines and two attach brackets.

The survival kit is designed to provide a 48-hour postlanding (water or land) survival capability for three crewmen between 40 degrees North and South latitudes.

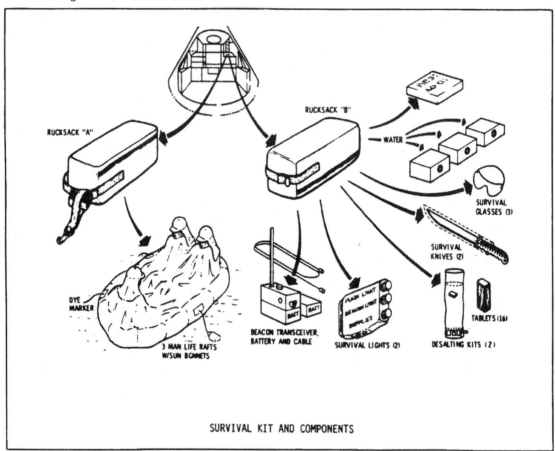

SURVIVAL KIT AND COMPONENTS

Biomedical Inflight Monitoring

The Apollo 7 crew inflight biomedical telemetry data received by the Manned Space Flight Network will be relayed for instantaneous display at Mission Control Center. Heart rate and breathing rate data will be displayed on the flight surgeons console during spacecraft passes over network stations. Heart rate and respiration rate average, range and deviation are computed and displayed on the digital TV screens. In addition, the instantaneous heart rate, real time and delayed EKG and respiration are recorded on strip charts for each man.

Biomedical data observed by the flight surgeon and his team in the Life Support Systems Staff Support Room will be correlated with spacecraft and spacesuit environmental data displays.

Blood pressure and body temperature are no longer taken as they were in earlier manned flight programs.

CREW BIOGRAPHIES

NAME: Walter M. Schirra, Jr. (Captain, USN)

BIRTHPLACE AND DATE: Mar. 12, 1923, Hackensack. N.J. Parents, Mr. and Mrs. Walter M. Schirra, Sr., reside in Point Loma, Calif.

PHYSICAL DESCRIPTION: Brown hair; brown eyes; height, 5 feet 10 inches; weight: 175 pounds.

EDUCATION: Graduated from Dwight Morrow High School, Englewood, N.J.; B.S., U.S. Naval Academy, 1945; received honorary Doctorate in Astronautical Engineering, Lafayette College, 1966.

MARITAL STATUS: Married to the former Josephine Fraser of Seattle.

CHILDREN: Walter M., III, June 23, 1950; Suzanne, Sept. 29, 1957.

ORGANIZATIONS: Member, Society of Experimental Test Pilots; Fellow, American Astronautical Society.

SPECIAL HONORS: Three Distinguished Flying Crosses, two Air Medals; two NASA Distinguished Service Medals; NASA Exceptional Service Medal; Navy Astronaut Wings; Distinguished Alumnus Award, Newark College of Engineering; Collier Trophy; SETP Kincheloe Award; AIAA Award; American Astronautical Society, Flight Achievement Award; co-recipient of 1966 Harmon Aviation Trophy.

EXPERIENCE: Flight training, Naval Air Station, Pensacola, Fla.

As exchange pilot with U.S. Air Force, 154th Fighter Bomber Squadron, flew 90 combat missions in F-8 E's in Korea; took part in development of Sidewinder Missile at the Naval Ordnance Test Station, China Lake, Calif; project pilot for F7U3 Cutlass and instructor pilot for Cutlass and FJ3 Fury; flew F3H-2N Demons in the 124th Fighter Squadron on board the carrier, U.S.S. LEXINGTON in the Pacific.

He attended Naval Air Safety Officer School, University of Southern California and completed test pilot training at Naval Air Test Center, Patuxent River, Md.; later was assigned there in suitability development work on the F4H.

He has accumulated more than 4,300 hours flying time, with 3,300 hours in jets.

ASSIGNMENTS: Capt. Schirra was one of the seven Mercury astronauts named by NASA in April 1959.

He piloted the six-orbit "Sigma 7" Mercury flight Oct. 3, 1962—a flight of 9 hours 13 minutes. He attained an altitude of 175 statute miles and traveled 144,000 miles before landing. Sigma 7 was recovered in the Pacific Ocean about 275 miles northeast of Midway Island.

Schirra has since served as backup command pilot for Gemini 3; Dec. 15-16, 1965, was command pilot on Gemini 6. Highlight was successful rendezvous of Gemini 6 with the already orbiting Gemini 7 spacecraft — the first rendezvous of two manned spacecraft. Known as a "textbook" pilot, Schirra remained in the spacecraft following his Mercury and Gemini flights.

NAME: Donn F. Eisele (Major, USAF) NASA Astronaut

BIRTHPLACE AND DATE: June 23, 1930, in Columbus, Ohio

PHYSICAL DESCRIPTION: Brown hair; blue eyes; height: 5 feet 9 inches; weight: 150 pounds.

EDUCATION: Graduated from West High School, Columbus; B.S. degree from the U.S. Naval Academy in 1952 and M.S. in Astronautics, 1960, USAF Institute of Technology, Wright-Patterson AFB, Ohio.

MARITAL STATUS: Married former Harriet E. Hamilton of Gnadenhutten, Ohio; her parents, Mr. And Mrs. Harry D. Hamilton, live there.

CHILDREN: Melinda S., July 25, 1954; Donn H., March 24, 1956; Jon J., Oct. 21, 1964.

ORGANIZATIONS: Member, Tau Beta Pi, national engineering society.

EXPERIENCE: Graduated from the U.S. Naval Academy and chose a career in the Air Force, 1952. Graduate of USAF Aerospace Research Pilot School, Edwards AFB, Calif.

Project engineer and experimental test pilot at USAF Special Weapons Center, Kirtland AFB, N.M.

More than 4,000 hours flying time 3,500 hours in jets.

Maj. Eisele, one of the third group of astronauts selected by NASA. in October 1963.

NAME: Walter Cunningham (civ.) NASA Astronaut

BIRTHPLACE AND DATE: March 16, 1932, Creston, Iowa; considers Santa Monica, Calif. hometown. Parents, Mr. and Mrs. Walter W. Cunningham, reside in Venice, Calif.

PHYSICAL DESCRIPTION: Blond hair; hazel eyes; height: 5 feet 10 inches; weight: 155 pounds.

EDUCATION: Graduated from Venice High School, Venice. Calif.; received B.A. with honors in Physics, 1960 and M.A. in Physics, 1961, from UCLA; has completed work, UCLA, on doctorate in Physics with exception of thesis.

MARITAL STATUS: Married to former Lo Ella Irby, Norwalk, Calif. Her mother, Mrs. Nellie Marie Maynard resides in Oxnard, Calif.

CHILDREN: Brian, Sept. 12, 1960; Kimberly, Feb. 12, 1963.

OTHER ACTIVITIES: Sports enthusiast, particularly interested in gymnastics and handball.

ORGANIZATIONS: Member, American Geophysical Union, American Institute of Aeronautics and Astronautics, Sigma Pi Sigma, and Sigma Xi.

EXPERIENCE: Joined the Navy in 1951 and began flight training in 1952. Joined a Marine squadron in 1953 and served on active duty until August 1956. Now is Marine reservist, with rank of Major.

Was research scientist for Rand Corp. before joining NASA; worked on classified defense studies and problems of Earth's magnetosphere at Rand.

At UCLA, in conjunction with doctoral thesis problem he developed and tested a search coil magnetometer which was later flown aboard the first NASA Orbiting Geophysical Observatory satellite.

Has 3,500 hours of flying time, more than 2,800 hours in jets.

Cunningham was one of the third group of astronauts selected by NASA in Oct. 1963.

The Crew on Launch Day

Following is a timetable of crew activities just before launch. (all times are shown in hours and minutes before liftoff).

T-9:00 -	Backup crew alerted
T-8:30 -	Backup crew to LC-34 for spacecraft pre-launch checkouts.
T-4:50 -	Flight crew alerted
T-4:35 -	Medical examinations
T-4:15 -	Breakfast
T-3:45 -	Don pressure suits
T-2:46 -	Leave Manned Spacecraft Operations Building for Pad-34 via Crew Transfer Van.
T-2:30 -	Arrive at Pad-34
T-2:26 -	Enter elevator to spacecraft level
T-2:25 -	Begin spacecraft ingress.

APOLLO 7 TEST PROGRAM

Spacecraft 2TV-1 Manned Thermal Vacuum Test

An eight-day thermal vacuum manned test of an Apollo Command and Service Module similar to the Apollo 7 spacecraft was run last June in the Manned Spacecraft Center's Space Environment Simulation Laboratory, chamber A. All of the test objectives, aimed mostly toward qualifying the spacecraft for manned orbital flight, were met.

The test objectives:

*Verify command module heat-shield structure under cold-soak space environment.

*Demonstrate capability of electrical power system radiators to handle fuel cell heat transfer needs.

*Verify material changes made in the command module.

*Verify Earth recovery system compatibility with space environment.

*Operate integrated spacecraft systems and subsystems in simulated space environment, both in pressurized and depressurized modes.

*Gather thermal data for use in flight vehicle thermal analysis.

*Determine environmental control system evaporator water consumption rate in space environment.

Astronaut crew for the test was Joseph P. Kerwin, Vance D. Brand and Joe H. Engle.

Command Module Flammability Testing

Following a series of more than 100 tests in which fires were intentionally set in the cabin of a boilerplate Apollo Command Module, NASA decided to use cabin atmosphere of 60 per cent oxygen and 40 per cent nitrogen on the launch pad.

The tests were run in three phases: 100 per cent oxygen at 6 psi, 100 per cent oxygen at 16 psi, and 60-40 oxygen nitrogen at 16 psi. While ignition was difficult in the pure oxygen at 16 psi atmosphere, fires had a tendency to spread, and in about half the tests spread beyond acceptable limits without extinguishing themselves.

Fire propagation tests run at 100 per cent oxygen at 6 psi and the 60-40 mix at 16 psi produced acceptable results. The test series showed that the command module interior is adequately protected against the ignition and spread of an accidental fire in the orbital cabin atmosphere of 100 per cent oxygen at 6 psi.

Apollo boilerplate spacecraft 1224, used in the flammability testing, incorporated the materials changes that have been made in the Command Module — stainless steel instead of aluminum for oxygen lines, protective covers over wiring bundles and replacement of other materials for minimizing flammability.

Representative Command Module materials were ignited in 33 separate tests in the 60-40 16 psi atmosphere and data were gathered on combustion history, temperature, pressure, crew visibility and analyses of gaseous products resulting from combustion.

Test fires were ignited by electrically-heated nichrome wire coils. Placement of igniters was determined by these criteria: proximity to flammable materials such as silicone clamps and spacers; apparent propagation paths such as wire bundles, connectors and terminal boards; large masses of nonmetallic materials; evaluation of earlier fixes of flammability hazards, and proximity to stowage areas containing flammable materials, such as food packets, crew equipment and flight documents.

Igniters were used in most of the tests to assure ignition. The igniters provided a more severe ignition source than would have the overloading of spacecraft wiring.

Results of the flammability tests in the 60-40 oxygen-nitrogen atmosphere at 16 psi showed that the command module is adequately protected against propagation of an accidental fire during prelaunch activities. Some changes were made as a result of the test series, such as removal of acoustic insulation from the spacecraft air circulation duct.

Operationally, the changes in launch pad cabin atmosphere resulting from the flammability test series have required no changes in the spacecraft system which supplies and controls the cabin atmosphere. The crew suit loops will carry 100 per cent oxygen at a pressure slightly higher than cabin pressure to avoid leakage into the suit loop. Some four hours after orbital insertion, the 60-40 oxygen-nitrogen mix will have been gradually replaced by 100 per cent oxygen at 5 Psi.

Apollo Parachute Development Testing

In the evolution of the Apollo Command Module, the weight has grown from a drawing-board figure of 9,500 pounds five years ago to 12,659 pounds for Apollo 7.

The Command Modules heavier weight made it necessary to modify the drogue and main parachutes in the Apollo Earth landing system.

Initial testing of parachute modifications began in July 1967 with a series of 24 drop tests at the Naval Air Test Facility, El Centro, Calif. Dummy test loads ranging from 5,400 to 13,000 pounds were air-dropped to test opening shock loads on drogue and main parachutes as well as to verify the advantages of additional reefing stages.

A series of drop tests of the all-up Apollo Earth landing system began in April 1968 using a 13,000 pound boilerplate Apollo spacecraft. A total of seven air drops of the complete system, simulating worst-case, abort and normal entry conditions, was conducted. The Earth landing system qualification was successfully completed in July 1968.

Modifications to the Apollo landing system parachutes include increasing the diameter of the drogue chutes from 13.7 feet to 16.5 feet, and employing two-stage reefing in the 83.3-feet diameter main parachutes to provide three phases of inflation — reefed, partial-reefed and full open to lessen opening shock.

Sea Habitability Tests

Apollo command module post-landing systems underwent an extensive series of tests last spring in an indoor tank at the Manned Spacecraft Center and in a 48-hour manned test in the Gulf of Mexico south of Galveston.

Spacecraft 007A was used for both tests and was similar to Apollo 7 in weight, center-of-gravity and postlanding systems.

The 48-hour sea test, April 5-7, subjected all spacecraft post-landing systems to a sea environment.

Systems and equipment tested and measured for performance were the uprighting system, the post-landing ventilation system, spacecraft recovery aids, (VHF recovery beacon, flashing light, sea dye, grappling hook, survival radio, swimmer interphone) VHF-AM communications, electrical systems and crew comfort and survival equipment.

Spacecraft 007A was hoisted from the deck of MV Retriever into the water apex down in about 18 fathoms, with waves running 3-4 feet and winds of 12-14 knots. Crewmen for the sea test were James A.Lovell, commander, Stuart A. Roosa, Command Module pilot, and Charles M. Duke, Jr., Lunar Module pilot.

The uprighting system rotated the spacecraft from the Stable II (apex down) position to Stable I (apex up) within six minutes after the uprighting bag compressors were turned on. Pressure checks were made on the bags every four hours throughout the test.

The post-landing ventilation system proved adequate and satisfactory for crew comfort. In the daytime the system kept the crew comfortable at low mode while at night it was cycled on every 30 minutes only to purge the cabin of excess carbon dioxide.

The VHF recovery beacon was activated shortly alter the test started and was left on for 24 hours. C-119 and HC-130 aircraft made ranging runs at varying altitudes, and acquisition and loss-of-signal ranges were all satisfactory. Similar aircraft ranging runs were made with the spacecraft VHF-AM radio as well as periodic voice checks between the spacecraft and the ship.

Tests with a training-model survival radio in the beacon mode were satisfactory, but the radio was not modulating properly in the voice mode and transmissions were not received by the ranging aircraft. The training radio was substituted since a flight-item radio was unavailable at the time of the sea tests.

When in the beacon mode, the survival radio's signal interfered with the spacecraft VHF-AM reception to the extent that reception of anything else was impossible.

Standby swimmers reported good communications with the crew in four tests of the swimmer interphones during the two-day period.

Aircraft ranging runs were also made on the spacecraft flashing light which was activated for 12 hours each night in the high mode (174 flashes-per-minute) and low mode (210 flashes-per-minute). In the low mode, aircraft pilots acquired the light at 9-10 miles from 10,000 feet, and in both high and low modes, spotted the light at 6-7 miles ranges from 1,200 feet.

Samples of sea water were taken aboard the spacecraft with a hand-held squeeze pump through the steam duct, and desalted. The crew reported the water was drinkable.

The sea dye marker, deployed shortly after the start of the test, emitted a dye slick about 1,000 yards long and 10 yards wide which was easily visible from the air.

Wave heights varied from one to four feet in the two days and wind velocity was recorded at one time to 14 knots.

The crew reported no motion sickness or any other ill effects from the test.

Tank testing, May 7-8, ran for 27 hours. The test was aimed primarily at determining whether the post-landing ventilating system could maintain habitable conditions for three crewmen under design limit conditions. Simulated wave motions and day-night environmental cycles (temperature, humidity) were induced throughout the test.

Crew biomedical instrumentation readouts were made on heart and breathing rates. Additional measurements of skin temperatures, cabin interior temperatures and carbon dioxide concentrations were made by the crew.

Other than a heat rash on the leg of one crewman, no ill effects were suffered by the crew. They reported sound sleep in the command module couches and no problems with motion sickness.

Land Impact Tests

The Apollo spacecraft is designed for landing on water but the possibility that it may land on the ground cannot be ignored.

Instrumented Apollo boilerplate Command Module and airframe spacecraft underwent a series of land-impact tests at the MSC Land and Water Impact Facility to determine accelerations in a beach landing following a possible off-the-pad abort.

Spacecraft pitch altitude and forward velocity were varied in the tests, and vertical velocity for three main chutes deployed (32 fps) and two main chutes (38 fps) onto simulated Cape Kennedy hard-packed beach sand provided data on abort landings. Data were gathered through 108 channels of accelerometers and strain gauges.

Test drops were also made with the spacecraft rolled 180 degrees, a condition that caused the spacecraft to roll over after impact.

Impact damage to spacecraft structure in these conditions was acceptable. Slight damage was sustained by other equipment in the cabin but in general the tests showed that likelihood of serious crew injury in an off-the-pad abort emergency landing was remote.

Vibro-Acoustic Testing

The structural integrity of the Apollo spacecraft under launch and boost dynamics were thoroughly tested in late 1967 and early 1968 at the MSC Vibration and Acoustic Test Facility. Vehicle for the vibro-acoustic test series was Apollo spacecraft 105 Command Service Module identical to Apollo 7 from a structural and systems standpoint.

Among the test objectives were qualification of the unified crew hatch tests of wiring and plumbing under launch vibrations, and verification of individual spacecraft components in the vibro-acoustic environment.

Tests were run at low and high frequencies to simulate such conditions as an abort at maximum dynamic pressure (max Q), transonic and max Q normal profiles, and off-limit acoustic stresses. Low-frequency vibration tests were conducted in the spacecraft longitudinal axis and in one lateral axis at frequencies ranging from 4 to 20 Hz. Acoustic tests simulated random actual-flight vibration conditions.

MAJOR APOLLO CONTRACTORS

Contractor	Item
Bellcomm Washington, D.C.	Apollo Systems Engineering
The Boeing Co. Washington, D.C.	Technical Integration and Evaluation
General Electric. Apollo Support Department. Daytona Beach, Fla.	Apollo Checkout and Reliability
North American Rockwell Corp. Space Div., Downey, Calif.	Spacecraft Command and Service Modules
Massachusetts Institute of Technology, Cambridge, Mass.	Guidance & Navigation (Technical Management)
General Motors Corp., AC Electronics Div., Milwaukee	Guidance & Navigation (Manufacturing)
Avco Corp., Wilmington, Mass.	Heat Shield Ablative Material

MAJOR SATURN IB CONTRACTORS

S-IB Stage

Chrysler Corp. Space Division New Orleans, La.	First Stage
Rocketdyne Division North American Rockwell Corp. Canoga Park, Calif.	H-1 Engines
Ling-Temco-Vought Dallas, Tex.	S-IB Tanks
Hayes International Corp. Birmingham, Ala.	S-IB Fins

S-IVB Stage

McDonnell Douglas Corp. Huntington Beach, Calif.	Second Stage
Rocketdyne Division North American Rockwell Corp. Canoga Park, Calif.	J-2 Engines
TRW Inc. Cleveland, Ohio	150-pound thrust attitude control engine
Vickers Detroit, Mich.	Pumps
Bell-Aerosystems, Inc. Buffalo, N.Y.	Fuel and oxidizer tank assemblies for Auxiliary Propulsion System

Instrument Unit

Federal Systems Division IBM Huntsville, Ala.	Prime Contractor
Bendix Corp. Eclipse Pioneer Division Teterboro, N. J.	St-124M Inertial Platform
Electronic Communication, Inc. St. Petersburg, Fla.	Control Computer
Federal Systems Division IBM Oswego, N.Y.	Digital Computer, Data Adapter

APOLLO PROGRAM OFFICIALS

Dr. George E. Mueller	Associate Administrator for Manned Space Flight, NASA Headquarters
Lt. Gen. Samuel C. Phillips	Director, Apollo Program Office, OMSF, NASA Headquarters
William C. Schneider	Apollo Mission Director, OMSF NASA Headquarters
Chester M. Lee	Assistant Mission Director, OMSF, NASA Headquarters
Col. Thomas H. McMullen	Assistant Mission Director, OMSF, NASA Headquarters
Maj. Gen. John D. Stevenson	Director, Mission Operations, OMSF, NASA Headquarters
Dr. Robert R. Gilruth	Director, Manned Spacecraft Center, Houston
George M. Low	Manager, Apollo Spacecraft Program Office, MSC
Kenneth S. Kleinknecht	Manager, Apollo Spacecraft Office, MSC
Donald K. Slayton	Director, Flight Crew Operations, MSC
Christopher C. Kraft, Jr.	Director, Flight Operations, MSC
Glynn Lunney Eugene F. Kranz Gerald D. Griffin	Apollo 7 Flight Directors, Flight Operations, MSC
Dr. Wernher von Braun	Director, Marshall Space Flight Center, Huntsville, Ala.
Brig. Gen. Edmund F. O'Connor	Director, Industrial Operations MSFC

William Teir	Manager, Saturn I, IB Program Office, MSFC
W. D. Brown	Manager, Engine Program Office, MSFC
Dr. Kurt H. Debus	Director, John F. Kennedy Space Center, Fla.
Miles Ross	Deputy Director, Center Operation Operations, KSC
Rocco A. Petrone	Director, Launch Operations, KSC
Walter J. Kapryan	Deputy Director, Launch Operations, KSC
Rear Adm. Roderick O. Middleton	Apollo Program Manager, KSC
Paul C. Donnelly	Launch Operations Manager, KSC
Gerald Truszynski	Associate Administrator, Tracking and Data Acquisition, NASA Headquarters
Norman Pozinsky	Director, Network Support Implementation Division, OTDA
Dr. John F. Clark	Director, Goddard Space Flight Center, Greenbelt, Md.
Ozro M. Covington	Assistant Director for Manned Space Flight Tracking, GSFC
Henry F. Thompson	Deputy Assistant Director for Manned Space Flight Support, GSFC
H. William Wood	Chief, Manned Flight Operations Division, GSFC
Tecwyn Roberts	Chief, Manned Flight Engineering Division, GSFC
L. R. Stelter	Chief, NASA Communications Division, GSFC
Maj. Gen. Vincent G. Huston	USAF, DOD Manager of Manned Space Flight Support Operations
Maj. Gen. David M. Jones	USAF, Deputy DOD Manager of Manned Space Flight Support Operations, Commander USAF Eastern Test Range
Rear Adm. P. S. McManus	USN, Commander (combined) Task Force 140 Primary Recovery Area
Rear Adm. F. E. Bakutis	USN, Commander (combined) Task Force 130 Pacific Recovery Area
Col. Royce G. Olson	USAF, Director, DOD Manned Space Flight Office
Brig. Gen. Allison C. Brooks	USAF, Commander Aerospace Rescue and Recovery Service

MISSION OPERATION REPORT

APOLLO 7

(AS 205) MISSION

Donn F. Eisele   Walter M. Schirra, Jr.   Walter Cunningham

OFFICE OF MANNED SPACE FLIGHT

FOR INTERNAL USE ONLY

Pre-Launch
Mission Operation Report

No. M-932-68-07
MEMORANDUM

To: A/Administrator   1 October 1968

From: MA/Apollo Program Director

Subject: Apollo 7 Mission (AS-205)

No earlier than 11 October 1968, we plan to launch the next Apollo/Saturn IB mission, Apollo 7. This will be the first manned Apollo flight, the first flight of a Block II Apollo Command/Service Module (CSM 101) and the fifth of a Saturn IB launch vehicle (SA 205).

The purpose of this mission is to demonstrate: CSM/crew performance, CSM rendezvous capability, and crew/vehicle/support facilities performance during a manned CSM mission. These objectives can be accomplished within three days. The mission is open ended to eleven days to acquire additional data and evaluate the aspects of long duration manned space flight.

The launch will be the third Saturn IB from launch Complex 34 at Cape Kennedy. The nominal launch window opens at 1100 EDT and closes five hours later at 1600 EDT based on the requirement for a fine IMU alignment for rendezvous.

The nominal mission will comprise: ascent to orbit (123 x 153 nm); separation of the CSM from the S-IVB stage, CSM transposition and simulated docking with the S-IVB; CSM separation from the S-IVB and later rendezvous; evaluation of long duration manned space flight; automatic deorbit and reentry; and recovery of the CM in the Atlantic Ocean approximately 300 nm ENE of Bermuda.

Sam C. Phillips
Lt. General, USAF
APPROVAL:

George E. Mueller
Associate Administrator for
Manned Space Flight

Report No. M-932-68-07
MISSION OPERATION REPORT

APOLLO 7 (AS 205) MISSION
Donn F. Eisele Walter M. Schirra, Jr. Walter Cunningham
OFFICE OF MANNED SPACE FLIGHT

FOR INTERNAL USE ONLY

FOREWORD

MISSION OPERATION REPORTS are published expressly for the use of NASA Senior Management, as required by the Administrator in NASA Instruction 6-2-10, dated August 15, 1963. The purpose of these reports is to provide NASA Senior Management with timely, complete, and definitive information on flight mission plans, and to establish official mission objectives which provide the basis for assessment of mission accomplishment.

Initial reports are prepared and issued for each flight project just prior to launch. Following launch, updating reports for each mission are issued to keep General Management currently informed of definitive mission results as provided in NASA Instruction 6-2-10.

Because of their sometimes highly technical orientation, distribution of these reports is limited to personnel having program-project management responsibilities. The Office of Public Affairs publishes a comprehensive series of pre-launch and post launch reports on NASA flight missions, which are available for general distribution.

Published and Distributed by PROGRAM and SPECIAL REPORTS DIVISION (XP) EXECUTIVE SECRETARIAT - NASA HEADQUARTERS

M-932-68-07

GENERAL

The goal of the Apollo Program is to enhance the manned space flight capability of the United States by developing, through logical and orderly evolution, the ability to land men on the Moon and return them safely to Earth.

To accomplish the goal of lunar landing and return in this decade, the Apollo Program has focused on the development of a highly reliable launch vehicle and spacecraft system. The program has been developed to utilize two launch vehicles and a common spacecraft system (see Figure 1). Each launch vehicle system — the Saturn V and the Saturn IB — has a specific purpose in the program. The Saturn V, with a total thrust of 7.5 million pounds, will be used to launch a full lunar payload; and, the smaller Saturn IB is used to launch spacecraft module payloads for integrated systems verification in a near Earth orbit. The Saturn IB develops a thrust of 1.6 million pounds.

The Apollo 7 mission is the fifth Saturn IB (SA-205) launch and is the first flight of a Block II Command and Service Module (CSM-101) as well as being the first manned Apollo flight. The mission is designed to test the CSM, support facilities and Flight and Ground Crew performance in a near Earth orbit.

PROGRAM DEVELOPMENT

The first Saturn vehicle was successfully flown on 27 October 1961 to initiate operations of the Saturn I Program. A total of ten Saturn I vehicles (SA-1 to SA-10) were successfully flight tested to provide information on the integration of launch vehicle and spacecraft and to provide operational experience with large multi-engined booster stages (S-I, S-IV).

The next generation of vehicles, developed under the Saturn IB Program, featured an uprated first stage (S-IB) and a more powerful new second stage (S-IVB). The first Saturn IB was launched on 26 February 1966. The first three Saturn IB missions (AS-201, AS-203 and AS-202) successfully tested the performance of the launch vehicle and spacecraft combination, separation of the stages, behavior of liquid hydrogen in a weightless environment, performance of the Command Module heat shield at low Earth orbital entry conditions, and recovery operations.

The planned fourth Saturn IB mission (AS-204) scheduled for early 1967 was intended to be the first manned Apollo flight. This mission was not flown because of a spacecraft fire, during a manned pre-launch test, that took the lives of the prime flight crew and severely damaged the spacecraft. The SA-204 launch vehicle was later assigned to the Apollo 5 mission.

The Apollo 4 mission was successfully executed on 9 November 1967. This mission initiated the use of the Saturn V launch vehicle (SA-501) and required an orbital restart of the S-IVB third stage. The spacecraft for this mission consisted of an unmanned Command and Service Module (CSM) and a Lunar Module Test Article (LTA). The CSM Service Propulsion System (SPS) was exercised, including restart, and the Command Module Block II heat shield was subjected to the combination of high heat load, high heat rate, and aerodynamic loads representative of lunar return entry.

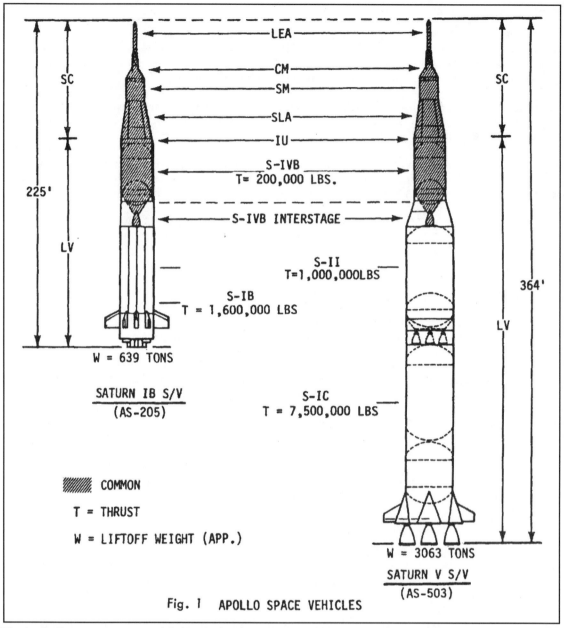

Fig. 1   APOLLO SPACE VEHICLES

The Apollo 5 mission was successfully launched and completed on 22 January 1968. This was the fourth mission utilizing Saturn IB vehicles (AS-204). This flight provided for unmanned orbital testing of the Lunar Module (LM-1). The LM structure, staging, proper operation of the Lunar Module Ascent Propulsion System (APS) and Descent Propulsion System (DPS), including restart, was verified. Satisfactory performance of the S-IVB/Instrument Unit (IU) in orbit was also demonstrated.

The Apollo 6 mission (second unmanned Saturn V) was successfully launched on 4 April 1968. Some flight anomalies encountered included oscillation related to propulsion structural longitudinal coupling, Spacecraft Lunar Module Adapter (SLA) area structural integrity and certain malfunctions of the J-2 engines in the S-II and S-IVB stages. The spacecraft flew the planned trajectory, but high velocity re-entry conditions were not achieved. A majority of the mission objectives for Apollo 6 were accomplished.

The Apollo 7 mission will provide the first manned orbital tests of the Block II Command and Service Modules.

THE APOLLO 7 MISSION

The Apollo 7 mission will be the fifth Saturn IB mission. This manned mission is intended to verify proper operation of the Command and Service Module (CSM) systems and operational capabilities of the CSM, crew and Manned Space Flight

Network (MSFN) support facilities in an Earth orbital environment. Planned duration is slightly less than 11 days, however, this full duration is not required for mission success.

In addition to fundamental spacecraft checkout and crew operations, Apollo 7 will qualify the CSM forward heat shield (flat apex area), determine Environmental Control System (ECS) radiator performance and the amount of coating degradation, perform transposition and simulated docking and evaluate CSM active rendezvous activities. Additional evaluation of the S-IVB attitude control system, safing of the S-IVB stage for rendezvous activities and evaluating the S-IVB orbital coast lifetime capability will be performed.

The Apollo 7 mission ascent-to-orbit will include the S-IB boost phase and the S-IVB orbit insertion burn. The spacecraft will remain attached to the S-IVB in a 123 x 153 nautical mile orbit for two revolutions. During this time activities will consist primarily of spacecraft subsystems checkout.

The CSM will separate from the S-IVB, transpose and perform a simulated docking maneuver using the S-IVB/SLA as a docking target. Photographs of the S-IVB and SLA will be taken during the transposition and docking maneuvers.

After completion of the simulated docking, the SM/Reaction Control System (RCS) will be used to perform an initial phasing maneuver for a rendezvous with the S-IVB. The CSM active rendezvous will be a two impulse transfer ellipse utilizing the Service Propulsion System (SPS) for the coelliptic and corrective combination maneuvers. The rendezvous with the S-IVB will be completed at approximately 30 hours into the mission.

Following a period of station keeping with the S-IVB, the spacecraft will separate and begin a drifting flight phase for nominally nine days. This period will be devoted to evaluation of crew activities, crew/spacecraft interface, subsystems performance and mission support facilities. The drifting flight phase will be interrupted by as many as five SPS burns. The primary purpose of these maneuvers is to evaluate the propulsion system and various spacecraft control modes.

The deorbit maneuver will be a Guidance, Navigation and Control System (GNCS) controlled SPS burn. Entry will be controlled automatically by the GNCS and monitored by the crew. Splashdown will occur in the Atlantic recovery area. The maximum planned mission time is slightly less than 11 days. Figure 2 presents a mission summary.

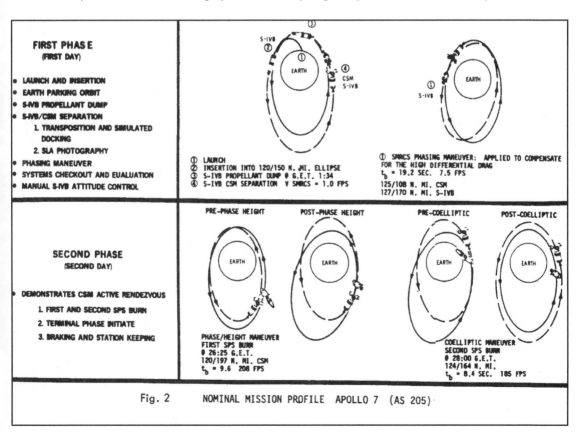

Fig. 2   NOMINAL MISSION PROFILE APOLLO 7 (AS 205)

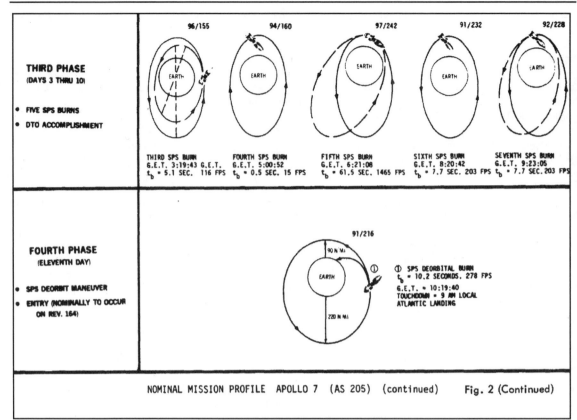

NOMINAL MISSION PROFILE   APOLLO 7   (AS 205)   (continued)   Fig. 2 (Continued)

NASA MISSION OBJECTIVES FOR APOLLO 7

PRIMARY OBJECTIVES

Demonstrate CSM/crew performance

Demonstrate crew/space vehicle/mission support facilities performance during a manned CSM mission

Demonstrate CSM rendezvous capability

Sam C. Phillips	George E. Mueller
Lt. General, USAF	Associate Administrator for
Apollo Program Director	Manned Space Flight
Date: 27 Sept 68	Date: 30 Sept 68

DETAILED TEST OBJECTIVES

The following detail amplifies and defines more explicitly basic tests, measurements and evaluations which are planned to achieve the primary objectives given previously.

Launch Vehicle

- Demonstrate orbital safing of the S-IVB

- Demonstrate launch vehicle attitude control

- Qualify J-2 engine Augmented Spark Ignition (ASI) line modification

Spacecraft

- Determine ECS radiator heat rejection and obtain data on the thermal degradation

- Obtain data on the Block II forward heat shield Thermal Protection System

- Perform an Inertial Measurement Unit (IMU) orientation determination and a star pattern visibility check in daylight

- Perform IMU alignments using the sextant

- Perform an SPS burn in the space environment

- Demonstrate SPS minimum impulse burns in a space environment

- Perform GNCS controlled SPS and RCS Delta-V maneuvers

- Demonstrate GNCS automatic and manual attitude controlled RCS maneuvers

- Evaluate the ability of the GNCS to monitor entry from Earth orbit

- Demonstrate Stabilization and Control System (SCS) automatic and manual attitude controlled RCS maneuvers

- Demonstrate CSM SCS Delta-V capability

- Perform a CSM active rendezvous with the S-IVB

- Perform optical tracking of the target vehicle using the sextant

- Perform a CSM/S-IVB separation, transposition and simulated docking

- Determine performance of the ECS throughout the mission

- Demonstrate water management subsystem operation in the flight environment

- Perform onboard navigation using the technique of scanning telescope landmark tracking

- Perform manual thrust vector control (MTVC) "take over"

- Demonstrate a simulated CSM overpass of the Lunar Module (LM) rendezvous radar during lunar stay

- Obtain data on all CSM consumables

- Demonstrate fuel cell operation in a zero-g environment

- Verify adequacy of the propellant feed line thermal control system

- Monitor the primary and auxiliary gauging system

- Obtain IMU performance data in the flight environment

- Monitor the entry monitor subsystem (EMS) during SPS Delta-V and entry

- Obtain data on SCS capability to provide a suitable inertial reference in a flight environment

- Verify automatic pressure control of the cryogenic tank systems in zero-g

- Obtain data on the thermal stratification with and without the cryogenic fans of the cryogenic gas storage system (CGSS)

- Demonstrate the performance of the CSM/MSFN S-Band communications system

- Perform sextant midcourse navigation sightings using star/lunar landmark and star/lunar horizon

- Demonstrate S-Band updata link capability

- Operate the secondary cooling loop

- Obtain crew evaluation of intravehicular activity in general

- Obtain data on operation of the waste management system in the flight environment

- Accomplish the backup mode of Gyro Display Coupler (GDC)/Flight Director Attitude Indicator (FDAI) using the scanning telescope in preparation for Delta-V maneuver

- Demonstrate postlanding ventilation circuit operation

SECONDARY OBJECTIVES

Apollo secondary objectives are established by the development centers to provide additional engineering or scientific data. For Apollo 7 the secondary test objectives are as follows.

Launch Vehicle

- Evaluate launch vehicle orbital lifetime

- Demonstrate CSM manual launch vehicle orbital attitude control

Spacecraft

- Demonstrate CSM VHF voice communications with MSFN

- Obtain data on SLA deployment system operation

- Obtain data on SM/RCS pulse and steady-state performance

- Verify that the launch vehicle propellant pressure displays are adequate to warn of a common bulkhead reversal

- Obtain data on initial coning angle when in the spin mode as used during transearth flight

- Obtain data on propellant slosh damping following SPS cutoff. and following RCS burns

- Obtain data on procedural adequacy and operational use of the Crew Optical Alignment Sight (COAS)

- Obtain photographs of the CM rendezvous windows during discrete phases of the flight

- Perform manual out-of-window CSM attitude orientation for retro

- Monitor the GNCS and displays during launch

- Perform crew controlled manual S-IVB attitude maneuvers in three axes

- Obtain data via CSM-Apollo Range Instrumentation Aircraft (A/RIA) communications

- Obtain CSM structural vibration data

- Obtain selective high quality, color cloud photographs to study the fine structure of the Earth's weather system

SAFETY PLANNING

GENERAL

As a result of the normal developmental cycle as well as a reassessment following the AS-204 accident in January of 1967, a number of changes and additions have been made to the Apollo systems and procedures. Some 1800 changes were instigated as a result of the AS-204 accident. A detailed discussion of changes is not within the scope of this report though some items are covered in later descriptive sections. This section generalizes the procedural or program aspects of safety related improvements.

PRE-LAUNCH PROCEDURES

Procedures for maximum launch complex area safety are provided by "Apollo/Saturn IB Ground Safety Plan" K-1B-023. Overall safety conditions at the launch pad area are monitored by the Systems Safety Supervisor who has the authority to stop any operation when a condition exists which, in his opinion, is imminently hazardous.

All test procedures are required to contain applicable emergency procedures. Prior to implementation, these test procedures are reviewed by the KSC Safety Office which makes the final determination as to the hazardous classification of all tests. The procedures that are evaluated as hazardous are then compared against a set of checklists to ensure compliance with safety practices.

To ensure maximum readiness of personnel to cope with emergencies, personnel emergency procedure training and practice are given on a regular basis. In addition, training proficiency is reviewed before conducting all hazardous operations. The training program that has been initiated includes the use of fire-fighting equipment, toxic propellant safety, safety locker qualification, first aid and the handling of personnel requiring aid in the event of an emergency. It will also include the development of procedures and training in emergency crew egress. Certification of course completion is mandatory for Launch Complex (LC) 34 personnel.

RANGE SAFETY

The range safety system provides essentially real time space vehicle position, trajectory and impact prediction information from launch through orbital insertion. The Range Safety Officer (RSO) uses consoles, plotting boards, visual displays, and information from range observers for making his decision on safe or unsafe space vehicle trajectories. Primary control of range safety responsibility is passed from the KSC RSO to the Bermuda RSO as the vehicle progresses down range.

LAUNCH COUNTDOWN AND TURNAROUND CAPABILITY AS-205

Countdown for the Apollo 7 mission will begin with a pre-count period during which launch vehicle and spacecraft preparations will take place independently until coordinated space vehicle countdown activities begin. Table 1 shows the significant launch countdown events.

SCRUB/TURNAROUND

Scrub/turnaround time is based upon the amount of work required to return the space vehicle to a safe condition and to accomplish the necessary normal re-testing in preparation for a second launch or simulated launch attempt. Planning guidelines used in the development of the data in this section are based upon a normal countdown followed by a 5-hour hold, scrub turnaround, and a second launch or simulated launch attempt. These times are minimal and do not allow serial time for repair or holds, or for re-testing of any system as a result of repair. Times listed do not consider any required unloading of hypergolic propellants and RP-1 from the space vehicle.

TURNAROUND CONDITIONS VS. TIME

Post LV Cryo Load (with LV Propellants Checks and with SC Cryo Re-Servicing)

The turnaround time from a scrub at post LV Cryo load with LV propulsion checks and with SC Cryo re-servicing is 52 hours, 30 minutes. Recycle time is 25 hours. Countdown time is 27 hours, 30 minutes.

Post LV Cryo Load (with No SC Cryo Re-Servicing)

The turnaround time from a scrub at post LV Cryo load with no SC Cryo re-servicing is 20 hours including 14 hours recycle and six hours countdown. SC Cryo quantity is the most critical consideration for the 20 hour scrub turnaround.

TABLE I

LAUNCH COUNTDOWN SEQUENCE OF EVENTS

Countdown Hrs:Min:Secs:	Event
24:00:00	Start Countdown Clock
24:00:00	Start CSM LH2 Servicing
16:45:00	MCC Command I/F Test
14:35:00	L/V Power Application
10:20:00	S/V EDS Test
09:30:00	Start L/V Ordnance Operations
06:55:00	CSM RF Voice Checks
06:50:00	SS Move to Park site
06:00:00	Six Hour Build in Hold (No Task Scheduled)
06:00:00	Start L/V Cryogenic Load
03:10:00	L/V Cryogenic Load Complete
03:00:00	Flight Crew Departs From MSOB
02:25:00	Flight Crew Ingress
00:50:00	Start Terminal Count
00:40:00	CSM Closeout Crew Clear Launch Area
00:33:00	Apollo Access Arm to Park — LES Arm
00:20:00	CSM RCS Static Fire
00:15:00	CSM to Internal Power
00:10:00	S-IVB Chilldown
00:05:00	Apollo Access Arm to Retract Position
00:02:43	Start Auto Launch Sequence
00:00:28	L/V to Internal Power
00:00:03	Ignition Command
00:00:00	Lift-off

Pre LV Cryo Load (with SC Cryo Re-Servicing Only)

For a hold greater than 24 hours after SC Cryo loading, the turnaround time from a scrub at pre LV Cryo load with SC Cryo re-servicing only is 47 hours. Recycle time is 19 hours, 30 minutes. Countdown time is 27 hours, 30 minutes.

Pre LV Cryo Load (with No SC Cryo Re-Servicing)

If a scrub occurs prior to LV cryogenic loading (T-6 hours) and after SC Cryo loading (T-19 hours), a hold condition can be established for a 24 hour period prior to picking up the countdown. This is based upon a 25 hour hold capability of the SC cryogenic system from originally scheduled T-0 of the countdown.

DETAILED FLIGHT MISSION DESCRIPTION

NOMINAL MISSION

Pre-Launch

The AS-205 space vehicle for the Apollo 7 mission will be launched from Launch Complex 34 at Cape Kennedy, Florida. The launch window opens at 1100 hours EDT and closes at approximately 1600 hours EDT and is based on the requirement for a fine IMU alignment during the night pass prior to the coelliptic maneuver (NSR).

Launch and Parking Orbit

The H-1 engines of the S-IB stage are ignited three seconds prior to lift-off. A detailed sequence of events from lift-off to parking orbit insertion is shown in Table 2.

Following insertion into a 123 x 153 nm parking orbit, the spacecraft/S-IVB combination is pitched until the longitudinal axis lies in the plane of the local horizontal.

As the S-IVB/CSM approaches the United States at the end of the first revolution, the remaining S-IVB propellants and cold gases are dumped through the J-2 engine. This procedure takes approximately five minutes and adds to the velocity vector causing the apogee to be raised to approximately 168 nm.

S-IVB/CSM Separation

S-IVB/CSM separation occurs at approximately three hours Ground Elapsed Time (GET) and is initiated such that 30 minutes of daylight remain. Separation is accomplished by firing each of the four +X SM thrusters. Following S-IVB/CSM separation, the CSM translates forward and fires four -X SM thrusters to damp the relative velocity between the S-IVB and CSM. This is followed by a CSM pitch maneuver of 180° for viewing and photographing the deployed SLA.

TABLE 2

LAUNCH PHASE

TIME Min:Sec	EVENT
-00:03	Ignition
00:00	Lift-off
00:10	Start roll program to align fin Plane I to 72° launch azimuth
00:21	Start pitch program
00:38	Terminate roll program
00:52	Terminate time tilt phase of pitch program, initiate gravity tilt
02:15	Tilt arrest halts pitch program
02:21	S-IB inboard engine cut-off
02:24	S-IB outboard engine cut-off
02:25	S-IVB ullage rocket ignition
02:25	S-IB/S-IVB separation
02:26	S-IVB ignition; J-2 thrust buildup
02:37	Jettison three ullage rocket cases
02:44	Jettison launch escape tower
07:34	Propellant utilization (P.U.) shift
09:16	S-IB stage impact
10:15	S-IVB Engine cut-off
10:25	Orbital insertion conditions attained

Resulting orbit (965 nm Range)

Inclination	31.59°
Period	88.47 minutes
Apogee	153 nm
Perigee	123 nm

CSM//S-IVB Rendezvous

During the pass over Ascension station (approx. 3-1/2 hours GET) the CSM makes a horizontal retrograde RCS maneuver to set up the proper phasing for the rendezvous maneuver planned to occur about 23 hours later. This maneuver will counteract the effect of the differential drag between the two vehicles.

The second day into the mission (approx. 26-1/2 hours GET), during the seventeenth revolution, the CSM will be leading the S-IVB by about 70 nm and will perform the first SPS maneuver.

This is the first of two impulse burns to transfer to the desired phase angle and differential height offset for the coelliptic setup of the CSM behind and below the S-IVB, and correct for any small out-of-phase angle that may have built up.

Residual Delta-Vs will be trimmed out using the RCS following all SPS rendezvous maneuvers. The relative motion between the S-IVB and CSM is shown in Figure 3. If there are significant errors in the first SPS burn setup, a second corrective combination maneuver will be scheduled during the next revolution over Antigua.

During the eighteenth revolution, the second SPS burn coelliptic maneuver is performed to place the CSM behind and below the S-IVB. This maneuver, as with the previous ones, is ground computed because the CSM does not have the necessary onboard logic. Onboard optical tracking will continue after this second SPS burn so the CSM can compute the upcoming terminal phase burns.

Terminal Phase Initiation (TPI)

TPI occurs about one hour after the second SPS burn (coelliptic maneuver, NSR) and during the nineteenth revolution, when the CSM is over Ascension. TPI will be initiated when the CSM line-of-sight angle to the S-IVB reaches approximately 27°, the range about 15 nm and the vehicles about 26 minutes from sunrise. The TPI maneuver will be performed with the RCS. About 15 minutes later, an onboard calculated correction maneuver will be performed.

Terminal Phase Finalization (TPF) maneuver will commence at about 29-1/2 hours GET when the CSM is about one nm from the S-IVB. The braking approach will begin using the RCS and, soon after, station keeping at about 100 to 200 ft. will begin. During station keeping, velocity match, line-of-sight, control and attitude maneuvering will be accomplished with the RCS. As the vehicles pass over the United States after about 30 minutes of station keeping, the CSM will leave the vicinity of the S-IVB by applying a small posigrade RCS maneuver.

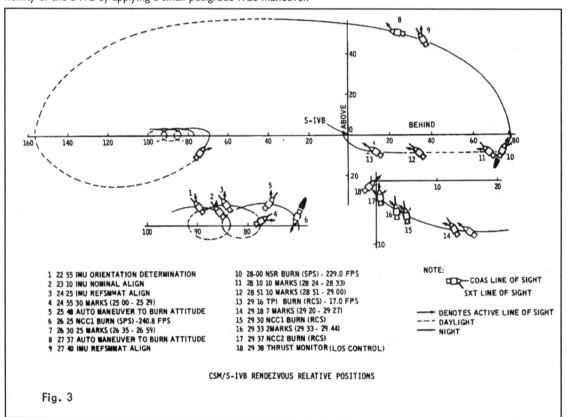

1	22 55 IMU ORIENTATION DETERMINATION	10	28-00 NSR BURN (SPS) - 229.0 FPS
2	23 10 IMU NOMINAL ALIGN	11	28 10 10 MARKS (28 24 - 28 33)
3	24 25 IMU REFSMMAT ALIGN	12	28 51 10 MARKS (28 51 - 29 00)
4	24 55 30 MARKS (25 00 - 25 29)	13	29 16 TPI BURN (RCS) - 17.0 FPS
5	25 48 AUTO MANEUVER TO BURN ATTITUDE	14	29 18 7 MARKS (29 20 - 29 27)
6	26 25 NCC1 BURN (SPS) -240.8 FPS	15	29 30 NCC1 BURN (RCS)
7	26 30 25 MARKS (26 35 - 26 59)	16	29 33 2MARKS (29 33 - 29 44)
8	27 37 AUTO MANEUVER TO BURN ATTITUDE	17	29 37 NCC2 BURN (RCS)
9	27 40 IMU REFSMMAT ALIGN	18	29 38 THRUST MONITOR (LOS CONTROL)

NOTE:

COAS LINE OF SIGHT
SXT LINE OF SIGHT

DENOTES ACTIVE LINE OF SIGHT
DAYLIGHT
NIGHT

CSM/S-IVB RENDEZVOUS RELATIVE POSITIONS

Fig. 3

CSM Operations

The third SPS burn occurs during the 58th revolution over the Eastern Test Range (ETR). The burn is performed under Guidance and Navigation (G&N) control.

The fourth SPS burn is performed during the 76th revolution under the SCS Delta-V mode and is a minimum impulse burn of 0.5 second in duration.

The fifth SPS burn occurs during the 104th revolution at approximately six days and 21 hours GET. The burn is performed under G&N control for the first 30 seconds, after which manual takeover is expected. The resulting Delta-V is applied partially in plane but the major portion is out of plane.

The sixth SPS burn is planned to occur during the 133rd revolution, nine days and 21 hours GET, and will be performed under SCS Delta-V mode.

Deorbit Maneuver (Eighth SPS Burn)

The last of eight scheduled SPS burns is a G&N Delta-V mode burn of approximately 10 seconds which deorbits the spacecraft. At burn termination, approximately 620 seconds remain for the flight crew to verify deorbit conditions, separate from the SM, and orient the CM to the entry attitude. The deorbit maneuver is initiated with the spacecraft in a retro attitude and pitched down below the line-of-sight to the horizon. This retro attitude allows the flight crew to verify the proper deorbit attitude and to manually control the spacecraft should the G&N system fail to function normally.

Re-Entry and Landing

Shortly after deorbit, the SM is jettisoned and the CM is oriented to the proper entry attitude. Landing of the CM following the nominal re-entry trajectory control occurs about 300 nm ENE of Bermuda.

Table 3 and Figure 4 present the sequence of events for the Apollo 7 mission.

Figure 5 shows the ground tracks for each revolution during the first 25 hours of the mission.

CONTINGENCY OPERATIONS

If an anomaly occurs after lift-off that would prevent the AS-205 space vehicle from following its nominal flight plan, an abort or an alternate mission will be initiated. An abort would provide only for an acceptable CM recovery while an alternate mission would attempt to achieve some of the mission objectives before providing for an acceptable CM recovery.

APOLLO 7 MISSION SEQUENCE OF EVENTS
INSERTION TO SPLASHDOWN

DAY (HOURS)	EVENT	REV. NO.	GET DAY:HR:MIN	COMMENT
1 (0-24)	INSERTION	1	0:00:10	123 BY 153 N.MI. ORBIT
	S/IVB/CSM SEPARATION (3SEC BURN)	2	0:02:55	SM RCS SEPARATION FROM S-IVB
	S-IVB TAKE-OVER DEMONSTRATION			
	TRANSPOSITION & SIMULATED DOCKING WITH THE S-IVB	2-3		SLA PHOTOGRAPHY
	SM RCS PHASING BURN (19SEC)	3	0:03:30	SET UP PROPER PHASE OFFSET FOR RENDEZVOUS
	CSM SYSTEM CHECKOUT			
	CRYOGENIC STRATIFICATION TEST 1			
	SXT CALIBRATION TEST			
	COAS CALIBRATION			
2 (24-48)	FIRST SPS BURN (10SEC)	17	1:02:25	CORRECTIVE COMBINATION MANEUVER
	SECOND SPS BURN (8SEC)	18	1:04:00	COELLIPTIC MANEUVER (NSR)
	S-IVB RENDEZVOUS TERMINAL PHASE INITIATE	19	1:05:23	RCS BURN 42SEC.
	RENDEZVOUS COMPLETED		1:05:41	
	S-IVB POST RENDEZVOUS TRACKING	20	1:06:20	TRACK AT 80 AND 160NM
3 (48-72)	S-IVB TRACKING AT 320 NM			
	SCT STAR COUNT TEST 1			
4 (72-96)	WSMR LM RR TEST 1			
	LANDMARK TRACKING			
	SCT STAR COUNT TEST 2			
	THIRD SPS BURN (5SEC)	58	3:19:43	POSITION & SIZE ELLIPSE FOR CM RCS DE-ORBIT TO ETR, SETS UP AUX GAUGING SYSTEM TEST (96/155 NM ORBIT)
	SLOSH DAMPING TEST 1			
	ECS RADIATOR TEST			
5 (96-120)	MIDCOURSE NAVIGATION			
	CRYOGENIC STRATIFICATION TEST 2			

TABLE 3

APOLLO 7 SEQUENCE OF EVENTS (CONTINUED)

DAY (HOURS)	EVENT	REV. NO.	GET DAY:HR:MIN	COMMENT
6 (120-144)	FOURTH SPS BURN (1/2 SEC)	77	5:00:52	MINIMUM IMPULSE TEST
	SLOSH DAMPING TEST 2			
	SCT STAR COUNT TEST 3			
	SPS COLD SOAK			
	LANDMARK TRACKING			
7 (144-168)	FIFTH SPS BURN (62 SEC)	105	6:21:08	GAUGING TEST, ADJUST ELLIPSE FOR LIFETIME, POSITION AND SIZE ELLIPSE FOR CM RCS DEORBIT. (MOSTLY OUT OF PLANE 97/242NM ORBIT.)
	PASSIVE THERMAL CONTROL TEST 1			
	MIDCOURSE NAVIGATION			
	WINDOW PHOTOGRAPHY			
8 (168-192)	ECS SECONDARY COOLANT LOOP TEST			
9 (192-216)	WSMR LM RR TEST 2			
	SCT STAR COUNT TEST 1 (HD)			
	SCS BACKUP ALIGN			
	SIXTH SPS BURN (1/2 SEC)	134	8:18:13	MINIMUM IMPULSE TEST
	PASSIVE THERMAL CONTROL TEST 2,3			
10 (216-240)	SEVENTH SPS BURN (8 SEC)	150	9:23:05	TIME ANOMALY ADJUST FOR DEORBIT BURN (92/228NM ORBIT)
	SXT CALIBRATION PIPA & EMS BIAS			
11 (240-COMP)	WINDOW PHOTOGRAPHY			
	CRYOGENIC STRATIFICATION TEST 3			
	EIGHTH SPS BURN (10SEC)	163	10:19:40	DEORBIT
	SPLASHDOWN	164	10:20:11	

TABLE 3 (CONT.)

Aborts

During launch, the velocity, altitude, atmosphere, and launch configuration change drastically; therefore, several abort modes, each adapted to a portion of the launch trajectory, are required. Mode I aborts protect the spacecraft and crew while the launch vehicle is on the pad and during atmospheric flight. They utilize the Launch Escape System (LES) for safe separation, and the aborts result in a suborbital trajectory with landings in the Atlantic Continuous Recovery Area (ACRA). Mode II abort capability begins once the Launch Escape Tower (LET) has been jettisoned and continues until the contingency orbit insertions capability begins or until the resulting landings threaten the African coast. Mode II aborts consist of a manual CSM separation from the launch vehicle, CM/SM separation, an entry orientation maneuver, and an open loop full lift entry. These aborts result in a suborbital trajectory with landings in the ACRA also. The mode III abort capability begins once the mode II landings threaten the African coast and continues until nominal insertion. The mode III aborts consist of a manual CSM separation, a fixed attitude Service Propulsion System (SPS) retrograde burn, CM/SM separation, an entry orientation maneuver, and an open loop, bank-left 55° entry. These abort maneuvers result in a suborbital trajectory with landings at the Atlantic Discrete Recovery Area (ADRA). The mode IV, or contingency orbit insertion (COI) capability, begins once the SPS can be used to insert the CSM into a safe orbit and continues until the launch vehicle has obtained a safe orbit. The COI maneuver consists of a manual CSM separation, a fixed-attitude, SPS posigrade burn resulting in a 75 nm perigee altitude, and subsequent SPS deorbit to a planned landing area. These maneuvers result in a safe orbital trajectory from which an alternate mission or an immediate deorbit can be planned.

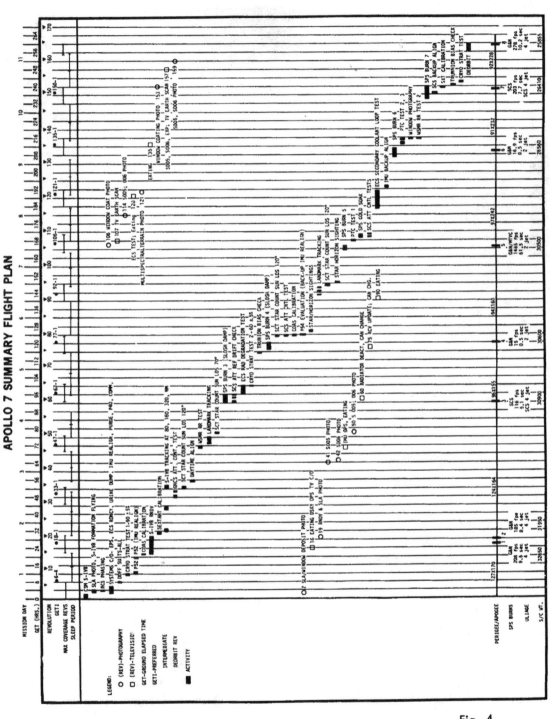

Fig. 4

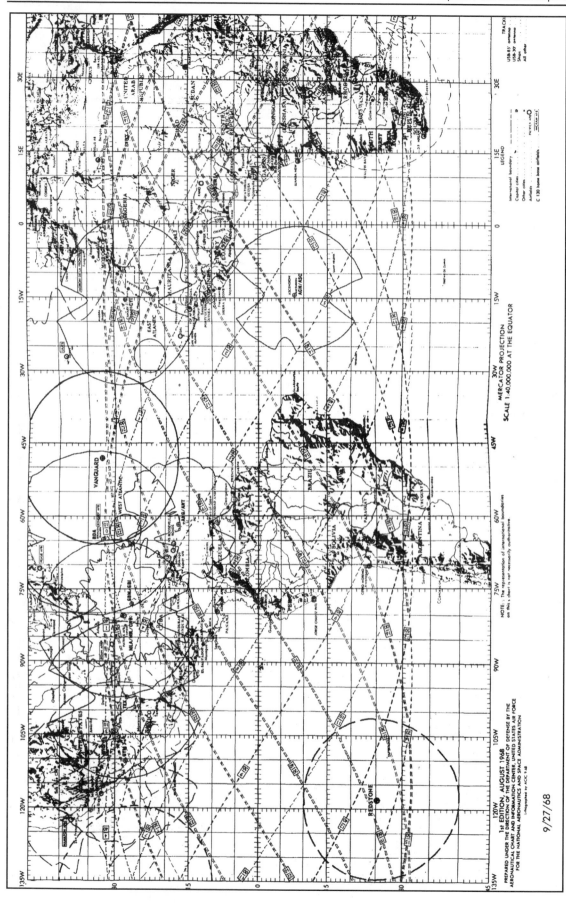

9/27/68

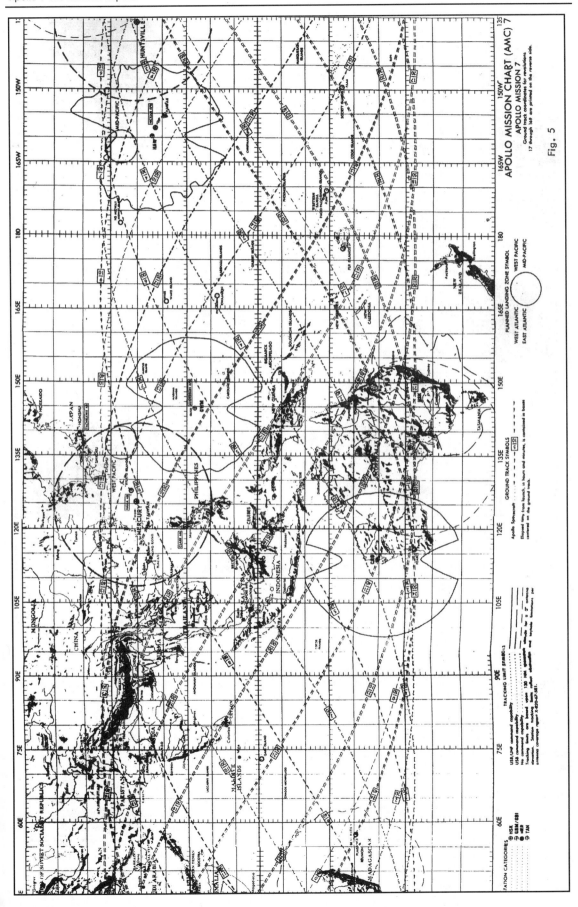

Fig. 5

Alternate Missions

Three general alternate missions (1-day, 2-day and 3-day) are considered with specific variations depending on whether or not the S-IVB stage is available, spacecraft system life-time problems, and the amount of available SPS propellant. An alternate rendezvous plan considering a 1-day delay is also considered. Missions greater than three days in duration will be planned in real time.

Many of the Detailed Test Objectives (DTO) for this mission require spacecraft translation maneuvers and/or specific attitude orientation. Each of the alternate mission profiles schedule as many of these profile related DTO's as possible. A summary is presented in Table 4.

Since none of the proposed alternate mission profiles schedule more maneuvers or require longer system duty cycles than the nominal mission, it is concluded that the consumables margins would be larger than for the nominal missions.

MISSION PRIORITY	1	5	6	7	11	12	13	14	18	38	
DTO#	7.19	3.15	3.14	1.13	2.5	20.13	1.10	20.8	2.6	57.21	
ALTERNATE MISSION	RADIATOR TEST	SPS PERFORMANCE	SPS MINIMUM IMPULSE	GNCS ΔV CONTROL	SCS ΔV CONTROL	CSM-ACTIVE RENDEZVOUS	SEXTANT TRACKING	TRANSPOSITION AND DOCKING	GNCS/MTVC ΔV TAKE OVER	SLA DEPLOYMENT	COMMENTS
1B				◑				●		●	
1D	○			◑				●		●	S-IVB RELATED TEST OBJECTIVES SATISFIED IF COI=0
2B	●	●	◑	◑	●		○	○	●		
2C	●		●	●	●				○		MANUAL TAKE OVER BURN MUST BE AT LEAST 35 SECONDS LONG
3A	●	●	◑	●	●	●	●	●	●	●	
3B	●	●	●	●	●				●		
3C	●		●	●	●				○		MANUAL TAKE OVER BURN MUST BE AT LEAST 35 SECONDS LONG
ALTERNATE RENDEZVOUS	●	●	●	●	●	●	●	●	●	●	

● FULFILLED

◑ PARTIALLY FULFILLED

○ POSSIBLY FULFILLED

DETAILED TEST OBJECTIVE ACCOMPLISHMENT
FOR THE APOLLO 7 ALTERNATE MISSIONS

TABLE 4

One-Day Mission Plans

There are two plans being considered for 1-day missions. The first terminates with a landing in the Middle Pacific Recovery Zone in the sixth revolution. The second terminates with a landing in the west Atlantic near the end of the first day. Both of these alternates follow the nominal operational trajectory plan until deorbit.

Two-Day Mission Plans

Two 2-day mission plans, alternates 2b and 2c, are being considered. Two days does not permit all test objectives to be met.

Alternate 2b- Alternate 2b assumes that an SCS COI burn of less than 31 seconds has occurred. The first maneuver will be a GNCS burn in revolution 16 over Carnarvon to adjust the propellant level for the gauging system test. If the COI did not satisfy the SCS test requirement, this maneuver would be under SCS control. If the COI were between 28 and 31 seconds, this maneuver could be a minimum-impulse test. A 57 second burn for the SPS performance, gauging and GNCS/MTVC tests will occur over Cape Kennedy in revolution 19. A minimum impulse test will be performed over Carnarvon in revolution 29 and the GNCS deorbit burn over Hawaii occurs in revolution 32 for a west Atlantic landing in revolution 33.

Alternate 2c - In the second 2-day plan, alternate 2c, it is assumed that a COI burn of more than 31 seconds has occurred. The COI burn will suffice for the SCS test. The first scheduled maneuver will be performed over Cape Kennedy in revolution 17. The burn objective will be a minimum impulse test. The second maneuver will occur two revolutions later over Cape Kennedy. Burn objectives will depend on the exact propellant level. The most desirable objective would be a GNCS MTVC maneuver. This requires a minimum maneuver time of 35 seconds. If this duration is impossible, the maneuver will be a GNCS-controlled, orbit-shaping maneuver that used whatever Delta-V is available. The third maneuver will be a second minimum impulse test. The maneuver will occur over Carnarvon in revolution 29. The deorbit maneuver will occur over Hawaii in revolution 32 and landing will be in the west Atlantic in revolution 33.

Three-Day Mission Plans

The three-day missions may allow all primary mission objectives to be scheduled. Three plans are presented, alternates 3a, 36 and 3c.

Alternate 3a - In the first plan, alternate 3a, it is assumed that the S-IVB is available. The rendezvous will occur as in the nominal mission. In revolution 28 an SCS burn will occur over Carnarvon to adjust the level for the SPS performance and gauging system test. These tests will be performed over Cape Kennedy in revolution 32. A minimum-impulse test will be performed shortly prior to the GNCS deorbit burn, which occurs in revolution 45 over Hawaii. Landing will be in revolution 46 in the west Atlantic.

Alternate 3b - The second three-day plan, alternate 3b, considers that the S-IVB is not available and that a COI burn of less than 31 seconds has occurred. The first maneuver will be a GNCS-controlled maneuver in revolution 17 over Cape Kennedy to adjust the propellant level for SPS performance and gauging system tests. If the COI burn did not provide a satisfactory SCS test, this maneuver will be under SCS control. The second maneuver will be a minimum-impulse test over Cape Kennedy two revolutions later. The SPS performance and gauging system tests will occur over Cape Kennedy in revolution 32. A second minimum-impulse test will be performed shortly prior to the GNCS deorbit, which occurs in revolution 47 over Hawaii.

Alternate 3c - The third three-day plan, alternate 3c, considers that the S-IVB is unavailable and that a COI burn of more than 31 seconds has occurred. The COI burn will suffice for an SCS test. The first maneuver will be a minimum-impulse test over Cape Kennedy in revolution 17. The second maneuver will occur over Cape Kennedy two revolutions later. The objective of this maneuver will be determined by the propellant level as on alternate 2c. The second minimum-impulse test will occur over Cape Kennedy in revolution 32. The GNCS deorbit burn will occur over Hawaii in revolution 46 to produce a landing in the west Atlantic in revolution 47.

Alternate Rendezvous Plan

The only alternate rendezvous plan being considered is a 1-day delay. Alternate rendezvous plans with a delay of one revolution are not considered because of the loss of good MSFN coverage. A rendezvous delay of more than one day is not considered because of the drag uncertainties of the S-IVB. A 1-day delay in the rendezvous allows approximately the same maneuver plan, the same station coverage, and the same lighting.

The plan involves deleting the phasing maneuver at 26 hours, 25 minutes GET and making, instead, a SM RCS maneuver to reestablish the near nominal phasing (CSM leading by about 75 nm) one day later. The SM RCS burn of about 12 fps has been scheduled to occur over Ascension in revolution 18 at about 27 hours, 30 minutes GET. The phasing and concentricity maneuvers necessary for rendezvous slip approximately one day and the terminal phase will follow essentially the same plan as that of the nominal. The remainder of the mission follows the nominal operational trajectory.

SPACE VEHICLE DESCRIPTION

The Apollo 7 Mission will be performed by an Apollo Saturn IB space vehicle designated AS-205, which consists of a two stage Saturn IB Launch Vehicle (SA-205)and an Apollo Block II Spacecraft (CSM-101) (Figure 6).

The Saturn IB Launch Vehicle consists of two propulsion stages and an Instrument Unit (IU). The Apollo Spacecraft payload for Apollo 7 consists of a launch escape assembly, Block II Command and Service Modules and a Spacecraft LM Adapter. There will be no Lunar Module Test Article on this flight. This is the first flight of a Block II Command and Service Module. A list of current weights for the space vehicle is contained in Table 5.

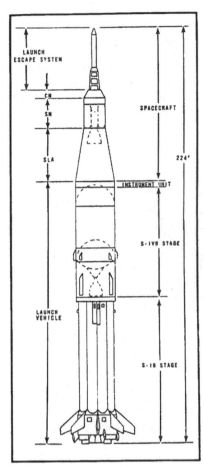

Fig. 6

LAUNCH VEHICLE DESCRIPTION

First Stage (S-IB)

The S-IB stage, Figure 7, of the launch vehicle is 80 feet long and 21.5 feet in diameter. The principle components of this stage, are four 70-inch-diameter LOX containers mounted alternately with four 70-inch-diameter fuel containers in a circular pattern around a 105-inch-diameter LOX center tank, a thrust assembly, eight H-1 engines, and a spider beam assembly. Eight aerodynamic fins stabilize the vehicle in flight. Pre-flight support is also provided by a holddown fitting on each fin.

The eight 200,000 pound thrust H-1 engines produce a total thrust of 1.6 million pounds at lift-off. Four fixed engines are arranged in a square pattern inboard of the four steerable outboard engines. The outer engines are hydraulically gimbaled to provide thrust vector control. Staging retrofire is provided by four solid rocket motors, each producing a thrust of 36,000 lbs. for 1.5 second.

Second Stage (S-IVB)

The S-IVB stage (Figure 8) has a diameter of 22 feet and a length of 59 feet. It is a semi monocoque structure consisting basically of an aft inter-stage, an aft skirt, a thrust structure, a divided propellant container and a forward skirt. The aft interstage, (S-IVB inter-stage) connects the S-IB to the S-IVB stage. The aft inter-stage also contains the retro-rockets necessary for separation of the S-IB and S-IVB.

TABLE 5

AS-205 SPACE VEHICLE WEIGHT SUMMARY

STAGE OR MODULE	INERT WEIGHT	TOTAL EXPENDABLES	TOTAL WEIGHT	NOTE (Optional)
S-IB Stage	84,401	895,098	979,499	85,000 lbs at separation
S-IVB Interstage	6,478		6,478	
S-IVB Stage	25,285	230,635	255,920	28,565 lbs at insertion
Instrument Unit	4,280		4,280	
Spacecraft LM Adapter	3,943		3,943	
Service Module	10,664	9,539	20,203	11,216 lbs at separation
Command Module	12,077	277	12,354	11,994 lbs at splashdown
Launch Escape Assembly	8,874		8,874	

Launch Vehicle at Ignition (S-IB, I/S, S-IVB, IU). . . . .   1,246,177 lbs

Spacecraft at Ignition (SLA, CSM, LEA). . . . .   45,374 lbs

Space Vehicle at Ignition . . . .   1,291,783 lbs

Thrust Buildup Propellant Utilization. . . . .   13,809 lbs

Space Vehicle at lift-off. . . . .   1,277,742 lbs

Space Vehicle in Orbit (S-IVB, IU, SLA, CSM) . . . .   66,850 lbs

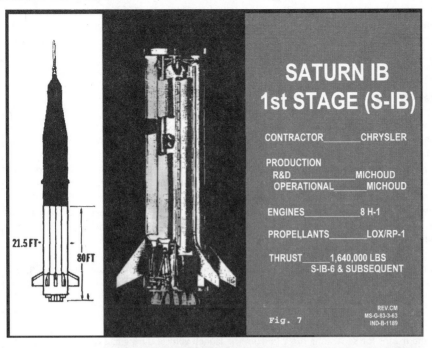

SATURN IB
1st STAGE (S-IB)

CONTRACTOR	CHRYSLER
PRODUCTION	
R&D	MICHOUD
OPERATIONAL	MICHOUD
ENGINES	8 H-1
PROPELLANTS	LOX/RP-1
THRUST	1,640,000 LBS
	S-IB-6 & SUBSEQUENT

REV.CM
MS-G-83-3-63
IND-B-1189

Fig. 7

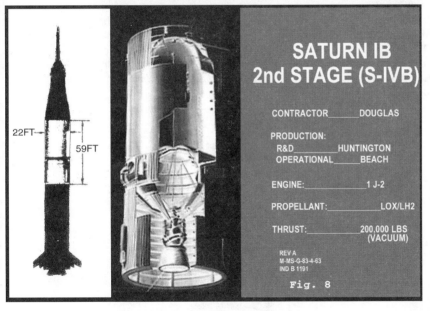

SATURN IB
2nd STAGE (S-IVB)

CONTRACTOR	DOUGLAS
PRODUCTION:	
R&D	HUNTINGTON
OPERATIONAL	BEACH
ENGINE:	1 J-2
PROPELLANT:	LOX/LH2
THRUST:	200,000 LBS
	(VACUUM)

REV A
M-MS-G-83-4-63
IND B 1191

Fig. 8

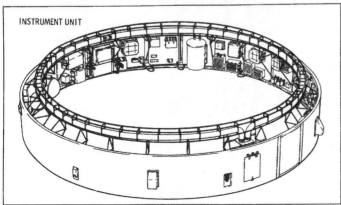

INSTRUMENT UNIT

Fig. 9

A single J-2 engine developing 200,000 pounds of thrust powers the S-IVB. During powered flight, pitch and yaw control is provided by gimbaling the J-2 engine and roll control is afforded by four 150 pound thrust hypergolic engines located in the Auxiliary Propulsion System (APS) modules. Three solid propellant ullage motors ensure settling of S-IVB propellants prior to J-2 engine ignition.

Instrument Unit (IU)

The IU structure, Figure 9, consists of three segments of honeycomb sandwich panels joined with splice plates to form a monocoque cylinder 21.7 feet in diameter and three feet high. Ring segment angles are bonded to the skin of the panels to provide mating surfaces to attach the IU to the S-IVB and SLA. Brackets are riveted to the inner face of the panel segments to provide mounting for the environmental conditioning cold plates.

The Instrument Unit contains the following: Electrical system, self-contained and battery powered; Environmental Control, provides thermal conditioning for the electrical components and guidance systems contained in the assembly;

Guidance and Control, used in solving guidance equations and controlling the attitude of the vehicle; Measuring and Telemetry, monitors and transmits flight parameters and vehicle operation information to ground stations; Radio Frequency, provides for tracking and command signals.

SPACECRAFT DESCRIPTION

AS-205 Spacecraft Safety Considerations

CSM 101 is a Block II spacecraft incorporating extensive design improvements over Block I. This spacecraft reflects stringent controls and criteria in the use of non metallic materials. Mechanical controls have been improved, general mobility of the astronauts has been enhanced by improving accessibility, and protection has been provided to components or controls susceptible to inadvertent bumping. Some aluminum tubing has been replaced with stainless steel and solder joints have been armored. A 60% oxygen and 40% nitrogen cabin atmosphere will be provided during count-down in order to reduce the fire hazard. The flight crew will continue to breathe 100% oxygen during this period through the suit circuit. After lift-off, the cabin will be purged and pressurized to five psi with 100% oxygen. A fire extinguisher has been added to the flight equipment. The reliability and efficiency of the overall communication system throughout the launch complex including the manned vehicle, has been significantly improved since the AS-204 accident.

The Block II spacecraft consists of a launch escape assembly (LEA), command module (CM), service module (SM), and the spacecraft lunar module adapter (SLA) (Figure 10).

Launch Escape Assembly (LEA)

The LEA (Figure 11) provides the means for separating the CM from the launch vehicle during pad or suborbital aborts. This assembly consists of a Q-ball Instrument assembly (nose cone), ballast compartment, canard surfaces, pitch control motor, tower jettison motor, launch escape motor, a structural skirt, an open-frame tower, and a boost protective cover (BPC). The structural skirt at the base of the housing which encloses the launch escape rocket motors, is secured to the forward portion of the tower. The BPC is attached to the aft end of the tower to protect the CM from heat during boost, and from exhaust damage by the launch escape and tower jettison motors. Explosive nuts, one in each tower leg well, secure the tower to the CM structure. Redundant analysis and tests (Launch escape motor case integrity, etc.) have been performed to maximize confidence in this emergency system.

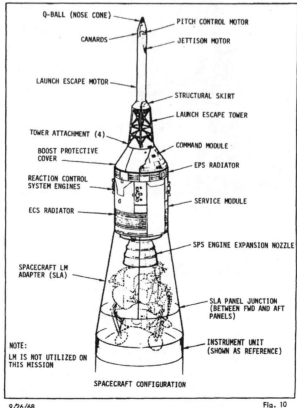

9/26/68   Fig. 10

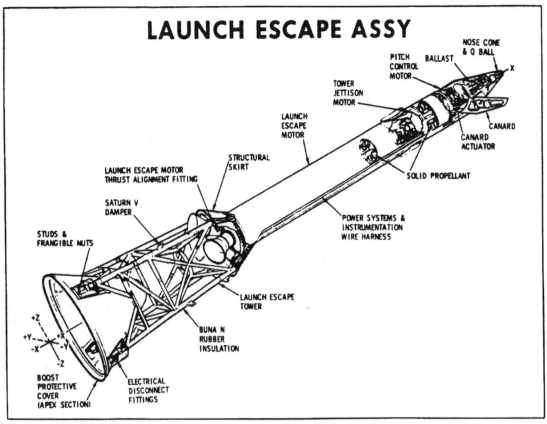

LAUNCH ESCAPE ASSY

9/26/68 Fig. 11

COMMAND MODULE (CM)

The CM (Figure 12) is the spacecraft control center and contains automatic and manual equipment to control and monitor the spacecraft systems. The CM also contains communications equipment and systems to provide for the safety and comfort of the flight crew. The primary structure is encompassed by three heat shields (coated with ablative material and joined or fastened to the primary structure) forming a truncated, conic structure. The CM consists of a forward compartment, a crew compartment, and an oft compartment.

Forward Compartment

The forward compartment consists of four 90-degree segments around the perimeter of the forward access tunnel. The forward compartment contains two negative pitch reaction control system engines, and the forward heat shield release mechanism. Also located in the forward compartment are the Earth landing system components.

The Earth Landing System (ELS) provides for safe return of the CM through automatic sequence of drogue and main parachute deployment. It also includes equipment to be deployed and activated after landing to aid recovery. The ELS features two drogue chutes, three pilot chutes and three main chutes. Deployment sequence is initiated by baroswitches. Postlanding equipment includes inflatable bags to upright the floating CM if it stabilizes in an apex down attitude, sea dye marker with 12-hour effectiveness, a flashing beacon and a VHF recovery beacon transmitter. Operation of the ELS under abort conditions is essentially the same as in nominal re-entry descent except for RCS propellant pre-impact preparations.

Crew Compartment

The crew compartment or inner structure is a sealed cabin with pressurization maintained by the Environmental Control System (ECS). The compartment, protected by a heat shield, contains controls and displays for operation of the spacecraft and spacecraft systems. The crew couches and restraint harness assemblies, hatch covers, window shades, etc. are located here. It is also provided with crew equipment, food and water, waste management provisions, survival equipment, and scientific experiments equipment. Access hatches, observation windows, and equipment bays complete the items in this area.

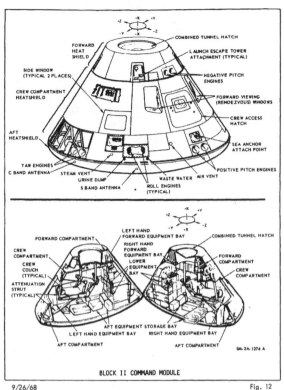

BLOCK II COMMAND MODULE

9/26/68   Fig. 12

CM Impact Attenuation System

During a water impact the CM deceleration force will vary, depending on wave shape and horizontal velocity at impact. The impact attenuation system reduces the impact forces acting on the crew to a value within their tolerance level. A major portion of the energy (75 to 90 per cent) is absorbed by the impact surface (water) and the deformation of the CM structure.

The impact system is divided into two subsystems: external and internal. The external subsystem consists of crushable structure located in the aft compartment. The internal system consists of the eight crushable core attenuation struts used to connect the crew couch to the CM inner structure.

Crew Couches

The spacecraft contains three couches bolted together to form a single unitized structure (Figure 13). The primary function of the couches is to support the crew during acceleration/decelerations up to 30 g's forward and aft (±X), 18 g's up and down (±Z), and 15 g's laterally (±Y). Secondary functions of the crew couches are: position crew at duty stations and provide support for the translation and rotation hand controls, lights, and other equipment.

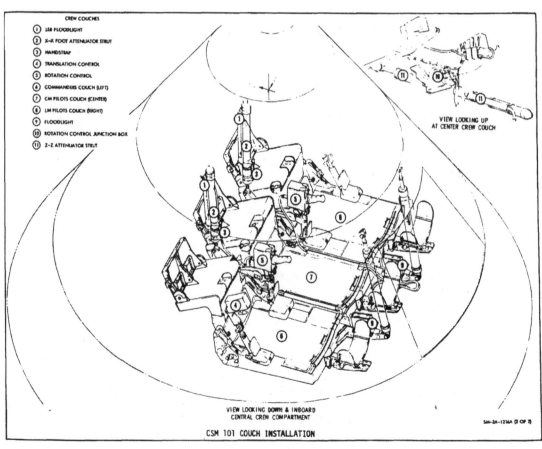

CSM 101 COUCH INSTALLATION

Fig. 13

Crew Couch Structure.

The crew couch structure consists of three crew couches fabricated of aluminum and weighing approximately 240 pounds. Beta cloth has been selected as the couch fabric. The left and right couches are identical. The center couch connects the left and right couch into a single unified structure. Crew couch positions are shown in Figure 14.

Crew Couch Attachments.

The couches support a number of items, with the primary items being the rotation and translation controls. The translation control is located on the right armrest of the left couch and the left armrest of the right couch. The latter rotation control can also be attached to the Lower Equipment Bay (LEB) for maneuvering the CSM during Guidance and Navigation System (G&N) functions.

CM Mechanical Controls

Mechanical controls are provided in the crew compartment for manual operation of the side access hatch covers, and forward access hatch covers. Manual override levers are used for the ECS cabin pressure relief valve. Tools for opening or securing the hatch covers and operating ECS manual backup valves, are in the stowage area aft of the work table in the lower equipment bay.

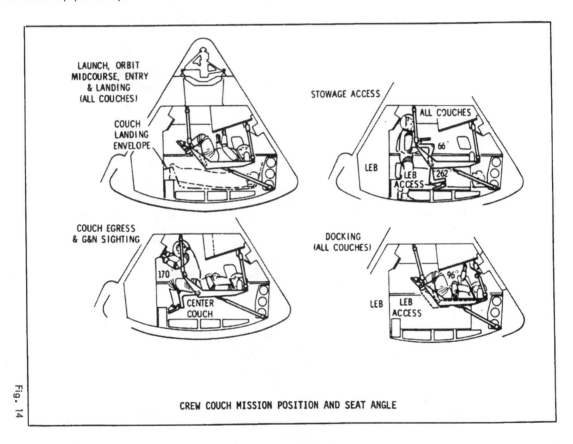

Fig. 14

CREW COUCH MISSION POSITION AND SEAT ANGLE

Side Access Hatch

Side access to the crew compartment is through an outward-opening single integrated hatch assembly and adapter frame (Figure 15). The hatch can be opened from the inside or outside in five seconds regardless of internal pressure. The hatch includes a primary flexible thermal seal, hinges, and a hatch and linkage mechanism. The adapter frame, which closes out the area between the inner and outer structure, provides the structural continuity for transmitting primary structure loads around the hatch opening without transmitting the tension or compression loads to the hatch. The inner structure adapter frame contains a single primary pressure seal.

Door deployment is accomplished by a single handle with ratchet mechanism which operates the latch. The latch and linkage mechanism provides a hatch lock for pressure loads and for pressure sealing of the crew compartment. The internal lever operation is perpendicular to the hatch with the inboard stroke driving the latches closed while the outboard stroke drives the latches open. The hatch will open 100 degrees minimum. A stored energy counter-balance system is provided to assist in opening the hatch in both normal and emergency conditions and attenuate the opening and closing velocity of the hatch.

The hatch is normally latched and unlatched manually from the inside by a lever permanently attached to the hatch operating system. Five actuations of 60 degrees per stroke will fully engage or disengage the 15 latches that engage the inner structure adapter. External operation is accomplished using a Ground Support Equipment (GSE) or an in-flight tool. Should the linkage jam or be unable to close and hold the hatch, auxiliary devices ore provided to hold the hatch closed.

A manually operated vent valve is located in the hatch. The valve is capable of venting the cabin from 5 to 0.1 psig in one minute. The valve may be operated from the inside or outside by a suited crewman.

The hatch mechanism operates the Boost Protective Cover (BPC) mechanism for normal and emergency modes, and is sequenced to insure release of the BPC hatch prior to unlocking the CM hatch. The BPC is hinged and retained with a tethering device when the combined unified and BPC hatch are opened. A permanent release handle (D-ring) is utilized on the outside of the BPC to manually unlatch the drive mechanism.

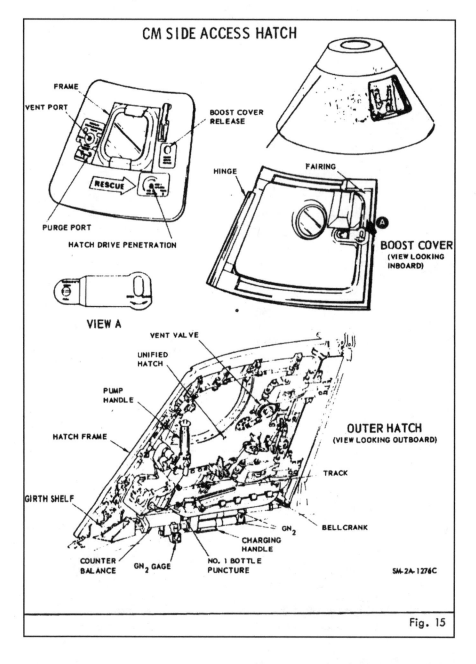

Fig. 15

Windows and Shades

Five windows are provided through the inner structure and heat shield of the CM: two forward viewing and two side observation windows, and a hatch window. During orbital flight, photographs of external objects will be taken through the viewing and observation windows. The inner windows are made of tempered silica glass with 0.25-inch-thick double panes, separated by 0.1 inch of space, and have a softening temperature point of 2000°F. The outer windows are made of amorphous-fused silicon with a single 0.7-inch-thick pane. Each pane contains an anti-reflecting coating on the external surface, and has a blue-red reflective coating on the inner surface for filtering out most infrared and all ultraviolet rays. The glass has a softening temperature point of 2800°F, and a melting point of 3110°F.

Shades are provided for controlling external light entering the CM. The aluminum sheet shades are opaque for zero-light transmittal, have a non reflective inner surface, and are held in place by "wing" levers.

Protection Panels

The protection panels prevent loose equipment (tools, etc.) and debris getting into the various nooks and crevices in the crew compartment. They also suppress fire by closing out the equipment bays with covers around the aft bulkhead and protect the ECS tubing from the zero g activities of the crew and the pre-launch activities of ground personnel.

The protection panels (also referred to as close-out panels) are a series of aluminum panels and covers that fair the irregular structure to the equipment bays and wire troughs and covers. The panels vary in thickness and are attached to secondary structures by captive fasteners. Access panels and penetrations are located at or over equipment and connectors needed for the mission.

Aft Compartment

The aft compartment is the area encompassed by the aft portion of the crew compartment heat shield, aft heat shield, and aft portion of the primary structure. This compartment contains 10 reaction control engines, impact attenuation structure, instrumentation, and storage tanks for water, fuel, oxidizer, and gaseous helium. Four crushable ribs, along the spacecraft +Z axis, are provided as part of the impact attenuation structure to absorb energy during impact.

The aft heat shield, which encloses the large end of the CM, is a shallow, spherically contoured assembly. It is made of the same type of materials as other CM heat shields. However, the ablative material on this heat shield has a greater thickness for the dissipation of heat during entry. External provisions are made on this heat shield for connecting the CM to the SM.

SERVICE MODULE

The service module is a cylindrical structure formed by 1-inch-thick aluminum honeycomb panels (Figure 16). Radial beams, milled from aluminum alloy plates, separate the structure interior into six unequal sectors around a cylindrical center section. Equipment contained within the service module is accessible through maintenance doors located around the exterior surface of the module.

Radial beam trusses on the forward portion of the CM structure provide a means for securing the CM to the SM. Three alternate beams have compression pads for supporting the CM and the other three have shear-compression pads and tension ties. A flat center section in each tension tie incorporates redundant explosive charges for SM-CM separation. These beams and separation devices are enclosed within a fairing between the CM and SM.

The Service Propulsion System (SPS) provides thrust for major velocity changes of the spacecraft after S-IVB separation. The four main SPS propellant tanks are mounted on the lower bulkhead of the SM in bays formed by the radial beams. Two helium tanks mounted in the SM center section pressurize the SPS propellant tanks and the SPS engine. The engine is gimbal mounted to the aft bulkhead to permit alignment of the direction of thrust through the varying center of gravity of the spacecraft. Insulation of crinkled, aluminized mylar is used in all sectors of the SM and between the CM and SM to maintain the temperature of the propellants within operating limits.

Common Command and Service Module Systems

Guidance and Navigation (G&N) System

The G&N system measures spacecraft attitude and velocity, determines trajectory, controls spacecraft attitude, controls the thrust vector of the SPS engine, and provides abort information and display data. Primary determination of the spacecraft velocity and position, and computation of the trajectory parameters is accomplished by the Manned Space Flight Network (MSFN).

Stabilization and Control System (SCS)

The SCS provides control and monitoring of the spacecraft attitude, backup control of the thrust vector of the SPS engine and a backup inertial reference.

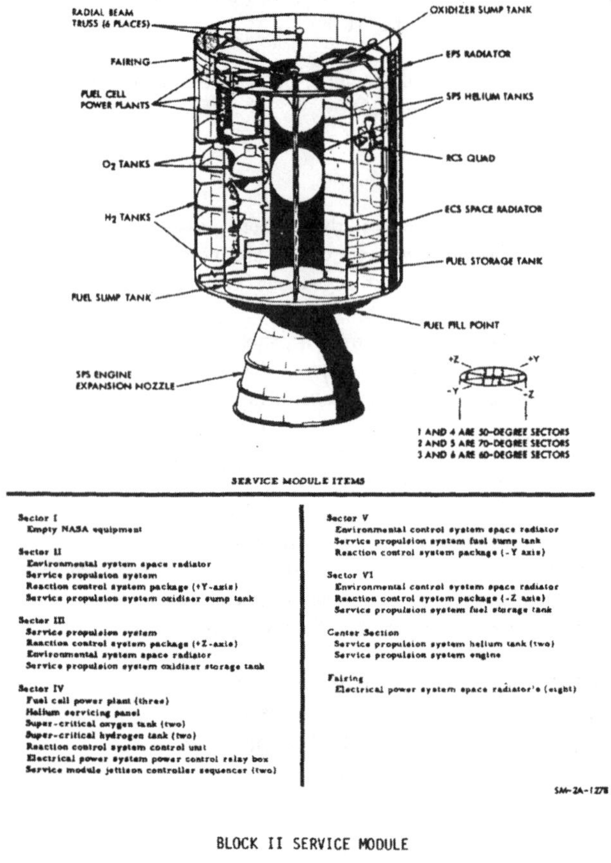

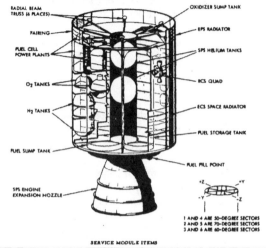

Major components of the SCS are attitude gyros, rate gyros, accelerometers and assorted indicators, sensors, signal processors and control assemblies.

Reaction Control System RCS

The RCS provides thrust for attitude maneuvers of the spacecraft in response to automatic control signals from the SCS in conjunction with the G&N system. The CM RCS includes two independent subsystems of six engines each, operating in tandem. A single subsystem is able to provide adequate attitude control should one subsystem fail. The SM RCS consists of four independent subsystems of four engines each, packaged as modules (quads) and located equidistant around the circumference near the top of the SM.

Electrical Power System EPS

The electrical power subsystem (EPS) consists of the equipment and reactants required to supply the electrical energy sources, power generation and controls, power conversion and conditioning, and power distribution to the electrical buses. Power is supplied to fulfill all command and service module (CSM) requirements.

The EPS can be functionally divided into four major categories:

Figure labels:

RADIAL BEAM TRUSS (6 PLACES)
FAIRING
FUEL CELL POWER PLANTS
O2 TANKS
H2 TANKS
FUEL SUMP TANK
SPS ENGINE EXPANSION NOZZLE

OXIDIZER SUMP TANK
EPS RADIATOR
SPS HELIUM TANKS
RCS QUAD
ECS SPACE RADIATOR
FUEL STORAGE TANK
FUEL FILL POINT

1 AND 4 ARE 50-DEGREE SECTORS
2 AND 5 ARE 70-DEGREE SECTORS
3 AND 6 ARE 60-DEGREE SECTORS

SERVICE MODULE ITEMS

Sector I
Empty NASA equipment

Sector II
Environmental system space radiator
Service propulsion system
Reaction control system package (+Y-axis)
Service propulsion system oxidizer sump tank

Sector III
Service propulsion system
Reaction control system package (+Z-axis)
Environmental system space radiator
Service propulsion system oxidizer storage tank

Sector IV
Fuel cell power plant (three)
Helium servicing panel
Super-critical oxygen tank (two)
Super-critical hydrogen tank (two)
Reaction control system control unit
Electrical power system power control relay box
Service module jettison controller sequencer (two)

Sector V
Environmental control system space radiator
Service propulsion system fuel dump tank
Reaction control system package (-Y axis)

Sector VI
Environmental control system space radiator
Reaction control system package (-Z axis)
Service propulsion system fuel storage tank

Center Section
Service propulsion system helium tank (two)
Service propulsion system engine

Fairing
Electrical power system space radiator's (eight)

SM-2A-1278

BLOCK II SERVICE MODULE

Fig. 16

Energy storage: Cryogenics storage, entry and postlanding batteries, pyrotechnic batteries.

Power generation: Fuel cell power plants.

Power conversion: Solid state inverters, battery charger.

Power distribution: D-C and A-C power buses, D-C and A-C sensing circuits, controls and displays.

The system operates in three modes: peak, average, and minimum mission loads. Peak loads occur during performance of major Delta-V maneuvers, including boost. These are of relatively short duration with D-C power being supplied by three fuel cell power plants supplemented by two of three entry batteries. A-C power is supplied by two of three inverters.

During drifting flight, minimum power is required. During these periods D-C power can be supplied by two fuel cell power plants with one on open circuit and A-C power by one or two inverters.

Energy Storage

The primary source of energy is provided by the cryogenic gas storage system that provides fuel (H2) and oxidizer (O2) to the power generating system located in the service module. Cryogenic consumption is dependent on energy demand by the power generating and/or environmental control subsystems. Manual control can be used when required.

A secondary source of energy storage is provided by five silver oxide-zinc batteries located in the CM. Three rechargeable entry and postlanding batteries supply sequencer logic power at all times, supplemental D-C power for peak loads, all operating power required for entry and postlanding, and can be connected to power either or both pyro circuits. Two pyro batteries provide energy for activation of pyro devices throughout all phases of a mission.

Environmental Control System (ECS)

The ECS provides a controlled cabin environment and dispersion of CM equipment heat loads. Proper cabin environment is maintained by the cabin pressure and temperature control subsystem, which regulates the pressure of the oxygen supplied by the EPS and regulates the temperature by circulation through the cabin heat exchanger. The water-glycol coolant subsystem absorbs and transports heat from and to the cabin heat exchanger and from the electronic equipment.

Telecommunication (T/C) System

The T/C system provides for the acquisition, processing, storage, transmission and reception of telemetry, and tracking, and ranging data between the spacecraft and ground stations. Radio Frequency (RF) electronics include VHF/FM transmitter, VHF/AM transceiver, C-Band transponder, Unified S-Band equipment, VHF recovery beacon and HF transceiver. Antennas are VHF omnidirectional, S-Band omni-directional, VHF and HF recovery, and C-Band. Voice communications between the crew and the MSFN is provided by the USB and VHF frequencies. Real time television is transmitted from the CM to the MSFN via the USB system.

Sequential (SEQ) Systems

The SEQ systems provide safety for the crew during the ascent and descent phases of a mission. Major subsystems are the sequential events control system (SECS), emergency detection system (EDS), launch escape system (LES), and Earth landing system (ELS). The system interfaces with the RCS or the SPS during an abort.

The Sequential Events Control System (SECS) consists of controllers that provide automatic and semi-automatic control for initiation or termination of functional events during various phases of a mission.

The Emergency Detection System (EDS) senses booster malfunction and, under certain conditions, provides automatic abort initiation, via the IU, between lift-off and prior to S-IB engine shutdown.

Spacecraft LM Adapter

The spacecraft LM adapter (SLA) is a truncated conical structure which connects the CSM to the launch vehicle instrument unit. This adapter, constructed of eight 2-inch-thick aluminum panels, is 154 inches in diameter at the forward end (SM interface) and 260 inches at the aft end. Separation of the spacecraft from the SLA is accomplished by means of explosive charges which permit the four SLA forward panels to disengage from the CSM and rotate outward 45 degrees from vertical. The four aft panels remain attached to the S-IVB instrument unit. For the Apollo 7 mission a cross-shaped stiffener is installed within the SLA in place of the LM. The SM SPS nozzle extends into the SLA which also houses an umbilical cable for connecting circuits between the launch vehicle and the spacecraft.

The SLA for the AS-205 mission has been modified with additional longitudinal reinforcement, an exterior cork layer and vent holes for pressurization equalization and acquisition lights as an aid to rendezvous.

Significant Configuration Changes from Block I Spacecraft

1.   Addition of S-band equipment for deep space communications.

2.   Removal of the HF transceiver, antenna and mounts, tie and stow harness and strengthening of the cold plate.

3.   Removal of the C-Band transponder and all associated mounting hardware and harness in the Lower
        Equipment Bay.

4.   VHF recovery antenna installation changes — flexible whiskers adjacent to antenna on CM structure to provide
        a ground plane.

5.   Communications system modifications and cobra cable redesign.

6.   Incorporation of the unified hatch assembly.

7.   Improved capabilities of components of the Earth Landing System (ELS).

8.   Incorporation of unitized crew couches.

9   Addition of a CM TV camera.

10.   Addition of portable fire extinguisher.

11.   Increased flight qualification and operational instrumentation.

12.   Incorporation of full crew support systems.

13.   Addition of three emergency oxygen masks.

HUMAN SYSTEM PROVISIONS

AS-205 SPACE SUITS

The Apollo space suit (Block II) (Figure 17) has evolved into its present configuration basically because of the changing goals of each manned spacecraft program.

Since the objective of the Apollo program is a manned lunar landing it has been necessary to develop a space suit assembly with life support systems which have a lunar surface extravehicular (EV) capability.

In addition, the space suit must provide intravehicular protection compatible with both the command and lunar modules during both pressurized and unpressurized flight. In the intravehicular (IV) mode, the suit consists of the pressure garment assembly (PGA) and cover layer, constant wear garment (CWG), waste management system, communications carrier, and the inflight coverall garment (ICG). Deleted are those subsystems designated as EV systems, such as the Portable Life Support System (PLSS), Oxygen Purge System (OPS) and the liquid cooling garment (LCG). Since the AS-205 mission is to be low Earth orbit and restricted to intravehicular activity, certain extravehicular hardware will not be flown.

Major Suit Changes Subsequent to the AS-204 Fire

1.   Beta and Teflon fabric utilization for fire protection.

2.   Integration of the Thermo Meteoroid Garment and Pressure Garment Assembly into one assembly.

3.   Fluorel coating of hoses.

4.   Light weight optimization of the Command Module Pilot's suit.

Flight Apparel and Related Equipment

The following items of flight apparel and related equipment will be required to support the AS-205 mission:

a.	IV pressure garment assembly (PGA) -	1 required
b.	EV pressure garment assembly (PGA) -	2 required
c.	Constant wear garment (CWG) -	6 required
d.	Communications carrier -	3 required
e.	Inflight coverall garment (ICG) -	3 required
f.	Maintenance kit (MK) -	1 required
g.	Inflight helmet stowage bag (IF HSB) -	3 required
h.	Bio-instrumentation System -	3 required
i.	Sleep station restraints (sleeping bags) -	2 required

The following paragraphs summarize the design concepts of the hardware to be provided for the AS-205 mission.

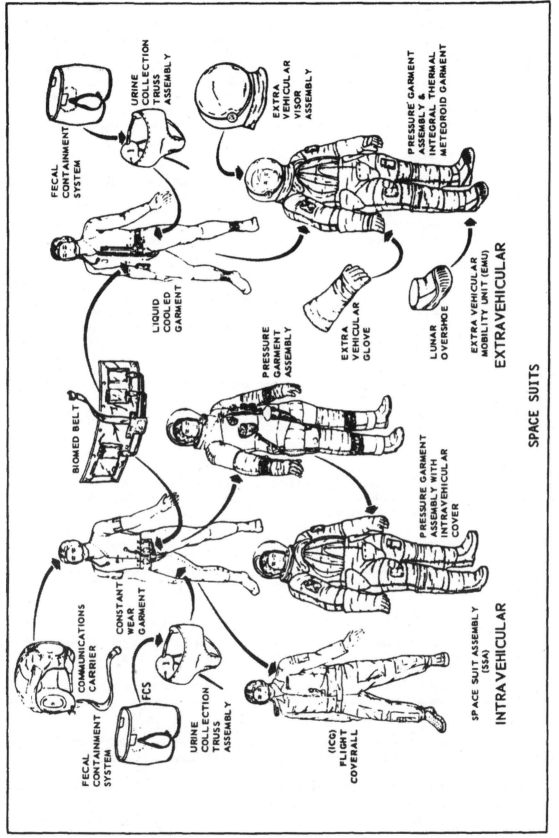

Fig. 17

Pressure Garment Assembly (PGA)

The PGA is an anthropomorphic pressure vessel which furnishes protection against the hostile environments associated with space flight while providing a mobility capability sufficient to accomplish useful work. Two models of the PGA will be provided; an IV version and an EV version. The IV model for the CSM center couch position (Command Module Pilot) has been optimized for a non-EVA mission by removing the relatively bulky integrated thermal meteoroid garment and substituting a light weight cover for abrasion and fire protection. All EV connectors and interfaces have also been removed to lighten and simplify its performance. For example, the dual gas connectors, water connector, PLSS attachments, etc., have been removed. The EV version of the PGA will be flown in the outboard CSM couches, which are the Command Pilot and the Lunar Module Pilot positions, to evaluate interfaces and performance capabilities.

Constant Wear Garment (CWG)

The CWG is a cotton undergarment worn beneath the PGA, ICG, or by itself as desired by the pilots. It contains provisions to accommodate the bio-instrumentation, waste management systems, and communications equipment. While worn with the PGA it provides skin abrasion protection, acts as a perspiration wick, and offers insulation for heat or cold as required. In the unsuited mode it is used primarily for insulation and as a carrier for the instrumentation and communications equipment. The Bio-belt Assembly is attached to the CWG being worn.

Communications Carrier

The communications carrier is a headset containing dual microphones and earphones for suited communications. Lightweight headsets are provided for unsuited modes. The carrier offers crew protection during high ambient noise environments and is designed to maintain microphone position with respect to the mouth during suited modes.

Inflight Coverall Garment (ICG)

The ICG is a two piece form fitting garment intended to be worn over the CWG. It is made of coated fiberglass for fire protection. Its purpose is to provide a comfortable garment for use in long periods of pressurized cabin mode. Pockets are provided for crewmen's personal items, provisions are included for communications equipment attachment, and Velcro-soled boots are available to assist off-couch movement in zero g.

Maintenance Kit (MK)

The maintenance kit is provided to service the PGA at routine intervals of the mission to maintain ease of operation and effect repairs if required. The kit contains lubricants, mending tape, and replacement seals. The PGA will be qualified to operate without this kit; however, PGA performance is enhanced through its use.

Inflight Helmet Stowage Bag (IF HSB)

The HSB's are light-weight coated cloth bags for stowage of the PGA helmets when doffed in the spacecraft. Provisions are made to attach the bags to the CM bulkhead when in use.

BIOINSTRUMENTATION SYSTEM

The Bio-instrumentation System enables the monitoring and analysis of critical physiological and bio-environmental parameters in order to assess astronaut performance and stress to ensure their safety and effectiveness.

The Bio-instrumentation System senses and transmits astronaut physiological conditions electrically to the telemetry system. The system is composed of sensors, signal conditioners, a biomed belt and wire signal carriers. One Biobelt is issued per crewman and attached to the CWG being worn.

The ground support portions of the bio-instrumentation system consists of remote site receiving-sending and formatting equipment and the Manned Spacecraft Center (MSC) receiving signal conditioning and computer processing facilities.

Data received at MSC is displayed on the aeromedical consoles in the Mission Control Center in various ways, such as: real-time display on digital rate meter, digital to TV rate display, and strip chart recorder. In addition, the data is further processed offline (i.e., not in real-time) to determine medically significant environmental physiological trends and relationships.

Since direct voice communication with the astronauts and up-to-date mission information is a vital part of medical monitoring and analysis, a world network of communication capabilities is provided to the aeromedical specialists.

MEDICAL ACTIVITIES

Medical activities during the Apollo 7 mission are limited to ground monitoring of bio-instrumentation data relayed from sensors worn by crew members. This permits the crew to devote full time to operational activities.

Pre and post-flight medical activities which require crew participation are pre-flight briefing and post-flight de-briefing, physical examinations, and medical evaluations in the fields of microbiology, immunology, hematology, biochemistry, cardiopulmonary physiology, bone densitometry and vestibular physiology.

Medical Kit

Medical supplies used for treatment of crewman in-flight emergencies, are stowed in the emergency medical kit. The kit contains oral drugs, injectable drugs, dressings and topical agents. The oral drugs and pills include pain capsules, stimulants, antibiotics, motion sickness pills, diarrhea pills, decongestants, and aspirin. The injectable drugs provide relief for pain and motion sickness. The dressings provided include compress bandages. First aid cream, sun cream, antibiotic ointment and eye drops are also provided.

The contents are packaged in a small two-zippered bag. The emergency medical kit bag is stowed in the Lower Equipment Bay (LEB) adjacent to a coldplate to maintain a cool temperature. The medical kit would be carried overboard in the event of evacuation during the recovery phase.

CREW PERSONAL HYGIENE

Crew personal hygiene equipment includes body cleanliness items, and the waste management system.

Body Cleanliness

A toothbrush and tube of tooth paste for each crewman is packaged with the food. Each man-meal package contains a wet-wipe cleansing towel. Three packages of dry towels and six tissue dispensers are stowed beneath the Command Module Pilot's couch.

Waste Management

Solid body wastes are collected in plastic defecation bags which contain a germicide to prevent bacteria and gas formation. The bags are sealed after use and stowed in empty food containers for post-flight analysis. Urine collection services are provided for use either while wearing the pressure suit or the inflight coveralls. Both devices attach to the spacecraft urine dump valve. Onboard waste storage areas are provided in the Right-Hand Equipment Bay (RHEB) and aft equipment storage bay.

CREW MEALS

Apollo 7 crewmen have a wide range of food items from which to select their daily mission menu. More than 60 items — cereals, fruit, beverages, main entrees and desserts — comprise the selection list of freeze-dried, bite-sized rehydratable food. Food is packaged and prepared in plastic bags, then squeezed directly into the mouth. Average daily caloric value of three meals will be 2500 calories per man.

Water is obtained from three dispensers; a portable dispenser for drinking water and two water spigots at the food preparation station. One supplies hot water for hot meals and the other cold water for beverages. The portable water dispenser emits half ounce spurts with each squeeze and the food preparation spigots dispense water in one ounce increments. Spacecraft potable water is a by-product of the electric power generation process by the fuel cells located in the Service Module.

SLEEP

Two sleeping stations are located under the two outboard couches. Two modes of restraint are utilized with the beta fabric sleeping bags. When wearing the PGA, crewmen sleep atop the bags and are restrained by straps. When wearing the CWG, they zip themselves into the sleeping bag. At least one crewman is awake at all times during the mission.

The sleeping bags are rolled and strapped to the side wall and aft bulkhead at launch. When unstowed, the free end will be attached to the LiOH storage boxes near the lower equipment bay.

OXYGEN MASKS

Three oxygen masks are provided for emergency breathing in the event of a sudden hostile environment in the cabin (e.g., smoke, toxic gas) during the shirt sleeve environment.

POST-LANDING VENTILATION (PLV) DUCTS

Three flexible, compressible ducts are provided in the Command Module to deliver outside ambient air to the immediate facial area of each crewman after splashdown and prior to hatch opening.

SURVIVAL EQUIPMENT

Survival kits are stowed in the crew compartment Right-Hand Forward Equipment Bay (RHFEB) for the post-landing phase of the mission. The major items (Figure 18) contained in each kit include 15 pounds of water, a desalter kit, a three-man life raft, radio transceiver, portable light, sun-glasses, and a machete. Life vests worn by the crew during lift-off and entry are placed in the space suit stowage bag during the orbit phase of the mission.

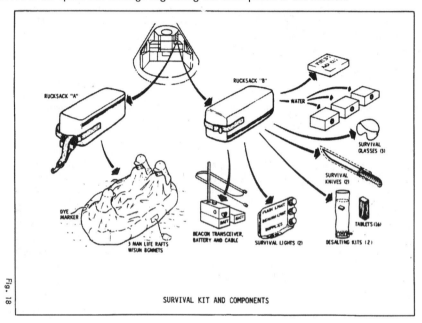

Fig. 18

SURVIVAL KIT AND COMPONENTS

LAUNCH COMPLEX

The AS-205 space vehicle will be launched from Complex 34 (LC 34) at Cape Kennedy (Figure 19). This Complex was initially designed and constructed for Saturn I Block I vehicle launchings. Subsequent modifications enabled LC 34 to support Saturn IB launchings. Mission AS-201 and AS-202 were launched from this complex.

Major components of LC 34 include the Service Structure, Launch Pedestal, Umbilical Tower, Automatic Ground Control Station (AGCS), fuel storage areas and Launch Control Center (LCC). The service structure is of rigid truss construction, approximately 250 feet high. It has eight vertically adjustable service platforms inside the silo enclosures which provide the area needed to properly service the vehicle during assembly and pre-launch check-out. A railway provides mobility for the service structure from the launch pad to the off pad anchor area.

The LC 34 pad area is of circular design with the major structures being; the umbilical tower, launch pedestal, the subterranean AGCS room and the service structure (when it is not in launch position). The AGCS beneath the ground at the foot of the umbilical tower contains computers and other checkout equipment. The umbilical tower (Figure 20) is a steel truss structure approximately 250 feet in height with four service arms. The launch pedestal is a massive square block with holddown arm assemblies bolted around a circular opening which provides access to the launch vehicle first stage.

As a prerequisite to the AS-205 launch and as a result of the AS-204 accident, LC 34 has been modified to include several redundant safety features. A slide wire emergency escape system has been installed. This escape system reaches from the

Apollo Access Arm (AAA), on the umbilical tower to a point at ground level 1200 feet away. The slide wire system is capable of transporting unconscious personnel.

Other additions include installation of emergency safety lockers at key locations throughout the service structure and umbilical tower. These lockers contain air packs, gas masks with smoke filters, fire blankets, axes, tools and other emergency items. Emergency rescue personnel have also been equipped with heat protective garments. Additional equipment and more specific procedures have been added to increase the fire fighting capabilities at the complex.

A hazardous gas detection system continuously samples selected areas of the space vehicle for critical concentrations of toxic, flammable, explosive and corrosive gases.

In addition to added safety equipment and emergency personnel several design changes have been incorporated in the umbilical tower and service structure to improve emergency personnel and crew evacuation capability.

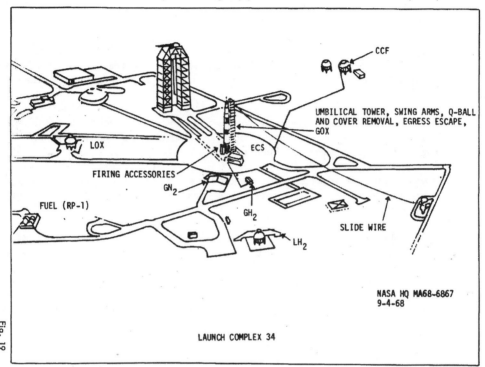

Fig. 19

LAUNCH COMPLEX 34

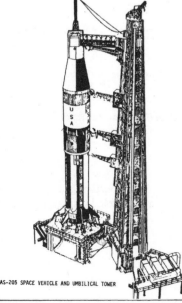

AS-205 SPACE VEHICLE AND UMBILICAL TOWER

Fig. 20

Changes were authorized to be made on LC 34 on 24 April 1967 and include:

1) Reconfiguring the environmental chamber (EC) adapter hood to provide a flatter egress path from the spacecraft.
2) Eliminating the step at each end of the Apollo access arm.
3) Incorporating two-way swinging doors on the Apollo access arm and on the access arm cab.
4) Providing smoke removal ventilation in the Apollo access arm cab.
5) Changing the arm retraction sequence to rotate the arm to a park position near the latch position at T-30 minutes to permit quick return to the command module. At T-4 minutes the arm will be swung to the stowed position.
6) Incorporating fire-resisting materials inside the Apollo access arm.

In addition a review was conducted of the LC 34 communications system and improvements were made to insure reliable communication between all test elements.

MISSION SUPPORT

Mission support is provided by the Launch Control Center (LCC) at KSC, the Mission Control Center at Houston (MCC) and by the Manned Space Flight Network (MSFN). All MSFN stations are remoted to MCC. The communication system linking the stations with the MCC has the capability of transmitting high speed data, low speed data, teletype traffic and voice communications.

An important part of Mission Support for all Gemini and Apollo missions has been the performance of Mission Simulations. As part of the basic philosophy of preplanning and training for every contingency a number of simulations are completed prior to an Apollo launch.

These simulations will orient and train Flight Crew and Flight Control personnel for most conceivable contingencies as well as for the nominal mission.

LAUNCH CONTROL CENTER (LCC)

The Launch Control Center (LCC) located approximately 1000 feet from the pad, serves as the focal point for monitoring and control of vehicle checkout and launch activities associated with the Apollo 7 mission. The LCC houses and protects launch team personnel, instrumentation and control equipment, and integrates all areas of the launch complex.

The firing room on the second floor houses the Ground Support Equipment (GSE) required for space vehicle control, monitoring, checkout, and for recording pre-launch operations. It also includes a glass enclosed observer room. The firing room is supported by an Operations Management Room (OMR).

The OMR is used by top management personnel to monitor the mission and to exercise operational judgment as required. The OMR has direct communication links with key operations personnel such as the Mission Director, Launch Director and Flight Director.

The equipment room on the first floor houses the necessary equipment to support the stations located in the firing room. This includes telemetry, tracking, closed-circuit television, communication, instrumentation, air conditioning, and power equipment.

All pre-launch operations are controlled from the LCC. However, the Mission Control Center (MCC) is responsible for flight mission control and, therefore, in order to assure that it is in flight-ready condition at launch time, LCC must operate in conjunction with MCC.

The LCC performs the following specific functions in preparation and launch of Apollo missions:

    a.   Monitors and controls pre-launch preparation of the space vehicle.

    b.   Monitors and controls, with appropriate recording and displays, checkout of the space vehicle at the launch pad through countdown and launch.

    c.   Monitors and verifies status of the Ground Support Equipment (GSE) systems during all checkout and launch operations.

    d.   Monitors and analyzes, using inputs from the Central Instrumentation Facility (CIF), booster function during the launch, ascent and initial powered flight.

MISSION CONTROL CENTER

Mission Control Center (MCC) is located in Manned Spacecraft Center (MSC) Building 30 at Houston, Texas. The Mission Control Center provides centralized mission control from lift-off through recovery, and technical management in the areas of vehicle systems, flight dynamics, recovery support, and ground systems operations.

To perform this function, MCC utilizes four basic systems:

1. Communications, Command and Telemetry System (CCATS)

2. Real Time Computer Complex (RTCC)

3. Voice Communications System

4. The Display/Control System

These systems provide the flight operations team with the necessary real-time data and reference data for rapid assessment of mission progress. A functional description of data flow within MCC is shown in Figure 21.

<u>Communications, Command, and Telemetry System (CCATS)</u>

The CCATS in the MCC provides the capability of simultaneously performing the functions of digital communications data handling, telemetry data decommutation and distribution, and digital command initiation and control. All digital data transferred between the MCC and the Manned Space Flight Network are processed and distributed by the CCATS.

<u>Real Time Computer Complex (RTCC)</u>

The real-time computer complex (RTCC) receives data from the CCATS and provides the computation facilities in the MCC for flight dynamic analysis, telemetry processing, acquisition predictions, and flight controller display generation with call-up capability.

The primary functions of this complex are to process incoming tracking and telemetry data for evaluation of overall mission conditions. Parameters critical to this evaluation are position and velocity of the spacecraft establishing the go/no go information for each powered flight phase.

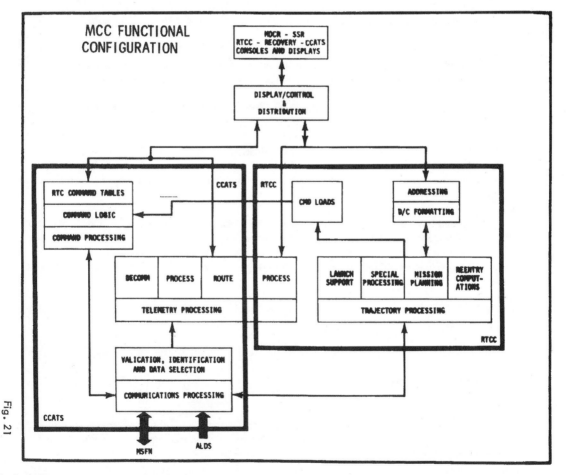

Fig. 21

To facilitate recovery operations, the computers predict where the spacecraft will be at any predetermined time throughout the mission. Also, the computers provide each tracking station with acquisition information which can be used for positioning antennas and advising station personnel of times they can expect to acquire the spacecraft. The computers are also used for processing telemetry information received from spacecraft to determine if spacecraft and launch vehicle systems are performing satisfactorily within predetermined environmental and operational parameters.

Voice Communications System

The voice communications system is comprised of voice intercom and public address equipment throughout MCC and various switching facilities to allow communications with the KSC launch area, with the spacecraft, the MSFN stations and other pertinent mission terminals.

Display/Control System

The display/control system provides mission control personnel with visual information concerning booster and vehicle systems, flight dynamics, the MSFN and recovery. This information is necessary to make the decision; which assure mission success and to advise proper actions through the voice circuits and the digital command system.

Mission Operations Control Room (MOCR)

The MOCR is the principal command and control center within MCC staffed with the key flight operations team responsible for overall management of a given flight. There are sixteen positions within the MOCR from which all aspects of a flight are monitored. The positions and primary responsibilities are as follows:

1.   Mission Director: Overall mission responsibility and control of flight test operations, which include launch preparation.

2.   Flight Operations Director: Responsible for successful completion of mission flight operations for all missions being supported.

3.   Flight Director: Responsible for detailed control of the mission from lift-off until conclusion of the flight.

4.   Department of Defense Representatives: Overall control of Department of Defense forces supporting the mission, including direction of the deployment of recovery forces, the operation of the recovery communications network, and the search, location and retrieval of the crew and spacecraft.

5.   Assistant Flight Director: Responsible to the Flight Director for detailed control of the mission from lift-off through conclusion of the flight; assumes the duties of the Flight Director during his absence.

6.   Public Affairs Officer: Responsible for providing information on the flight status to the public.

7.   Experiments and Flight Planning: Plans and monitors accomplishment of flight planning and scientific experiment activities.

8.   Operations and Procedures Officer: Responsible to the Flight Director for the detailed implementation of the MCC/Ground Operational Support Systems mission control procedures.

9.   Vehicle Systems Engineers: Monitors and evaluates the performance of all electrical, mechanical and life suppor equipment aboard the spacecraft.

10. Flight Dynamics Officer: Monitors and evaluates the flight parameters required to achieve a successful orbital flight; gives "GO" or "ABORT" recommendations to the Flight Director.

11. Retrofire Officer: Monitors impact prediction displays and is responsible for determination of retrofire times.

12. Booster Systems Engineer: Monitors propellant tank pressurization systems and advises the Flight Director of system abnormalities.

13. Guidance Officer: Detects Stage I and Stage II slow rate deviations and other programmed events, verifies proper performance of the Inertial Guidance System, commands onboard computation function and recommends action to the Flight Director.

14. Network Controller: Has detailed operational control of the Ground Operational Support System network.

15. Flight Surgeon: Directs all operational medical activities concerned with the mission, including the status of the flight crew.

16. Spacecraft Communicator: Voice communications with the astronauts, exchanging information on the progress of the mission.

Staff Support Rooms (SSR)

There are six SSR's located adjacent to each MOCR. These rooms are occupied by the technical specialists who are responsible for supporting their counterparts in the MOCR.

The six SSR's are:

Flight Dynamics	Flight Director
Vehicle Systems	Experiments Office
Life Systems	Project Office

Recovery Control Room

The Recovery Control Room is the command and control center for all recovery operations. Both DOD and NASA personnel are involved in this function. DOD personnel are responsible for detailed command and control of the recovery task forces, and the NASA personnel are responsible for coordination of recovery operations as required for mission support.

MANNED SPACE FLIGHT NETWORK (MSFN)

The Manned Space Flight Network is a worldwide ground operational support systems network, which is controlled by the MCC during Apollo missions. The network is composed of fixed stations (Figure 5), supplemented by mobile stations, which are optimally located within a global band extending from approximately 40° north latitude to 40° south latitude. The network performs four basic functions vital to mission success: tracking, telemetry, command, and communications (voice, television).

The data gathered by network sites as the spacecraft passes over their respective areas is transmitted to MCC where they are evaluated and used to provide the MOCR with continuous mission information. Station capabilities are summarized in Table 6.

The information is transmitted from the station by submarine cable, microwave, radio, landline and satellite. Telemetry data from the space vehicle provides information on which status of vehicle systems can be monitored. Continuous coverage is not possible since the spacecraft is out of range of network sites a portion of the time. Telemetry data are stored during such periods and periodically "dumped" over major receiving stations.

The command system provides MCC the capability to command the spacecraft as required by the mission. Communications with the astronauts is accomplished through voice and television circuits routed to MCC.

The mobile facilities consist of Apollo instrumented ships and Apollo Range Instrumentation Aircraft (A/RIA). The purpose of these facilities is to augment land-based MSFN stations during certain critical mission phases such as insertion, injection, re-entry and recovery. Locations for Apollo 7 are listed in Table 7.

MSFN Interfaces

The Manned Space Flight Network has three primary interfaces during a mission, Space Vehicle, NASCOM, MCC.

1. Space Vehicle - The telemetry from all stages and modules of a space vehicle are monitored by the MSFN. The launch vehicle transmitters and receivers perform telemetry, tracking and command functions. Equipment in the Instrument Unit, and the Command and Service Module has in addition, voice and television transmission equipment to interface the MSFN. Realtime television transmission from the CM to the MSFN is planned.

2. NASA Communications (NASCOM) - The NASCOM Network is a global system which provides the operational ground communications for all NASA programs. In effect NASCOM connects the MSFN stations and supplementary stations to the MCC (Figure 22). To accomplish these connections, NASCOM utilizes switching centers at Honolulu (HON), Canberra (ACSW), and London (LON) with supplementary DOD centers at Wheeler AFB, Hawaii and Cape Kennedy, Florida. The Goddard Space Flight Center (GSFC) Communication Center located

at Greenbelt, Maryland receives all data passing through the switching centers and received by the Intelsat Communication Satellites. These received data are then processed and routed to MCC or to another applicable station.

3.   MCC - Figure 22 shows the communications interfaces for MCC and the MSFN. It is noted that MCC has two primary interfaces, one with GSFC and the other with KSC via the Apollo Launch Data System.

Network Configuration for the AS-205 Mission.

Systems / Facilities	TRACKING				USB			TLM					CMD			Data Processing		Comm					Other		Remarks
	C-band (high speed)	C-band (low speed)	ODOP	USB	Voice	Command	TLM	VHF Links	FM Remoting	Mag Tape Recording	Decom	Displays	UHF Commanding	CMD Destruct	DRUL Remoting 642B	642B TLM	642B CMD	High Speed Data	Wideband Data	TTY	Voice (SCAMA)	Voice VHF A/G	Biometer	SPAN	
PAT / CNV	2 / 1	2 /	/ 1											1											Launch Abort Contingency
MLA / TEL-IV	2	2																							
CIF / MIL				2	2	2	2	2	2	2	2		2		2	2	2	2		2	2	2	2		
GBI / GBM	2	2		1	1	1	1	1	1	1	1		1	1	1	1	1	1		1	1	1			
ANT / ANG		3		3	3	3	3		3	3	3		3	1	3	3	3	3		3	3	3			
BDA / CYI	2	2 / 3		2 / 3	2 / 3	2 / 3	2 / 3	2 / 3	2 / 3	2 / 3	2 / 3	1	2 / 3	1		2 / 3	2 / 3	2 / 3	3	2 / 3	2 / 3	2 / 3	3	3	Launch Abort Contingency
ASC / ACN		3		3	3	3	3	3	3	3	3		3			3	3	3		3	3	3			
PRE / TAN		3						3		3										3	3	3			
CRO / WOM	3	3 / 3		3	3	3	3	3	3	3	3		3			3	3	3		3 / 3	3 / 3	3	3	3	
GWM / HAW		3		3 / 3	3 / 3	3 / 3	3 / 3	3 / 3	3 / 3	3 / 3	3 / 3		3 / 3			3 / 3	3 / 3	3 / 3		3 / 3	3 / 3	3 / 3			
CAL / GDS		3		3	3	3	3		3	3	3		3			3	3	3		3 / 3	3 / 3	3			
GYM / WHS		3		3	3	3	3	3	3	3	3		3			3	3	3		3 / 3	3 / 3				
TEX / GTK		3		3	3	3	3	3	3	3	3		3	1		3	3	3		3	3	3			Backup to BDA
LIMA / HSK		3		3	3	3	3		3	3	3					3	3	3		3 / 3	3		3		
HSKX / KSC				3*		3*																			
MAD / MADX		3		3 / 3*	3	3	3 / 3*		3	3	3					3	3	3		3	3				
ARIA / RED		3		3 / 3	3	3 / 3	3	3		3 / 3	3					3	3	3		3 / 3	3	3			Reentry Support
VAN / MER	2 / 3		2 / 3	2 / 3	2 / 3	2 / 3	2 / 3	2 / 3		2 / 3	2 / 3		2			2 / 3	2 / 3	2 / 3		2 / 3	2 / 3	2 / 3			Insertion Ship Alt. Reentry
HTV	3		3		3		3			3	3	3								3	3	3			Reentry

LEGEND:
1 LAUNCH   3 ORBIT   * - RECEIVE and RECORD ONLY
2 LAUNCH AND ORBIT   4 LAUNCH ABORT

TABLE 6

TABLE 7

MSFN MOBILE FACILITIES

APOLLO SHIPS (4 required)

FUNCTION	SUPPORT	LOCATION	NAME
Apollo Insertion Ship	Insertion, abort contingencies	32.7°N, 48°W	USNS VANGUARD
Apollo Injection Ship	Orbital event support and gap filler	25°S, 118°W	USNS REDSTONE
Apollo Injection Ship	Alternate reentry area support and orbital gap filler	25°N, 125°E	USNS MERCURY
Apollo Reentry Ship	Orbital gap filler – Test and evaluation basis	25°N, 136°W	USNS HUNTSVILLE

APOLLO AIRCRAFT (5 required)

A/RIA will support the mission on specified revolutions from assigned Test Support Positions (TSP) from Rev 2 thru 107. In addition, A/RIA will cover reentry (400,000 ft) thru crew recovery. A/RIA #1, #2 and #3 will operate in the Pacific Sector and A/RIA #4 and #5 in the Atlantic.

Thirteen identified revolutions will be covered from 22 Test Support Positions.

RECOVERY OPERATIONS

Recovery operations begin with touchdown of the command module and are terminated with the retrieval of the command module and the astronauts. The recovery forces are made up of ships and aircraft deployed in the planned recovery areas. These areas include the primary landing areas and abort and contingency landing areas. Since all Apollo missions have a planned water primary landing area, recovery support equipment is included for this environment.

Upon command module splashdown, three recovery aids are activated:

1. VHF communications

2. Sea marker

3. Recovery light

The VHF communications system provides a repeating location signal and voice communication with the command module and recovery forces. The sea marker is a fluorescent dye which goes into solution coloring the water a bright yellow-green over an extended area. This dye, visible for a considerable distance, has an effective life of approximately twelve hours. The recovery light is automatically deployed after splashdown. It has a self-contained power supply capable of providing 15 to 20 flashes per minute for a 24 hour period.

Apollo recovery procedures are designed for a fast and safe recovery of the command module and crew. Prior to splashdown, recovery ships are directed to the closest proximity to the landing position possible. Helicopters with swim teams onboard are launched to deliver a flotation collar which they attach to the command module. The collar provides a survivable flotation capability for a minimum of 48 hours. Prior to the arrival of the swim team, the astronaut crew will assess the flotation status and capability of the module. Should the command module be in an inverted (Stable II) attitude, the crew will activate the uprighting system. When the command module achieves an upright (Stable I) attitude, the crew will remain in the command module or, if necessary, will leave in the inflatable life raft provided for the three crew members. The capability is provided for helicopter pickup of the command module, using the recovery pickup loop, or a near by ship may pick up the command module. The three crew members may be picked up by helicopter, ship or boat.

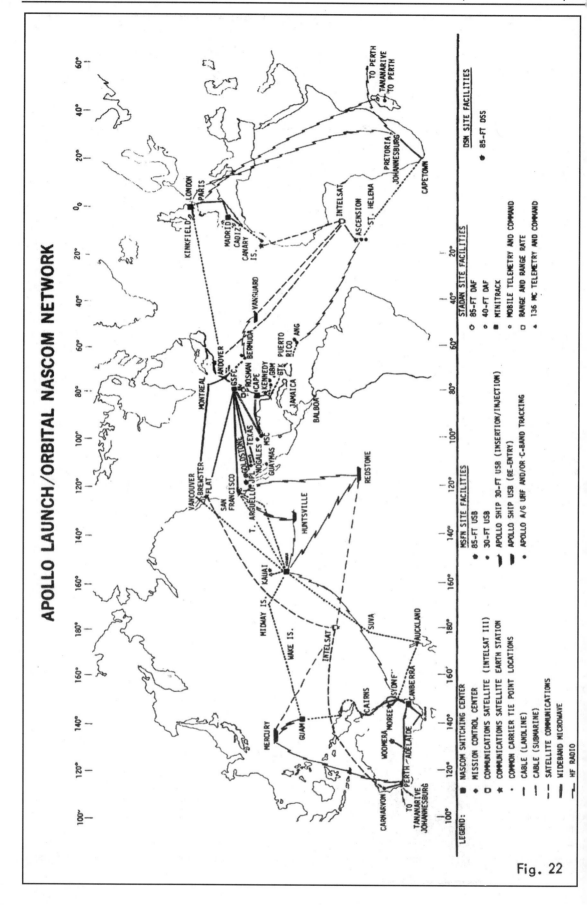

Fig. 22

APOLLO 7 RECOVERY

Recovery forces for the Apollo 7 mission will be deployed in both the Atlantic and Pacific Ocean (Figure 23). The recovery will be directed from the Recovery Control Room of the MCC and will be supported by two satellite recovery control centers: the Atlantic Recovery Control Center located at Norfolk, Virginia, and the Pacific Recovery Control Center located at Kunia in the Hawaiian Islands. In addition to the recovery control centers, there will be NASA representatives deployed with recovery forces throughout the worldwide DOD recovery network.

There are five recovery areas defined for the Apollo 7 mission as follows: Launch Site, Launch Abort, Primary, Secondary and Contingency.

LAUNCH SITE AREA

The launch site area is defined as that area in which the CM would land following a pad abort or an abort early in the launch phase.

The launch site area is illustrated in Figure 24. The possible CM landing points lie in a corridor within this area. This corridor is determined by wind profile data obtained periodically prior to launch. The corridor for Apollo 7 will be defined during the pre-launch period.

LAUNCH ABORT AREAS

The launch abort areas are those areas in which the CM will land following an abort initiated during the launch phase of the flight. For the Apollo 7 mission, the landing points following a launch abort lie between the launch site area and 3,200 nautical miles downrange. These areas are bounded by lines 50 nautical miles to either side of the spacecraft ground track (Figure 25).

a.   Launch Abort Area A: This area extends from the eastern extremity of the launch site to 1,900 nautical miles downrange. The downrange extremity of this area is commensurate with the exit from the "high-g" reentry abort region. Late Mode I aborts and a large portion of the Mode II aborts would result in a CM landing in this area.

b.   Launch Abort Area B: This area extends from 1,900 to 3,200 nautical miles downrange. Late Mode II aborts and all Mode III aborts would result in a CM landing in this area.

PRIMARY LANDING AREAS

Primary landing areas consist of those areas within or near the West Atlantic recovery zone where the probability of a CM landing is sufficiently high to warrant the requirement for primary recovery ship support. Included in this category are the nominal end-of-mission landing area and the majority of the GO/NO GO areas designated as the most desirable locations for landings on a periodic (usually, day-to-day) basis if early termination of the mission becomes necessary. These areas are defined by a 500 by 100 nautical mile ellipse along the ground track centered at a target point. The ellipse is designed to include the high probability landing point dispersions around the target point that may be caused by trajectory deviations during deorbit and entry (Figure 26).

SECONDARY LANDING AREA

A secondary landing area is an area within or near any of the four recovery zones, shown in Figure 23, where the probability of a landing is sufficiently high to warrant a requirement for at least secondary recovery ship support.

CONTINGENCY LANDING AREA

The contingency landing area is that area outside of the launch site, launch abort, primary and secondary landing areas within which a landing could possibly occur. These contingency landing areas are shown in Figure 23.

FLIGHT CREW

GENERAL

Approximately 1146 hours of crew training was programmed to prepare the flight crew to fly this first manned mission (see Table 8). The training coordinator, assisted by the crew commander, was responsible for the optimized accomplishment of the mission training program.

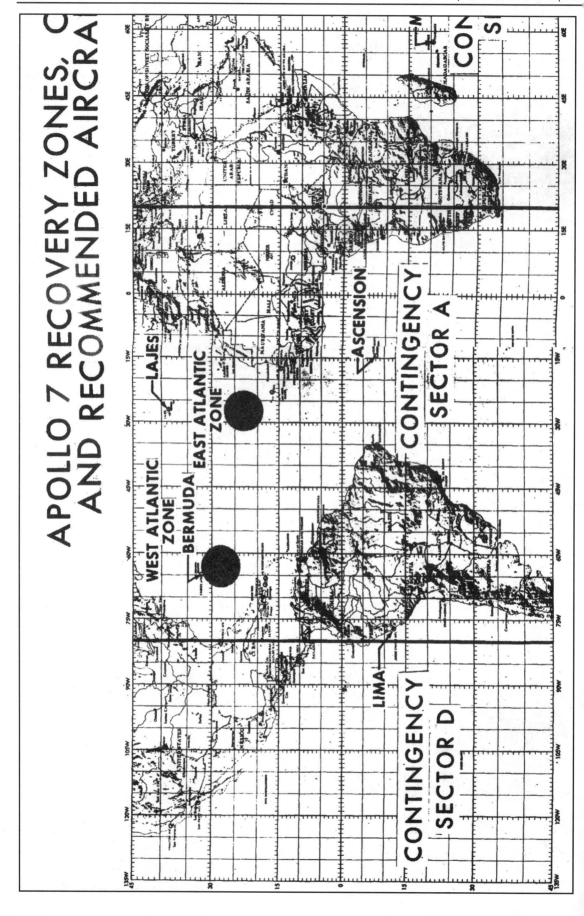

ZONES, CONTINGENCY AREA
AIRCRAFT STAGING BASES

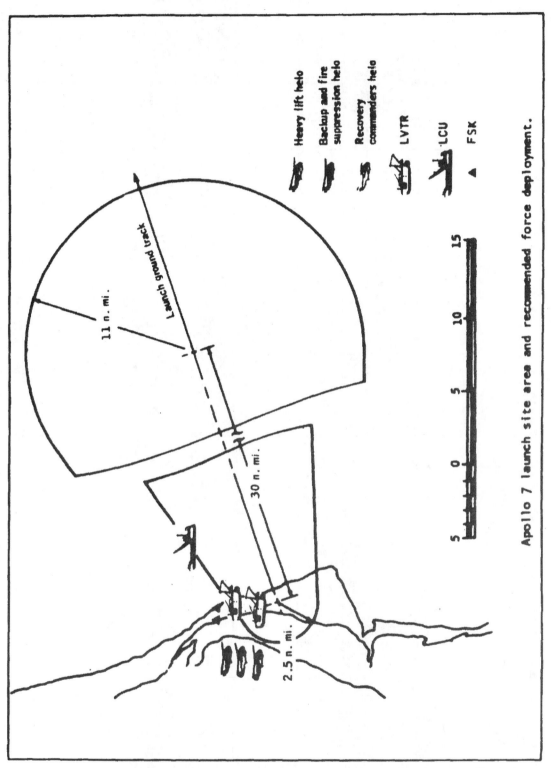

Apollo 7 launch site area and recommended force deployment.

Fig. 24

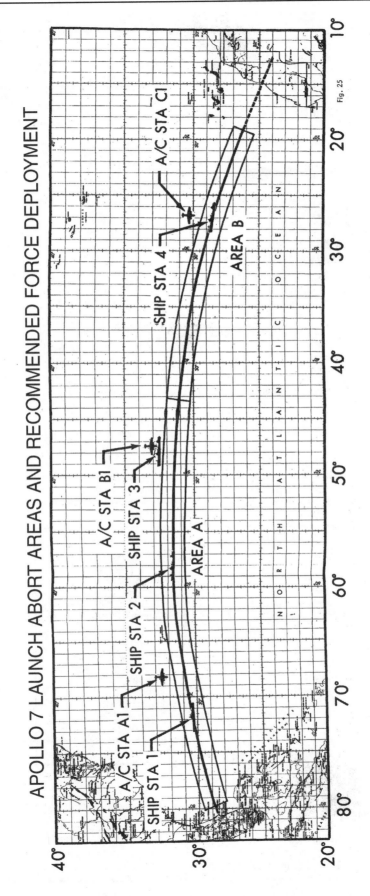

APOLLO 7 LAUNCH ABORT AREAS AND RECOMMENDED FORCE DEPLOYMENT

Fig. 25

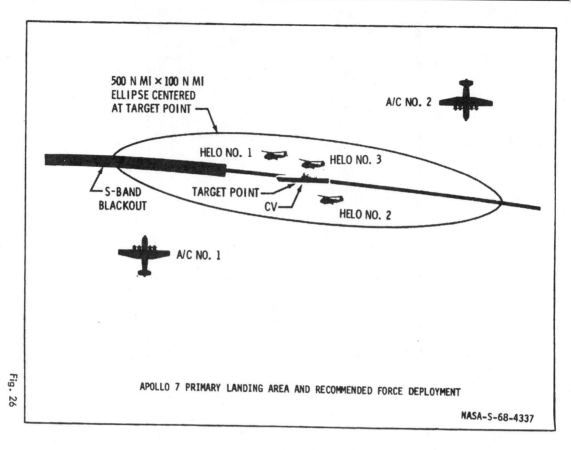

Fig. 26

APOLLO 7 PRIMARY LANDING AREA AND RECOMMENDED FORCE DEPLOYMENT

NASA-S-68-4337

TABLE 8

FORMAL FLIGHT CREW TRAINING TIME - APOLLO 7			
ACTIVITY	HOURS	ACTIVITY	HOURS
Briefings & Reviews		Simulator Training (CSM Simulators)	
CSM Systems	140		
Launch Vehicle	20	CMS	160
G&N Program	36	CMPS	60
Photography	8	DCPS	15
Experiments	8	Contractor Sim.	20
		Simulator Briefings	75
Procedures			
		Special Purpose Training	
OCP & TCP	60		
C/L & AOH	50	Stowage	20
Emer. & Abort	24	Egress	20
		Planetarium	20
Stowage	30	Spacecraft Fire Trng.	5
Flight Plan	50	IVA Training	9
Mission Rules	16		
Design & Accept.	60	TOTAL	1146
Flight Readiness	10		
Training	30		
Team	60		
Pilot	40		
Rendezvous	20		
S/C Test Participation			
S/C OCPs & TCPs (cockpit)	80		

In addition to the programmed training, many hours were spent at related training activities such as general study, physical conditioning, informal reviews and briefings. Mission support activities such as aircraft piloting, travel, pilots meetings, suit fits, physical examinations and mission development also necessarily consume time.

The flight crew contributes significantly to mission success in their pre mission integration role by applying an intense interest in the practical interrelationships of the "man in the loop" aspects encompassing all systems. Many system improvements have resulted from realistic simulations and constructive critical comment.

FLIGHT CREW ASSIGNMENTS

Prime Crew (Figure 27)

Command Pilot (CDR) Walter M. Schirra, Capt. USN

Command Module Pilot (CMP) Donn F. Eisele, Maj. USAF

Lunar Module Pilot (LMP) Walter Cunningham (Mr.)

Backup Crew (Figure 28)

Command Pilot (CDR) Thomas P. Stafford, Col., USAF

Command Module Pilot (CMP) John W. Young, Cdr. USN

Lunar Module Pilot (LMP) Eugene A. Cernan, Cdr. USN

Fig. 27

Fig. 28

PRIME CREW BIOGRAPHICAL DATA

Command Pilot (CDR)

Name: Walter M. Schirra, Jr. (Captain, USN)

Birth date: Born 12 March 1923

Physical Description: Height: 5 feet 10 inches; weight: 175 pounds

Education: Graduated from Dwight Morrow High School, Englewood, New Jersey, received a Bachelor of Science degree from the U.S. Naval Academy in 1945; recipient of an Honorary Doctorate in Astronautical Engineering from Lafayette College in 1966.

Organizations: Member of the Society of Experimental Test Pilots and a Fellow of the American Astronautical Society.

Special Honors: Received two Distinguished Flying Crosses and two Air Medals; two NASA Distinguished Service Medals; the NASA Exceptional Service Medal; the Navy Astronaut Wings; the Distinguished Alumnus Award from the Newark College of Engineering; the Collier Trophy; SETP Kincheloe Award; AIAA Award; and the American Astronautical Society Flight Achievement Award; and co-recipient of the 1966 Harmon Aviation Trophy.

Experience: Schirra received flight training at the Naval Air Station, Pensacola, Florida. As an exchange pilot with the United States Air Force, 154th Fighter Bomber Squadron, he flew 90 combat missions in F-84E aircraft in Korea. He also took part in the development of the Sidewinder Missile at the Naval Ordnance Training Station at China Lake, California, and was project pilot for the F7U3 Cutlass and instructor pilot for the Cutlass and the FJ3 Fury. He flew F3H-2N Demons while assigned as operations officer of the 124th Fighter Squadron on board the carrier LEXINGTON in the Pacific. He attended the Naval Air Safety Officer School at the University of Southern California and completed test pilot training at the Naval Air Test Center, Patuxent River, Maryland. He later was assigned at Patuxent in suitability development work on the F4H.

Current Assignment: Captain Schirra was one of the seven Mercury astronauts named by NASA in April 1959. On 3 October 1962, he piloted the six orbit "Sigma 7" Mercury flight — a flight which lasted 9 hours and 13 minutes.

Schirra has since served as backup command pilot for the Gemini 3 mission; and, on 15-16 December, he occupied the command pilot seat on the history-making Gemini 6 flight. The highlight of this mission was the successful rendezvous of Gemini 6 with the already orbiting Gemini 7 spacecraft, thus accomplishing the first rendezvous of two manned maneuverable spacecraft and establishing another space "first" for the United States. Known as a "textbook" pilot, Schirra remained in the spacecraft following his Mercury and Gemini flights and is the first astronaut to be brought aboard recovery ships twice in this manner.

Command Module Pilot (CMP)

Name: Donn F. Eisele (Major, USAF)

Birth date: 23 June 1930

Physical Description: Height: 5 feet 9 inches; weight; 150 pounds

Education: Graduated from West High School, Columbia, Ohio; received a Bachelor of Science degree from the United States Naval Academy in 1952 and a Master of Science degree in Astronautics in 1960 from the Air Force Institute of Technology, Wright-Patterson Air Force Base, Ohio.

Organizations: Member of Tau Beta Pi (national engineering society).

Experience: Eisele, an Air Force Major, graduated from the U.S. Naval Academy and chose a career in the Air Force. He is also a graduate of the Air Force Aerospace Research Pilot School at Edwards Air Force Base, California.

He was a project engineer and experimental test pilot at the Air Force Special Weapons Center at Kirtland Air Force Base, New Mexico. In this capacity, he flew experimental test flights in support of special weapons development programs.

Current Assignment: Major Eisele was one of the third group of astronauts selected by NASA in October 1963.

Lunar Module Pilot (LMP)

Name: Walter Cunningham (Mr.)

Birth date: Born 16 March 1932

Physical Description: Height: 5 feet 10 inches; weight: 155 pounds.

Education: Graduated from Venice High School, Venice, California; received a Bachelor of Arts degree with honors in Physics in 1960 and a Master of Arts degree in Physics in 1961 from the University of California at Los Angeles; has completed work at UCLA on doctorate in Physics with exception of thesis.

Organizations: Member of the American Geophysical Union, the American - Institute of Aeronautics and Astronautics, Sigma Pi Sigma, and Sigma Xi.

Experience: Cunningham joined the Navy in 1951 and began his flight training in 1952. In 1953 he joined a Marine squadron and served on active duty with the U.S. Marine Corps until August 1956. He is presently a Marine reservist with the rank of Major.

He worked as a research scientist for Rand Corporation prior to joining NASA. While with Rand, he worked on classified defense studies and problems of the Earth's magnetosphere.

His last work at UCLA was in conjunction with his doctoral thesis problem and consisted of developing and testing a search coil magnetometer which was later flown aboard the first NASA Orbiting Geophysical Observatory satellite.

Current Assignment: Mr. Cunningham was one of the third group of astronauts selected by NASA in October 1963.

BACKUP CREW BIOGRAPHICAL DATA

Command Pilot (CDR)

Name: Thomas P. Stafford (Colonel, USAF)

Birth date: Born 17 September 1930

Physical Description: Height: 6 feet; weight: 175 pounds

Education: Graduated from Weatherford High School, Weatherford, Oklahoma; received a Bachelor of Science degree from the United States Naval Academy in 1952; recipient of an Honorary Doctorate of Science from Oklahoma City University in 1967.

Organizations: Member of the Society of Experimental Test Pilots.

Special Honors: Awarded two NASA Exceptional Service Medals and the Air Force Astronaut Wings; the Distinguished Flying Cross; the AIAA Astronautics Award; and co-recipient of the 1966 Harmon International Aviation Trophy.

Experience: Stafford, an Air Force Colonel, was commissioned in the United States Air Force upon graduation from Annapolis. Following his flight training, he flew fighter interceptor aircraft in the United States and Germany and later attended the USAF Experimental Flight Test School at Edwards Air Force Base, California. He served as Chief of the Performance Branch at the USAF Aerospace Research Pilot School at Edwards and was responsible for the supervision and administration of the flying curriculum for student test pilots. He was also an instructor in flight test training and specialized academic subjects — establishing basic textbooks and directing the writing of flight test manuals for use by the staff and students. He is co-author of the Pilot's Handbook for Performance Flight Training and the *Aerodynamics Handbook for Performance Flight Testing*.

Current Assignment: Colonel Stafford was selected as an astronaut by NASA in September 1962. He has since served as backup pilot for the Gemini 3 flight. On 15 December 1965, he and command pilot Walter M. Schirra were launched on the Gemini 6 mission and subsequently participated in the first successful rendezvous of two manned maneuverable spacecraft by joining the already orbiting Gemini 7 crew. Gemini 6 returned to Earth after 25 hours 51 minutes and 24 seconds of flight. He made his second flight on 3 June 1966 as command pilot of the Gemini 9 mission. The flight ended after 72 hours and 20 minutes with a perfect reentry and recovery.

Command Module Pilot (CMP)

Name: John W. Young (Commander, USN)

Birth date: 24 September 1930.

Physical Description: Height: 5 feet 9 inches; weight: 165 pounds.

Education: Graduated from Orlando High School, Florida; received a Bachelor of Science degree in Aeronautical Engineering from the Georgia Institute of Technology in 1952.

Organizations: Member of the American Institute of Aeronautics and Astronautics and the Society of Experimental Test Pilots.

Special Honors: Awarded two NASA Exceptional Service Medals, the Navy Astronaut Wings, and the Distinguished Flying Cross.

Experience: Upon graduation from Georgia Tech, Young entered the U.S. Navy and holds the rank of Commander in that service.

He was a test pilot at the Naval Air Test Center from 1959 to 1962. Test projects included evaluations of the F8D and F4B fighter weapons systems. In 1962 he set world time-to-climb records of 3,000 and 25,000 meter altitudes in the F4B. Prior to his assignment to NASA he was Maintenance Officer of All-Weather-Fighter Squadron 143 at the Naval Air Station, Miramar, California.

Current Assignment: Commander Young was selected as an astronaut by NASA in September 1962. He served as pilot on the first manned Gemini flight — a 3-orbit mission, launched on 23 March 1965, during which the crew accomplished the first orbital trajectory modifications and the first lifting reentry of manned spacecraft. After this assignment, he was backup pilot for Gemini, 6. On 18 July 1966, Young occupied the command pilot seat for the Gemini 10 mission and, with Michael Collins as pilot, effected a successful rendezvous and docking with the Agena target vehicle. The flight was concluded after 3 days and 44 revolutions — during which Gemini 10 traveled a total distance of 1,275,091 statute miles. Splashdown occurred in the West Atlantic, 529 statute miles east of Cape Kennedy.

Lunar Module Pilot (LMP)

Name: Eugene A Cernan (Commander, USN)

Birth date : 14 March 1934

Physical Description: Height: 6 feet; weight: 170 pounds

Education: Graduated from Proviso Township High School in Maywood, Illinois; received a Bachelor of Science degree in Electrical Engineering from Purdue University and a Master of Science degree in Aeronautical Engineering from the U.S. Naval Postgraduate School.

Organizations: Member of Tau Beta Pi, national engineering society; Sigma Xi, national science research society; and Phi Gamma Delta, national social fraternity.

Special Honors: Awarded the NASA Exceptional Service Medal; the Navy Astronaut Wings; and the Distinguished Flying Cross.

Experience: Cernan, a United States Navy Commander, received his commission through the Navy ROTC program at Purdue. He entered flight training upon his graduation. Prior to attending the Naval Postgraduate School, he was assigned to Attack Squadron 126 and 113 at the Miramar, California, Naval Air Station.

Current Assignment: Commander Cernan was one of the third group of astronauts selected by NASA in October 1963. He occupied the pilot seat along side of command pilot Tom Stafford on the Gemini 9 mission. During this 3-day flight which began on 3 June 1966, Cernan logged two hours and ten minutes outside the spacecraft in extravehicular activity. The flight ended after 72 hours and 20 minutes with a perfect reentry and recovery.

MISSION MANAGEMENT RESPONSIBILITY

Title	Name	Organization
Director, Apollo Program	Lt. Gen. Samuel C. Phillips	NASA/OMSF
Director, Mission Operations	Maj. Gen. John D. Stevenson (Ret)	NASA/OMSF
Saturn Vehicle Prog. Mgr.	Col. William Teir	NASA/MSFC
Apollo Spacecraft Prog. Mgr.	Mr. George M. Low	NASA/MSC
Apollo Prog. Manager KSC	R. Adm. Roderick O. Middleton	NASA/KSC
Mission Director	Mr. William C. Schneider	NASA/OMSF
Assistant Mission Director	Capt. Chester M. Lee (Ret)	NASA/OMSF
Assistant Mission Director	Col. Thomas H. McMullen	NASA/OMSF
Director of Launch Operations	Mr. Rocco Petrone	NASA/KSC
Director of Flight Operations	Mr. Christopher C. Kraft	NASA/MSC
Launch Operations Manager	Mr. Paul C. Donnelly	NASA/KSC
Flight Directors	Mr. Glynn Lunney	NASA/MSC
	Mr. Eugene F. Kranz	
	Mr. Gerald D. Griffin	
Spacecraft Commander (Prime)	Capt. Walter M. Schirra	NASA/MSC
Spacecraft Commander (Backup)	Col. Thomas P. Stafford	NASA/MSC

PROGRAM MANAGEMENT

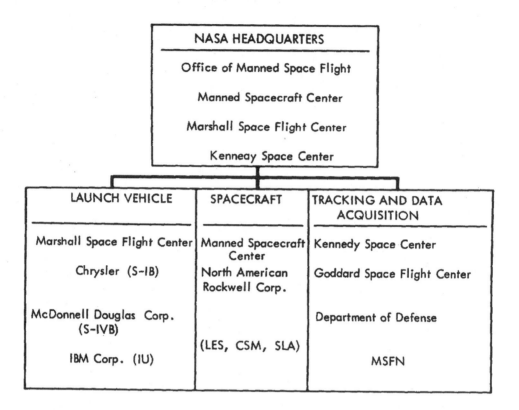

LIST OF ABBREVIATIONS

ACRA	Atlantic Contingency Recovery Area
AGCS	Automatic Ground Control Station
APS	Auxiliary Propulsion System
ARIA	Apollo Range Instrumentation Aircraft
AS	Apollo Saturn
BPC	Boost Protective Cover
CCATS	Communications, Command & Telemetry System
CM	Command Module
COAS	Crewman Optical Alignment Sight
COI	Contingency Orbit Insertion
CRYO	Cryogenic
CSM	Command/Service Module
CWG	Constant Wear Garment
DOD	Department of Defense
DTO's	Detailed Test Objectives
ECS	Environmental Control System
EDS	Emergency Detection System
ELS	Earth Landing System
EMS	Entry Monitor System
EMU	Extravehicular Mobility Unit
EPS	Electrical Power Subsystem
ETR	Eastern Test Range
EV	Extra Vehicular
EVA	Extra Vehicular Activity
GDC	Gyro Display Coupler
GET	Ground Elapsed Time

G&N	Guidance and Navigation
GNCS	Guidance Navigation and Control System
GSE	Ground Support Equipment
H2	Hydrogen
HF	High Frequency
ICG	In-flight Coverall Garment
IMU	Inertial Measurement Unit
IU	Instrument Unit
IV	Intra Vehicular
KSC	Kennedy Space Center
LC	Launch Complex
LCC	Launch Control Center
LCG	Liquid Cooling Garment
LEA	Launch Escape Assembly
LEB	Lower Equipment Bay
LES	Launch Escape System
LET	Launch Escape Tower
LM	Lunar Module
LOX	Liquid Oxygen
LTA	Lunar Test Article
LV	Launch Vehicle
MCC	Mission Control Center
MK	Maintenance Kit
MOCR	Mission Operation Control Room
MSC	Manned Spacecraft Center
MSFC	Marshall Space Flight Center
MSFN	Manned Space Flight Network
MTVC	Manual Thrust Vector Control
NSR	Coelliptic Maneuver
O2	Oxygen
OMR	Operations Management Room
OSR	Operations Support Room
PGA	Pressure Garment Assembly
PLSS	Portable Life Support System
PMP	Pre Modulation Processor
RCS	Reaction Control System
RP-1	Refined Kerosene
SC	Spacecraft
SCS	Stabilization and Control System
SECS	Sequential Events Control System
SLA	Spacecraft LM Adapter
SM	Service Module
SPS	Service Propulsion System
SSR	Staff Support Room
T/C	Telecommunications
TPI	Terminal Phase Initiation
USB	Unified S-Band
UHF	Ultra High Frequency

Report No. 932-68-07

POST LAUNCH
MISSION OPERATION REPORT

APOLLO 7/S-IVB RENDEZVOUS

APOLLO 7 ATLANTIC RECOVERY

SATURN IB VEHICLE

OFFICE OF MANNED SPACE FLIGHT

Post Launch
Mission Operation Report

No. M-932-68-07

MEMORANDUM

To: A/Acting Administrator
27 December 1968

From: MA/Apollo Program Director

Subject: Apollo 7 Mission (AS-205), Post Launch Report #1

We successfully launched the Apollo 7 mission from Launch Complex 34 at Cape Kennedy on Friday, 11 October 1968 and completed it as planned with recovery of the spacecraft and crew in the Atlantic recovery area on 22 October 1968. Initial evaluation of the flight based upon quick look data and crew debriefing, indicates that all mission objectives were attained. Further detailed analysis of all the data is continuing and appropriate refined results of the mission will be reported in technical reports.

Based on mission performance as described in this report I am recommending that the Apollo 7 mission be adjudged as having achieved agency pre-set primary objectives and considered a success.

Sam C. Phillips
Lt. General, USAF
Apollo Program Director

APPROVAL:
George E. Mueller
Associate Administrator for
Manned Space Flight

GENERAL

The Apollo 7 (AS-205) mission was successfully launched from Launch Complex 34 at Cape Kennedy on Friday, 11 October 1968 at 11:02:45 a.m. EDT. Initial review of test data indicates that overall performance of the launch vehicle, spacecraft and flight crew together with ground support and control facilities and personnel was satisfactory. Quick look assessment indicates that all test objectives were successfully accomplished.

All Launch Vehicle Systems performed satisfactorily throughout their expected lifetime. All spacecraft systems continued to function throughout the mission with some minor anomalies reported. Each anomaly was countered by a backup subsystem, a change in procedures, isolation or careful monitoring such that no loss of systems support resulted. Temperatures and consumables usages remained within specified limits throughout the mission. Further review of all test data will continue in order to provide a more detailed evaluation of performance.

Recovery of the flight crew and command module was successfully accomplished by the deployed recovery forces. The actual landing point at the time of touchdown was within one mile of the guidance system target point. The astronauts arrived on the deck of the prime recovery ship approximately one hour after touchdown and the command module less than two hours after touchdown.

NASA MISSION OBJECTIVES FOR APOLLO 7

PRIMARY OBJECTIVES

Demonstrate CSM/crew performance

Demonstrate crew/space vehicle/mission support facilities performance during a manned CSM mission

Demonstrate CSM rendezvous capability

Sam C. Phillips	George E. Mueller
Lt. General, USAF Apollo Program Director	Associate Administrator for Manned Space Flight
Date: 27 Sept 68	Date: 30 Sept 68

RESULTS OF APOLLO 7 MISSION

Based upon a review of the assessed performance of Apollo 7, launched 11 October 1968, and completed 22 October 1968, this mission is adjudged a success in accordance with the objectives stated above.

Sam C. Phillips	George E. Mueller
Lt. General, USAF Apollo Program Director	Associate Administrator for Manned Space Flight
Date: 29 Nov 68	Date: 27 Dec 68

COUNTDOWN

The terminal launch countdown for Apollo 7 began at T-18 hours 30 minutes at 10:30 a.m. EDT 10 October 1968 and proceeded to T-6 hours with no holds. At this point a scheduled 6-hour hold was initiated. The countdown was resumed at 05:00 a.m. EDT 11 October 1968 and continued to T-6 minutes 15 seconds when there was an unscheduled hold of 2 minutes and 45 seconds duration. This hold was to complete S-IVB thrust chamber jacket chilldown. The count was resumed at 10:56:30 a. m. EDT and continued to lift-off at 11:02:45 a.m. EDT with no further problems.

FLIGHT SUMMARY

The Apollo 7 Space Vehicle was launched from Cape Kennedy, Florida, at 11:02:45 a.m. EDT on 11 October 1968. Following a nominal boost phase, the spacecraft and S-IVB combination was inserted into an orbit of 123 by 153 nautical miles at 10 minutes 27 seconds Ground Elapsed Time (GET). Prior to separation of the command and service modules from the S-IVB, the crew manually controlled the CSM/S-IVB combination. After separation, a transposition and simulated docking exercise was completed.

Following completion of the transposition and simulated docking exercise, two phasing maneuvers for rendezvous were performed with the reaction control system. The rendezvous sequence was initiated over Carnarvon in revolution 17 at 26:24:55 GET with the first service propulsion maneuver. The second service propulsion maneuver was performed one revolution later to establish the necessary catch-up rate. The crew reported station-keeping with the S-IVB at 30:00:00 GET. A final separation maneuver from the S-IVB was performed in revolution 19 at 30:20:00 GET.

During the 10.8 day flight, eight planned maneuvers using the Service Propulsion System (SPS) were completed and all major test objectives were satisfied.

Almost without exception, spacecraft systems operated as intended. All temperatures remained within acceptable limits and essentially exhibited predicted behavior except for fuel cell No. 2 condenser exit temperature which ran higher than predicted. Consumables usage was always maintained at safe levels and permitted introduction of additional flight activities toward the end of the mission. Communications quality was generally good, and live television was transmitted to ground stations on seven occasions. A test of the rendezvous radar system was completed in support of later flights with the lunar module. Manual operation of the spacecraft by the crew was good. Even though they were somewhat hampered by head colds and congestion, the crew satisfactorily performed all flight plan functions and the photographic experiments were completed.

The deorbit maneuver (eighth service propulsion maneuver) occurred during revolution 163 over Hawaii at 259:39:16 GET in the Atlantic Ocean southeast of Bermuda, with recovery coordinates of 27°33' north latitude and 64° 04' west longitude. This landing point is within one mile of the guidance system target point. The crew was retrieved by helicopter, and both the spacecraft and crew were taken aboard the prime recovery ship, USS ESSEX.

Table I presents a summary of mission events.

TABLE I - SUMMARY OF MISSION EVENTS

Event	Planned	Actual
	Time, Hr:Min:Sec GET	

Launch Phase

Event	Planned	Actual
Lift-off (15:02:45.36 GMT)	00:00:00.2	00:00:00.4
Maximum dynamic pressure	00:01:15.6	00:01:15.5
S-IB inboard engine cutoff	00:02:20.3	00:02:20.7
S-IB outboard engine cutoff	00:02:23.3	00:02:24.3
S-IB/S-IVB separation	00:02:24.6	00:02:25.6
S-IVB engine ignition	00:02:26.0	00:02:27.1
Launch escape tower jettison	00:02:43.3	00:02:46.5
S-IVB engine cutoff	00:10:14.8	00:10:16.8

Orbital Phase

Event	Planned	Actual
Orbital insertion	00:10:14.8	00:10:26.8
S-IVB safing start	01:34:27.0	01:34:29.0
S-IVB safing terminate	01:46:28.0	01:46:30.0
S-IVB takeover	02:29:55.0	02:31:21.0
CSM/S-IVB separation	02:54:55.2	02:55:07.0
First phasing maneuver (RCS) start	03:20:00.0	03:20:09.9
First phasing maneuver (RCS) cutoff	03:20:16.3	03:20:37.3
Second phasing maneuver (RCS) start	15:52:00	15:52:00.0
Second phasing maneuver (RCS) cutoff	15:52:18.5	Not Available
First service propulsion ignition	26:24:55.2	26:24:55.7
First service propulsion cutoff	26:25:04.7	26:25:05.1
Second service propulsion ignition	28:00:56.0	28:00:56.5
Second service propulsion cutoff	28:01:03.8	28:01:04.3
Terminal phase initiate (RCS) start	29:18:34.0	29:17:55.0
Terminal phase initiate (RCS) cutoff		Not Available
Terminal phase finalize (RCS) start	29:53:34.0	29:54:33.0
Terminal phase finalize (RCS) cutoff		
Separation maneuver (RCS) start	30:20:00.0	30:20:00.0
Separation maneuver (RCS) cutoff	30:20:05.4	30:20:05.4
Third service propulsion ignition	75:47:58.6	75:48:00.3
Third service propulsion cutoff	75:48:07.8	75:48:09.3
Fourth service propulsion ignition	120:43:00.0	120:43:00.0
Fourth service propulsion cutoff	120:43:00.4	120:43:00.5
Fifth service propulsion ignition	165:00:00.0	165:00:00.0
Fifth service propulsion cutoff	165:01:05.9	155:01:07.6
Sixth service propulsion ignition	210:08:00.0	210:08:00.5
Sixth service propulsion cutoff	210:08:00.4	210:08:01.0
Seventh service propulsion ignition	239:06:11.0	239:06:11.0
Seventh service propulsion cutoff	239:06:18.8	239:06:18.9
Eighth service propulsion ignition	259:38:15.9	259:39:15.9
Eighth service propulsion cutoff	259:39:27.9	259:30:27.7

Entry Phase

Event	Planned	Actual
Command module/service module separation	259:43:33.2	259:43:33.2
Entry interface (400,000 feet)	259:53:26.0	259:53:25.0
Enter blackout	259:56:17	259:54:58
Leave blackout	259:59:14	259:59:46
Drogue deployment	260:03:28	260:03:22
Main parachute deployment	260:04:14	260:04:13
Landing	260:08:58	260:09:08

LAUNCH VEHICLE

Early engineering evaluation of the SA-205 Saturn IB launch vehicle indicates that all primary and secondary mission objectives were accomplished and that no significant anomalies occurred. All launch vehicle GSE appears to have performed satisfactorily. Preliminary powered flight trajectory through insertion into orbit indicates that both propulsive stages and the instrument unit performed within expected tolerances.

FIRST STAGE (S-IB)

Quick look data examined indicates that no anomalies or system discrepancies were encountered during first stage operation. Inboard engine cutoff was initiated by the low fuel level sensor and occurred 3.2 seconds after sensor actuation. Outboard engine cutoff, due to LOX depletion, occurred 3.7 seconds after inboard engine cutoff.

SECOND STAGE (S-IVB)

Preliminary review of flight data indicates that performance of the S-IVB stage and associated systems was normal. J-2 engine main stage operation was within one percent of expected performance. The S-IVB burn time was approximately 470 seconds, within one second of predicted.

The propellant utilization system was flown open loop and mixture ratio shift occurred close to the nominal time as a result of a switch selector event.

S-IVB orbital safing was conducted as planned and was successful. A single LOX tank vent was initiated just after J-2 cutoff. LOX dump began at approximately 94 minutes 29 seconds GET. The engine control bottle pressure decayed, as expected, to a pressure below that required for normal operation of the valve, thus preventing full closure. No adverse effects were noted.

The cold helium dump was performed satisfactorily.

The three programmed LH2 vent tank sequences occurred as expected after J-2 engine cutoff. Additional venting of the LH2 tank was required due to extra residuals and less liquid venting than experienced on AS-204. The S-IVB stage was safed through four additional ground commanded venting sequences.

INSTRUMENT UNIT AND OTHER SYSTEMS

The guidance and control systems performed satisfactorily. The control parameters at S-IB separation appear to be nominal.

The electrical and emergency detection systems performed as expected. The performance of the measuring systems on all stages appear to be very good. Preliminary indications are that four measurements were possible failures and that three measurements are questionable.

SPACECRAFT

Based on quick look evaluation of data covering the flight, performance of the Apollo spacecraft was satisfactory. No major anomalies occurred and those discrepancies that did appear did not adversely affect mission performance.

STRUCTURES

Structural loads were below design limit values for all phases of flight. The peak ground winds just prior to lift-off were within one knot of the structural red line; however, the measured launch vehicle strain data indicated that only 50 percent of the limit loads were encountered. Structural loads in the max q region were less than 25 percent of limit.

PROPULSION

All propulsion systems operated satisfactorily. Planned firings of both Service Propulsion System (SPS) and Reaction Control System (RCS) were accomplished. The actual times, durations, and velocity changes are summarized in Table II.

Service Propulsion System (SPS)

The eight planned firings of the service propulsion engine were performed, and the system operation was satisfactory in all aspects.

TABLE II ORBITAL MANEUVERS

Maneuver*	System	GET (hrs:min)	Burn Delta-V (fps)	Burn Time (Secs)	Initial Orbit (N.Mi.)	Resultant Orbit (N.Mi.)
Separation Translation and Dock	SM RCS	2:55	-	-	167x123	167x123
Initial Phasing for Rendezvous	SM RCS	3:20	16.3	5.7	167x123	165x124
Second Phasing for Rendezvous	SM RCS	15:52	18.5	6.5	165x124	164x120
SPS Burn #1	SPS	26:25	10	206	164x120	196x125
SPS Burn #2	SPS	28:01	7.8	175	196x125	153x114
Terminal Phase Initiate (TPI)	SM RCS	29:18	42.2	16.7	153x114	153x122
Terminal Phase Final (TPF)	SM RCS	29:55	N.A.	17.0	154x122	161x122
Separation Following Rendezvous	SM RCS	30:20	5.4	2	161x122	161x122
SPS Burn #3	SPS	75:48	9.3	215	159x122	160x90
SPS Burn #4	SPS	120:43	0.51	15.3	151x89	158x90
SPS Burn #5	SPS	165:00	67.6	1692	149x89	245x90
SPS Burn #6	SPS	210:08	0.5	18.6	236x90	236x90
SPS Burn #7	SPS	239:06	7.9	227	231x90	231x90
SPS Burn #8	SPS	259.39	11.8	350	223x90	-

*SPS Burn

#1 - NCC (Corrective Combination Maneuver)

#2 - MSR (Coelliptic Maneuver)

#3 - Position and size ellipse for CM RCS deorbit to ETR, Set up Aux Gauging System Test.

#4 - Minimum Impulse Burn

#5 - Gauging Test and Set up ellipse for lifetime. Position and size ellipse for CM RCS deorbit.

#6 - Minimum Impulse Burn

#7 - Time anomaly adjust for deorbit burn

#8 - Deorbit

The ignition time for the third maneuver was advanced 16 hours from the original flight plan to improve the margin of backup deorbit capability with the service module reaction control system. To ensure the verification of the propellant gauging system, the firing time for the third maneuver was increased from 61 to 66 seconds so that both propellant sensor points would be uncovered during steady-state engine operation. Propellant quantity data indicate that both sensors were uncovered.

After the third maneuver, a 3-hour SPS Thermal Control System cold-soak test was performed, with no notable change in temperatures within the system. Thermal characteristics of the system appeared to be better than anticipated for random, drifting flight since the rate of temperature decrease was less than predicted.

Reaction Control System (RCS)

The primary service module RCS quad heaters performed normally and maintained all quad package temperatures between 118° and 141° F during the mission.

The helium regulators for the service module reaction control system maintained the helium and propellant manifold pressures essentially constant. Propellant utilization was near the predicted nominal in most cases.

Zero helium leakage was indicated from the command module RCS prior to activation just before the deorbit maneuver. The command module engine heaters were not required because the engine injector temperatures remained above 46° F prior to system activation. The command module RCS performed normally from activation through landing.

Guidance and Control

Guidance and control system performance was satisfactory throughout the mission. The inertial measurement unit was aligned optically, as scheduled, within small tolerances. Backup alignment methods were demonstrated for the inertial measurement unit and the stabilization and control system attitude reference. Data were obtained on star visibility, landmark tracking, star/horizon sightings, and optics utilization. The guidance and navigation system, using optical tracking data, supported the rendezvous with the S-IVB. All significant attitude control modes in both the prime and the backup system were tested and appeared to perform satisfactorily. Thrust vector control of the service propulsion engine was demonstrated using both the guidance and navigation and the stabilization and control systems, and mid-maneuver manual takeover techniques were also successfully demonstrated.

Two hardware problems were encountered. The rotational hand controller minus-pitch breakout switch was reported to have operated inadvertently once early in the mission. The Flight Director Attitude Indicator No. I indicated an abnormal shift in the pitch axis when being driven by the back up attitude reference system. No operational capability was lost as a result of either problem.

ELECTRICAL POWER SYSTEM

The electrical power system maintained the ac and do voltages within nominal limits except for the discrepancies discussed in the following paragraphs.

The crew reported two ac bus I failure indications and one ac bus I and 2 failure indication early in the mission. The loss of voltage was verified by the onboard meter, and the voltage was restored to normal by resetting the ac bus sensors. The occurrences were coincident with the cryogenic oxygen tank fans and heaters cycling OFF in the automatic mode. An ac bus can be automatically disconnected by an overvoltage being detected by the ac overload sensing unit. After a procedural change was made to prevent the fans in both tanks from cycling OFF simultaneously, the problem did not recur for the remaining 200 hours of flight.

Two other occurrences were associated with activation of the cryogenic tank fans: a master alarm was observed at the beginning of the cryogenic heater cycle at the time both buses dropped out, and the digital event time started inadvertently once when the oxygen fans were turned on manually.

Fuel Cells

All power requirements imposed on the three fuel cells were satisfied.

Prior to the fifth service propulsion maneuver, the condenser exit temperature of fuel cell 2 increased from 160° to 180°F (nominal is from 155° to 165°F). The electrical load was removed from fuel cell 2 for approximately 54 minutes to permit cooling prior to the service propulsion maneuver. Performance of the fuel cell was satisfactory during the maneuver. Four days later, the electrical load was again removed from fuel cell 2 for a short period of time as a precautionary measure to insure proper performance during the deorbit maneuver.

The data indicate a possible malfunction or restriction in the regenerator bypass valve which controls glycol flow to the condenser exit. The result was that the glycol coolant entering the fuel cell from the spacecraft radiator was hotter than normal, and the condenser exit temperature subsequently increased under the higher power load. The load-sharing capability of the fuel cell was only slightly affected. Thermal control by the corresponding bypass valve in fuel cell I was abnormal in one instance; the condenser exit temperature increased slightly above the normal operating temperature during the first period when only two fuel cells were carrying the load. It operated normally after fuel cell 2 was returned to the bus, and the problem was not evident the second time fuel cell 2 was removed from the bus.

Batteries

The voltage and current delivered by the entry batteries and pyrotechnic batteries were within the range of normal battery performance throughout the mission. The charge rates on batteries A and B were much lower than expected.

However, subsequent ground test performed during and after the flight showed that two factors contributed to this condition: line impedance between the battery and charger, and the particular characteristics of the battery and battery charger system under the flight conditions.

The main bus voltage, as read out onboard at command module/service module separation, unexpectedly dropped to approximately 25.0 volts but then gradually increased to a nominal level prior to blackout.

THERMAL CONTROL

Temperatures of all passive elements of the spacecraft remained within limits for an earth orbit mission. The command module ablator temperature ranged from 3° to 95°F as expected. However, the service propulsion feedlines were warmer than expected; consequently, the heaters were not required. The monitored temperatures for the service propulsion and reaction control propellant and helium tanks slowly decreased throughout the mission. The "fracture mechanics" temperature limits were never approached during the flight. The thermal efficiency of the service module insulation appeared to be adequate based on the temperature histories of the tanks.

No specific instance of extended temperature increases were noted during the entire mission. Over the 3-hour period of the service propulsion system cold soak all quad tanks showed a definite cooling trend. This type of response is indicative of what will occur on a translunar mission when the vehicle is not in the passive thermal control mode and the service module is being cold soaked.

CRYOGENICS

The cryogenic storage system performed satisfactorily during the mission. Excess reactants were available because spacecraft power levels were slightly below those predicted for the mission.

Automatic quantity balancing in the oxygen tanks was accomplished within 1-1/2 percent even though the fans in oxygen tank 2 were not operated automatically for a major portion of the mission. Automatic quantity balancing in the hydrogen tanks and one manual quantity adjustment were successfully performed. The criteria for this mission were balancing to within 3 percent.

COMMUNICATIONS

The communications system, which includes voice, telemetry, updata link, television, and tracking capability, satisfactorily supported the mission.

The VHF and S-band voice links provided good communications. The onboard television equipment was operated on seven occasions with good picture quality. The playback voice performance varied in quality from noisy to good as received by the network sites during recorder dumps. Some dropouts of both real-time and playback telemetry were noted; however, overall telemetry performance was satisfactory.

Downlink data were lost momentarily at approximately 65 hours GET. Real-time telemetry and television were time-shared on the backup S-band FM mode until full communications capability was restored by switching to the alternate S-band transponder.

The VHF voice duplex-B mode was very good during the countdown and launch phase until about 7 minutes. At that time, voice quality became garbled on downlink recievers and did not completely clear until simplex A was selected over the Canary Islands tracking station. The operation of the duplex B mode was successfully reverified at about 7-1/2 hours into the mission. Present indications are that the problem was associated with improper ground operating procedures.

USS HUNTSVILLE lost contact with the spacecraft approximately two minutes early during the final revolution. S-band communications blackout at Merritt Island occurred at 259:54:58 GET; the signal was acquired by Bermuda at 259:59:46 GET, the first reported contact after blackout.

A test of the rendezvous radar transponder was successfully completed with the White Sands Missile Range during revolution 48. Approximately 47 seconds of data were obtained. The ground radar acquired and locked on the spacecraft transponder at a range of 390 nm and tracked to a range of 415 nm.

ENVIRONMENTAL CONTROL SYSTEM (ECS)

Performance of the environmental control system was satisfactory. During pre-launch operations, the cabin was purged to an atmosphere of 60 percent oxygen and 40 percent nitrogen. The crew was isolated from the cabin by the suit circuit, which contained 100 percent oxygen. Shortly after lift-off the cabin atmosphere was gradually enriched to pure oxygen at a pressure of 5.9 psi. Cabin leakage was estimated to have been 0.1 lb/hr as expected.

The radiators satisfactorily rejected the spacecraft heat loads to the extent that the evaporators were not required. The primary evaporator is required only when the heat loads exceed the radiator capability. Under the low, variable heat loads which existed, the evaporator operated erratically in the automatic mode, causing what appeared to be wick drying or subsequent flash freezing. The automatic control dynamics are such that this condition can be expected. The evaporator was serviced with water to keep it working but was subsequently turned off.

The secondary coolant loop was tested for eight hours with the secondary evaporator, which was serviced prior to flight. The test was begun with a heat load of 1400 watts; halfway through the test, the load was increased to 1800 watts. The dynamic response of the secondary evaporator was such that stable operation of the evaporator control system was achieved. Under the automatic demand, the evaporator was required about 50 minutes per revolution during the test. The secondary evaporator operated differently from the primary because the heat load was higher as a result of the lower capacity of the secondary radiators.

Moisture condensed on cold, uninsulated coolant lines, as anticipated, and was dumped overboard by the crew utilizing the urine transfer hose and cabin enrichment purge assembly. Some condensation was also noted in the suit umbilical hoses.

A water leak was observed at the B-nut connection to the waste water quick disconnect during the overboard dumps.

The urine dump system operated normally and no indication of freezing was observed.

Both cabin fans were operating at lift-off; however, one was turned off after orbital insertion to reduce the high noise level. The second cabin fan was subsequently turned off. The measured cabin temperature was between 65° and 75°F and was not significantly affected by fan operation.

EARTH LANDING SYSTEM (ELS)

The ELS performed satisfactorily. The crew reported that all parachutes disreefed and deployed properly. After landing, the spacecraft assumed a stable II (apex-down) attitude for 8 minutes, at which time the uprighting system was activated; 4.5 minutes later, the spacecraft was returned to the stable I (apex-up) attitude. Operation of the recovery aids was interrupted while the spacecraft was in the stable II attitude. Communications were reestablished and the flashing light was activated after the spacecraft was uprighted.

INSTRUMENTATION

The instrumentation performance was satisfactory throughout the mission except for the discrepancies noted. The performance of the data storage equipment was satisfactory throughout the mission.

At 11:09:23, the central timing equipment was reading correctly over USNS REDSTONE. At 12:07:26 GET, it was reading 00:42:09 GET, indicating a reset at 11:25:17 GET. The timing equipment was updated over Hawaii and continued to read correctly.

Two discrepancies were encountered with the biomedical instrumentation equipment; these are discussed under Crew Provisions.

FLIGHT CREW

CREW PROVISIONS

The crew equipment operated satisfactorily during the mission with the exception of the biomedical instrumentation equipment and the water metering dispenser.

Two discrepancies were encountered with the biomedical instrumentation equipment. First, a wire was broken at the connector to the EKG signal conditioner on each of two harnesses. In addition, the pin connectors to the sensors periodically became disconnected. Second, the dc-dc converter on the command module pilot was reported to have become warm. As a precautionary measure, the harnesses were disconnected from all three crewmen.

The manual triggering device for the water metering dispenser became increasingly difficult to operate as the mission progressed.

CREW PERFORMANCE

Crew performance was satisfactory throughout the mission, even though all three crewmen had head colds and congestion.

The mission was conducted essentially in accordance with the nominal flight plan. The only significant alteration to the flight plan was the rescheduling of the third service propulsion maneuver from the 58th to the 48th revolution. Additional photography was accommodated during the latter portion of the mission.

Two experiments, Synoptic Terrain Photography and Synoptic Weather Photography, were included on this mission. Preliminary information indicates that most of the terrain photography was performed. For meteorological photography, 27 phenomena were of interest; at least 7 were apparently photographed and 8 others may have been. The most successful was photography of tropical storms. Three storms were in view of the spacecraft, two of which reached hurricane intensity.

The deorbit, entry, and landing sequence were accomplished normally. Due to head colds and congestion, the crew elected to reenter with suits on and helmets off and stowed. The spacecraft assumed the stable II (apex-down) attitude after landing and was uprighted to the stable I (apex-up) position by inflation of the uprighting bags. The crew elected a helicopter pickup for the approximately 3-mile trip to the recovery carrier.

MISSION SUPPORT

FLIGHT CONTROL

Flight control performance was satisfactory for the entire mission; the only major ground system problem encountered was in the data recovery from the Manned Space Flight Network.

NETWORK

Network performance was satisfactory during the mission. Several minor problems were encountered, but none affected the mission operations. On launch day, an electrical power problem occurred at MCC causing loss of displays for about seven minutes but no interruption of computer and voice capabilities. A short circuit in the wiring to the cooling tower fan is suspected. At 169.02 GET problems were encountered with the main trunk cable connecting GSFC to MSC. Only a small amount of data was lost.

RECOVERY

Recovery operations were successfully effected in the West Atlantic by the prime recovery ship, USS ESSEX, on 22 October 1968. The following table lists the major recovery events on 22 October 1968:

Greenwich mean time, Hr: Min:	Event
11:05	S-band contact by recovery aircraft
11:08	Landing
11:32	Visual sighting by recovery aircraft
11:43	Flotation collar installed
12:00	Astronauts aboard helicopter
12:08	Astronauts aboard USS ESSEX
13:03	Spacecraft aboard USS ESSEX

The spacecraft landing point was estimated from ship position (by LORAN) and a helicopter bearing to be 27°33' north latitude, 64°04' west longitude. The sea condition at the recovery site was moderate.

Because the spacecraft assumed a stable II orientation for approximately 12 minutes after landing, the operation of the command module voice transmitters and recovery beacons was temporarily interrupted.

LAUNCH COMPLEX

No major problems occurred during the countdown. Launch damage to the pad was light compared with previous launches. Ground systems performance was as expected with no major anomalies.

Some of the minor anomalies that did occur are presented below:

1 . At T-31 minutes, during power transfer, the Flight Control Computer inverter detector switched from the primary to the secondary inverter as the result of a voltage transient during power transfer. The inverter was reset, and the IU power transfer was completed successfully.

2. All eight holddown arms released pneumatically. Six explosive release bolts were fired by post launch ignition but two others did not fire.

3. EDS GN2 supply was lost for approximately three minutes during countdown due to a stripped shaft on the motorized valve supplying LN2 to the low pressure vaporizers.

4. After close-out crew egress, the egress elevator failed to remain in the normal egress position at the 220 foot level. Preliminary investigation revealed two coils to be open.

5. The umbilical tower firex system was self actuated during lift-off. Water flow was stopped by remote control.

68-H-1052

68-H-1057

CONFIDENTIAL

;PACE ADMINISTRATION

NOTICE: This document may be exempt from public disclosure under the Freedom of Information Act (5 U.S.C. 552). Requests for its release to persons outside the U. S. Government should be handled under the provisions of NASA Policy Directive 1382.2.

W69-30,003 c.1

LINK SECURITY

NO. LKH-0133

(C-2)

APOLLO VII
TECHNICAL DEBRIEFING
Part I
(U)

PREPARED BY

MISSION OPERATIONS BRANCH
FLIGHT CREW SUPPORT DIVISION

GROUP 4
Downgraded at 3 year
intervals; declassified
after 12 years.

CLASSIFIED DOCUMENT - TITLE UNCLASSIFIED

This material contains information affecting the national defense of the United States within the meaning of the espionage laws, Title 18, U.S.C., Secs. 793 and 794, the transmission or revelation of which in any manner to an unauthorized person is prohibited by law.

MANNED SPACECRAFT CENTER

HOUSTON, TEXAS

OCTOBER 27, 1968

DATE	OPR		DOC	SUBJECT	SIGNATOR	LOC

CONFIDENTIAL

REP — What was wrong with the watch?

CUNNINGHAM — My watch, when I hit the RESET button, the minute hand went "chunk", and back 3 or 4 minutes.

EISELE — Incidentally, I don't know if you want to talk about watches, but I had a watch failure - the little pin. This little pin came out a couple of times. I've got it taped now; I finally taped it in flight. It came out launch morning, and I didn't want to fool around and have them run all over to get another watch, so I took it. It's the little pin that holds the band on. It came out in flight, and I put it back and taped it.

SCHIRRA — We told them to put new pins in those. Remember that? Way back - we picked those up with new pins in for flight. Let me cover the essential things before you get hung up on the watches.

EISELE — This is an old one; it works fine.

SCHIRRA — On the sensors, my two sternal sensors were placed too high, and I should know by now where they should be placed. I got tattoo marks from it. As a result, the fittings of the harness, the BIOMED harness I had in the past were violated, and that's why this thing came apart. To prevent it coming apart in flight, I taped it in flight, when we were in the constant wear garment and flight coveralls. Unfortunately, I wasn't thinking that much, but the stress then was applied to the connector to the amplifier, and it broke there at the signal conditioner. That's why that particular lead broke. The tape part held beautifully. That's what wiped out my sensors. Donn's broke at the same place; we don't know why it broke there, but it did break there.

EISELE — The only thing I could think of possibly is that when I exercised, I'd sit in the middle seat, and I put that left belt across my stomach to keep me from flying all over the spacecraft, but I'd do it very loosely; I'm not tied down. Possibly, in the act of running the exerciser, I might have bumped against the lap belt enough to break it. I don't know whether that's what happened or not, but I do know sometimes they'd call up and say they weren't getting some of the BIOMED. I looked, and there was a wire broken off right at the little fitting where it goes on the signal conditioner.

SCHIRRA — Walt's also failed in flight, as long as we're on that subject. We don't know why. We rewired all his to make it theoretically work. Basically, it ended up the configuration I had, except he used sternal leads instead of axillary leads.

EISELE — I don't think he had any mechanical failure; he just quit putting out a signal.

SCHIRRA — We're not sure if his conditioners failed or what; at any rate, I'd say that all three were very faulty. I suspect technique caused mine, placing the sensors. I might add in post flight I had very little disturbance from the BIOMED sensors. Donn had some very great residuals, and Walt had bleeding residual effects from the sensors, so we're not out of the woods on that area yet.

EISELE — Well, I couldn't even feel mine. It looked worse than it was - physically mottled skin. Spots where the things had been - but there are photos of Walt's positions. Let's go back to the suiting area again and bring up the watch. When I put my watch on - when my watch was put on is the word, I naturally would test it. I started T and stop it, then reset it. The minute hand went minus about 2 or 3 minutes; and Mr. Slayton was there and of course saw it too. We made a fast scurry, and I felt it didn't affect our suiting time line. It was still somewhere I felt because I could put the watch on the trailer as far as that goes. We did get an alternate watch which did fine.

SLAYTON — Those watches should have been properly checked, and that shouldn't have been delivered to the suit room; and second, they should have all been set.

SCHIRRA — They should have been synchronized with local time.

SLAYTON — We synchronized them with the clock in the suit room which sure isn't calibrated about anything, and the others synch in with the other one.

SCHIRRA — It was too late.

SLAYTON — In a way, I worry although other people should be. I have always had my watch, synched it, and checked it. Remember, back in the old days, we would go back into the control center and listen to WWV. It should have been done before you ever walked in the suit room.

SCHIRRA — That was a goof. Let's see. Is there anything else with suiting? I had no other problems with suiting. Donn, did you have any?

EISELE — I can't recall any particular problems.

SCHIRRA — I would like to say that the COMM stations in the suit room are not necessarily up to spec. We had trouble talking to each other; sometime you didn't get side tone with him. I very rarely had side tone at my console in the suit room. There we were, always trying to get "do you hear me?" One of the nice things there is a plus. I had this football player's chin strap which was perfect for me for launch and the first day. It turned out at the last minute that Marshall Horton gave me a cloth one to put in my suit pocket as a backup, saying "when you have a beard," - and I knew nothing about beards - "you might want this," and it turned out I used it to come home with. The plastic cup did not work with a beard on it. My face was highly irritable with a beard; you kept catching the beard in anything, and I could wear the cup - I had to wear the cloth underneath my chin. I would encourage crews to consider underneath the chin strap rather than across the chin with a beard.

EISELE — I wore a cloth one across the chin, and it bothered me some, too. But I just put up with it because it was all I had.

1.0 COUNTDOWN

1.2 Prime Ingress and Status Check

SCHIRRA — Once you get a beard, I would suggest under the chin strap because it really bugs you. I asked that bearded guy that ran that coffin box for us. He said it took him months to get over it. The tender skin that a beard has underneath it. The bristles, the whiskers pull.

1.2.1 SECS Pyro

SCHIRRA — SECS pyro is per OCP; no problem.

1.2.2 Suit Connections

SCHIRRA — Suit connections, we had no problems with that. Now, we configure - and knowing the backup crew knows what the other crews don't, the would-be lock-locks unlock to optimize egress. They really can slow you down.

EISELE — However, I found that I was lashed down in there; I don't know whether you guys knew it or not, but my lock-locks got pushed down anyway.

SCHIRRA — One of them does when we want to egress.

EISELE — So if we bump it. I just always just assume they are locked and check it before I start to disconnect.

SCHIRRA — It's nice if you can pop out that easily.

1.2.3 Comm Verification

COMM Verification, no problems with that. One technique we use during preflight is to use the HF loop. We can always talk to each other on HF loop. We never lose communications with anybody if we take the other loops (meaning VHF, UHF, or S-band), and turn those to RECEIVER ONLY; then you can transmit quietly across the cockpit. There are times when you should talk; we judge the elevator together, slide wire, and this kind of stuff. You need a private loop, a perfect example of it is when we were brought off from the elevator.

EISELE — The center guy can't get at his switches to change them like that. What I do is just keep my mouth shut and listen to what they are saying. I would go ahead and say it, and it goes out over the loop, but nobody else hears the rest of the conversation.

SCHIRRA — He could say yes, and they would say what the heck was that about.

EISELE — That's right.

SCHIRRA — You don't violate the security of leaving communications since you are receiving all the time. They say – "CDR checks switch to so and so"; you just go click, "Roger", and it doesn't put a power transit on the spacecraft. By flipping back to transmit/receive, the transit comes to your transmitter, so there's no problem with that. I think it's a very good technique to maintain crew discipline in the cockpit and when you need to talk with each other.

1.2.4 PGA Circuit Check

PGA circuit check, something the rest of the crews may not know: we had the backup and the CMP do some checks which saves all your energy. It saves a lot of work, and it's very hard to do, particularly to get the regulators from BOTH to OFF. That's almost impossible to do when you are pressurized. John Young did an outstanding job on that.

1.2.5 Cabin Closeout

Cabin closeout, there were no discrepancies. EDS checks were a surprise to the command pilot. If he will go through that during plugs out and CDDT and that stuff, it would help.

EISELE — Did we do them in the chamber?

SCHIRRA — No. No, it's with the booster. What's the other check? The CDG is integrated with the countdown now. There's one check...

EISELE — The FRT.

SCHIRRA — The FRT, that's it. The FRT, you'll see it.

1.2.6 EDS

SCHIRRA — We'd advise all command pilots to get an EDS briefing from the booster honcho to see the light sequence and how they do it because you play the abort light. For example, it's A then B; you've heard all that in the loop, but there are two bulbs in all of the lights. You could see each light work. Certain functions are alien to us, and it's the surprise that I'm getting at. So if he does FRT, he will see it. I believe all command pilots should go over that one.

1.2.7 The RCS Check

SCHIRRA — I had a waiver on that, and I said "be prepared for a no audible" because I didn't know. It was audible on all of them if you're very, very quiet. You can hear them on the ground, and in flight; you can hear them all the time because your helmet is off. Most of the time, it's off, so that was quite surprising. We didn't really know what we would hear. I'll take the part I had.

1.2.8 G & C Verification

The FDAI worked fine. GDC align we did at T minus 45 seconds, and if you check your needles on NULL early enough, you just hit GDC ALIGN anytime you want it. It's going to come in because the IMU is going to stay where it was. Gimbal Drive and Trim were fine. I guess the surprise was more on the pad than it was in the flight when the G&N flicked the gimbals around at plus or minus 2 degrees. You could feel it on the ground, but I didn't feel it in flight as much.

EISELE — Well, I did, but I also noticed that when you are in tight deadband, it drives you into the deadband and the jets fire.

SCHIRRA — Yes.

EISELE — A computer swinging that gimbal - swings it from zero plus 2 and then to minus 2 - makes these big arcs; it makes the spacecraft move and then you can get jet firing. You get a double confirmation.

SCHIRRA — Yes.

EISELE — In fact, the gimbals are being driven that way.

SCHIRRA — GDC Drive, no comment. I set the EMS RAI on the launch pad and left it there until I needed EMS roll ON. It stayed at 12 o'clock the whole mission until I was in position to use it. However, it worked during re-entry as it should have. The only part of the re-entry phase that the EMS worked properly, I might add. EDS power, no problem there. DELTA-V SET, we did have a problem, and I didn't talk about it prior to launch. The technique is to have the MODE switch in STANDBY. You then rotate the selector knob from OFF to DELTA-V SET, which is a counter clockwise motion, through DELTA-V, and as you come through DELTA-V, you stop when it reads 0.0. You then go to DELTA-V SET; it should still be 0.0. You then add whatever velocity you want to set in there. For example, in our case, it was 3000 feet per second. The first time I came across to DELTA-V SET, it was not 0.0. It was 90 000.0. So I looked at Donn, and he looked at me, and I flicked it back to OFF again; it came up again 0.0, and I went "shuuuuu." We had "Go Fever."

EISELE — But that was the first time we had ever seen or even heard of it.

SCHIRRA — It happened during the re-entry test, which really shook me. At any rate, we got an anomaly where it flames in at 90 000. We have never seen it before; we saw it with some frequency during the flight, both in NORMAL mode and in ENTRY mode. I don't think it affects the DELTA-V at all; it's just an anomaly that is in that system. The EMS is going to require some careful scrutiny. I should go out to North American and sit down with those people and explain it to them. That might be worthwhile. I do feel the piece of gear is very important to the lunar flight, and I felt sick that I didn't have it myself. I was worried about the computer for re-entry. It performed flawlessly, just beautifully on every burn, better than the G&C.

1.2.9 Launch Preparation

SCHIRRA — No problems with LCC Confirm Ready. We had a problem here, and it was resolved at the last minute, but it should have been resolved long before. The cabin should be 95 percent; however, the Cape was thinking 98. One thing about the cabin gas analyzer, I think was that it played the game as fine as we wanted it to. We stowed it before close-out, and that was a good deal. It took us 5 days to get our cabin up to over 90 percent, so no sense in waiting for that.

EISELE — We never did get to a 100.

SCHIRRA — Oh, one thing, we didn't log that, did we?

EISELE — Yes, it's all in there.

SCHIRRA — I know the numbers we did. Did we log that or did we leave the damn thing on?

EISELE — Oh, Walt says he thinks he left it on a whole day (laughter), and it still worked.

CUNNINGHAM — That is an extremely good battery.

SCHIRRA — I would suggest that you take the suit sample from the commander's suit, at suit close-out, with

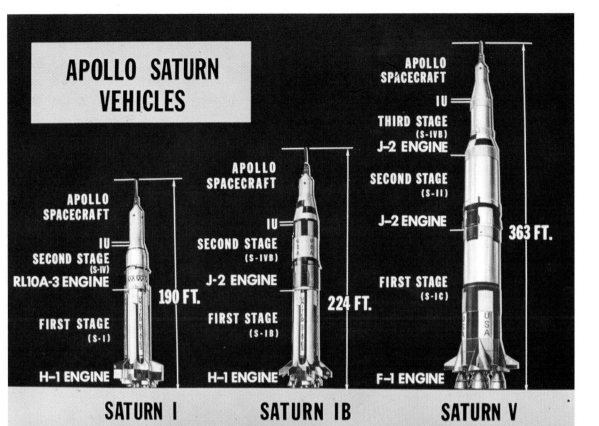

Apollo 7 Prime Crew (l to r below) Major Donn F. Eisele, Captain Walter M. Schirra Jr,
Mr. Walter Cunningham and Donald Slayton, Director Flight Crew Operations
at the MSC Houston. Briefing. October 9 1968

Apollo 7 prime crew, Walter Cunningham, Donn Eisele and Walter Schirra (above)
Apollo 7 at Complex 34 September 16 1968 - Saturn IB Booster during Countdown Demonstration Tests (below)

October 11 1968 224 ft tall Saturn IB lifts off at 11:03 am EDT from Complex 34. (above & right)

An AC-135 aircraft flying at more than 35,000 ft photographed the launch of Apollo 7 (below). The VAB appears to be closer than its actual ten mile distance. Photograph was made by an ALOTS (Airborne Lightweight Optical Tracking System) camera .

October 11 1968. SIVB during transposition and docking maneuvers at 125 nm. GET 3 hours 15 mins. Florida coastline from Flagler beach to Vero beach is in the background. Distance between vehicles is about 100 feet. The round white disc is a simulated docking target.
(above)
Fighting a cold Wally Schirra appears somewhat subdued during the flight.
(left)

This spectacular photograph of the exposed interior of the Saturn IVB was taken over Sonora NM during the second revolution of Apollo 7.

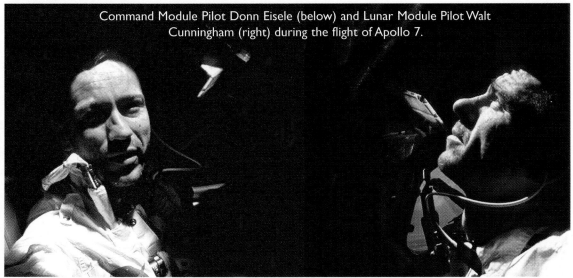

Command Module Pilot Donn Eisele (below) and Lunar Module Pilot Walt Cunningham (right) during the flight of Apollo 7.

Hurricane Gladys 150 miles Southwest of Tampa taken from 97 nm during the 91st rev at GET of 144 hrs 27 mins. Looking towards southwest with Cuba in background. Wind speeds were 80 knots.

All dozen of the world's five mile high peaks are in this remarkable picture. Mt Everest is at lower center. On the central horizon can be seen the 28,250 ft Mount Godwin-Austen (K-2) In the lower right is Mount Kanchenjunga (28,208 ft). The snow line is at 17,500 ft. Tibet is visible in the upper right.

Morning over the Gulf of Mexico at 122 nm altitude. Florida is a
dark silhouette. Taken during 134th orbit at 213 hrs 20 mins.

South America during 81st revolution (below left) . Port city of Antofagasta
Chile is in the half moon shaped bay in the lower left. At the center behind
the large salt lake is where Bolivia, Chile and Argentina meet.

Walt Cunningham writes with space pen. Note film
magazine floating in zero G above his right hand.

Aboard The USS Essex. Dr Donald Stulken Recovery Team Leader leads the crew after splashdown which was at 7.11 am EDT October 22 1968.

Aboard USS Essex October 22 1968.

Conversation with President Johnson via ship to shore telephone after splashdown. (above)

12 days and 4.5 million miles later the crew return to Cape Kennedy after splashing down 200 miles SSW of Bermuda. CVS on their caps signifies Navy Anti-submarine ops a function of USS Essex.

2 November 1968. President Johnson is presented with an Apollo 7 photograph at the awards program. The picture shows the SIVB. (left)

67-H-756

67-H-774

67-H-892

67-H-928

67-H-930

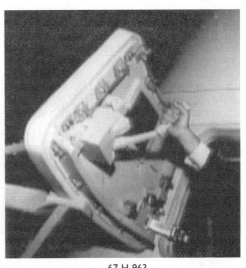

67-H-963

68-H-729

68-H-818

68-H-904

68-H-905

68-H-906

68-H-907

GSE, and then scrub off on that. That makes it a lot cleaner and it's extra weight and gear that is axiomatic. We ran humidity surveys and gas analyzer surveys, RAD surveys, and I hope they are over with.

1.2.10 Systems Prep

SCHIRRA — No problem.

1.2.11 Crew Comfort

EISELE — I got cold.

SCHIRRA — Yes, but I had warned you that you were going to get warm; and during boost, we got warm, just after we got into orbit. We were just a little warm; we did get warm a little bit.

EISELE — But in preflight, it was quite cool in the suit loop.

SCHIRRA — It was so cold that that was what probably triggered my cold off. It may very well be. It wasn't shivering cold, but I guess we were a little reluctant to tell them to change the flow because it was fairly late, and remember those cats in 190th floor? One hundred ninety feet level, that's where they had to come to do that. We got cold fairly late in the count.

CUNNINGHAM — Yes, it wasn't bad.

SLAYTON — It wasn't at the press conference because there were a lot of people bugging us about - you caught cold during the dove hunt, you know. I remember when I was with you I didn't have one. I am sure the question will come up again.

SCHIRRA — It really got quite cold. I guess the discomfort was considerable.

1.2.12 Crew Station Controls and Displays

SCHIRRA — No problems.

1.2.13 Distinction of Sounds Countdown to Lift Off

SCHIRRA — Man, oh man, was that a Mother. I am going to use the word "Mother" and quote me on it, but when it lights off, there is no way you know when you have lift-off. It's just a thundering herd down there. If I had a hold-kill on that thing, it probably would have taken 10 seconds to make my mind up that I had one. When I heard ignition, it developed a real violent, shaking sound; it's very unreal. At lift-off, I could barely see the darn clock. Countdown to lift-off.

1.2.14 Vehicle Sway Prior to Ignition

SCHIRRA — Are you talking about the last 3 minutes when things are going automatic?

EISELE — You can tell things are happening. I don't know exactly what's happening. You don't know what the sequence is, but you can tell, feel, and hear, at very low levels some fluids running around; and you can hear the engines thumping and feel the whole stack shake a little, and you know something is going on down there. You can't tell exactly what it is. It's very evident that the vehicle sways.

SCHIRRA — It sure was vibrating up a storm. Low frequency massive amplitudes is the way it felt. That's overstated, but there was no doubt in your mind that you were being shook. I thought the world was coming to an end.

EISELE — We could see the vehicle sway; at least, I could. I could look out and watch the white room structure go back-and-forth.

SCHIRRA — No, you're talking about lifting.

CUNNINGHAM — No, this is prior to ignition.

SCHIRRA — Well, there was motion.

CUNNINGHAM — You could see it. I moved a foot or two either side.

SLAYTON — What do you think that Saturn V is going to sound like?

CUNNINGHAM — Oh, golly.

SLAYTON — That was pretty good wind.

SCHIRRA — All I've got to say is that those poor cats are going to have to be hanging on for at least the first 10 seconds. I heard "clear tower" though. I heard that come up.

SLAYTON — You heard that?

CUNNINGHAM — I thought, "Thank God, I passed that one."

2.0 POWERED
FLIGHT

2.1 S-IB Ignition

2.2 Lift-Off

SCHIRRA — Okay. I think we described the ignition.

The lift-off - all those words should be used: vibrations, sensations, isolations and instrumentation. The time I had lift-off, and when I had it, I couldn't hear.

SLAYTON — You didn't hear Stu calling?

SCHIRRA — No. At least, I don't recall hearing him.

EISELE — I think I remember hearing Stu say lift-off. The light came on, and then somebody said so.

SCHIRRA — Well, I said lift-off.

EISELE — Well, maybe you did. I heard somebody say lift off.

SCHIRRA — Well, whatever, it's hard for you to tell if you heard Stu or me say it.

EISELE — Yes, maybe I don't recall hearing Stu. It seems like I said it first. Stu said he wasn't going to say it until he was positive, and that's fine with me. Then the clock started. At lift-off, the very heavy vibrations stopped.

CUNNINGHAM — Yes, you could feel the change in the vibrations at lift-off.

SCHIRRA — When you left the hold downs, then the vibrations simmered down a little bit, considerably so. That might have been my detection at lift off.

CUNNINGHAM — Well, that's kind of what I felt, too, because when I got to thinking about it afterwards, I knew when we lifted off. And how did I know? I couldn't feel any acceleration or motion, and I think it was just the change in the vibration spectrum that you could feel from this kind of heavy carrying on; then all of a sudden, it dropped off. It didn't go to nothing; you could still feel something, but it was a pronounced change.

SCHIRRA — It was a change.

2.3 L/V Lights

CUNNINGHAM — At that time, the lift-off light came on, and the clock started. So I kind of figured that's what lift-off cue was for me.

SCHIRRA — It wasn't enough to cue me, because I didn't have the whole feel. I knew I didn't because those other things kept adding up. Then things started unwinding very fast. I knew that was the whole cue:

2.4 Roll Program
2.5 Pitch Program
2.6 Roll Complete
2.7 Rate Change

Roll program, nominal pitch program, roll complete. The rate change, I don't know what that is. Is that the rate change that everybody has in their checklist that I don't have?

EISELE — That's the one you don't recognize.

SCHIRRA — I didn't recognize the 3 degrees per second versus 5 degrees.

2.8 Effect at Mach 1
Transient

Mach 1 - I was really worried about this, Mr. Slayton. I was worried about the fact that we could talk to each other with the COMM carriers on. I mean that the DB attenuation was very low, and yet this wasn't as noisy as the Atlas, Agena, or Titan. I was quite surprised.

SLAYTON — Was that Mach 1?

2.9 Max Q

SCHIRRA — Well, the noise was at max Q and Mach 1.

EISELE — I know it was, and I expected far worse.

CUNNINGHAM — I figured we wouldn't be able to hear each other or anything. I heard 1-Bravo!

EISELE — That's right.

CUNNINGHAM — I don't hear that in the simulator most of the time.

EISELE — It was a rumble and kind of muffled.

SCHIRRA — The most noise we had was the cabin venting which everybody is going to hear. You learn to hear that in the altitude chamber.

EISELE — Incidentally, that's a very welcome sound.

SCHIRRA — Schumm!

67-H-965

67-H-971

68-H-411

68-H-616

68-H-617

68-H-64

EISELE — After about 50 seconds or so when you're expecting rumble, rumble.

SCHIRRA — You figure you're going to dump and even have the lock off, and that's the point. On boost, I had the position for the two cabin vent valves in LOCK OFF so I could flick it into DUMP. Then I knew I was safe; I've got a closed loop suit circuit. If I dumped the cabin inadvertently, that's fine. Then I took the lock off, and I put the lock on when I got in orbit so I can't come into dump again without being at a low altitude or dumping because I want to. I think that's a good technique, for that reason in particular.

2.10 EDS Manual

CUNNINGHAM — The EDS MANUAL. I got out of sequence as I was going to turn it off instead of turn it on for the RCS propellants.

EISELE — Wally banged my hand away and I said "oops." That was a very good hand.

SCHIRRA — Yes, I remember, …think nothing dangerous there.

EISELE — That's why I formed a habit in that regard on those both time shared checkers. We both checked each other, and we did it on a simulator; one or the other would start to do something, start the wrong way or forget to do it when you should, and we've always just kind of overlapped each other that way, so I'm glad you did.

SCHIRRA — He watches me like a hawk when I play control modes, which is fine, and it helps. I think I prefer that technique to "somewhere," and I've heard Dave Scott and Milby were where they will cross over each other. I think that's very bad form, but this is the way two aviators or pilots work. You learn to work together in a pilot/ co-pilot relationship, and I think Donn and I've spent enough time on these systems together where we could overlap, and that was good.

2.11 GO/NO-GO for Staging

EISELE — Yes.

CUNNINGHAM — GO/NO-GO for staging is no strain; inboard cutoff right on time. As called out, outboard cut off. Sep, boy, was that a thrill! Every time we hit an event like this where there is a pyro or something, it's a crash.

2.12 Inboard Cut-Off

2.13 Outboard Cut-Off

EISELE — Hark to the cannon's roar. That's what it sounds like.

2.14 S-IB/S-IVB Sep

CUNNINGHAM — Conditions for explosions, including this landing…

EISELE — It always builds up on us.

CUNNINGHAM — It sounds like asking what gun is it today. Is it the 5 inch, or 38's that make a crack like that? It's more than a rifle, by far. It is really a loud noise, but it's a sharp sound. You'd think the whole back end blew off, which it did, of course, after fire.

2.15 S-IVB Engine Ignition

SCHIRRA — However, the ignition was as soft as a powder puff. I didn't even know it happened, except the light went off. The light was on, then went out.

EISELE — Well, you could feel the g's coming.

SCHIRRA — Yes, but there was no big deal. That was why we were really shocked when we got that first SPS light off. Pow!

CUNNINGHAM — That J2 comes up pretty smooth; it must have a very long thrust rise because we didn't feel any sharp change.

SCHIRRA — I hope that the flight quality notes a lot of g, in that, it sure felt like we got kicked. The SPS, that's where we need a soft light.

2.16 S-IVB Plume

I didn't see any S-IVB plume. I was playing EDS in rates and that sort of stuff, and starting gimbal motors. I did see the big fire, and Donn could probably describe it better than I. I saw it even where I was in the cockpit. We launched cockpit bright IFR, and I saw lots of fire come by us from the retro rockets from the first stage.

CUNNINGHAM — You could see those very good.

SCHIRRA — I'm sure he had a real good view of them.

EISELE — Yes, you could see kind of a sheet of flame come by the hatch.

SCHIRRA — Yes, real big flames.

SLAYTON — Looks like a catastrophe on TV.

SCHIRRA — Yes, well, that's what triggered me off when I said I caught a movie on that. Okay. Let's stand by for that. I kept telling about it as if we were at launch. The S-IVB plume, I don't recall anything like that unless that's what you were talking about here.

EISELE — No, we couldn't. At least, I never saw anything out the window on the plume for that.

SCHIRRA — Okay.

2.17 Scale Change

SCHIRRA — Scale Change. What I do after we're on the S-IVB is I go for 1 degree per second rather than the called out 10 degrees per second. Glynn Lunney and I worked this out together. I had the idea, and I showed it to him one day.

Here's my logic, and I'd like to get this one across. It's wrong to do it the way the OCP, the AOH, and everything else says. Our checklist may even still have it for all I know, but it was very late that I did this. But I go to 1 degree per second, and I can see guidance initiate which is very small; it's less than a degree per second rate. Then I go to 1 degree per second. If it gets bad, I'm at 1 g or less at this point. I can go to 5 degrees per second right down to 10 degrees per second. Just go click, click. We had a simulation where I had to do that, and I went right on down to my abort rules. I think that's the spot where they flagged us. At 1 degree per second, if something develops to make us aware that something is going wrong, you can detect guidance in initiate; you can detect the P00 shift; in our case it was 734. You can actually see a little bit of rate change. It is significant to see that, then have it masked in this large scale. So I would suggest that scale change should read 1 degree per second rather than the other, and I think if the guys play it that way, they'll see my point. By the way, Mr. Slayton, to orient to the next booster, we know the I-B's history.

SLAYTON — Yes.

2.18 Distinction of Sounds

SCHIRRA — Judging by the distinction of sounds, I would say everything that happened we heard. Wouldn't you?

EISELE — Yes, I believe that.

SCHIRRA — Thrusters, separations, all of that was heard.

2.19 Trajectory GO/NO-GO

Okay. Trajectories GO/NO-GO is the one we did not get a mode 4 call-out, and that really surprised me because we always had a mode 4 call-out.

EISELE — I didn't worry about it because we'd been given an onboard guidance GO. In other words, I knew the computer was good, and I had the little card up there with the velocities versus H-dot. We were coming right up the slot, right up the groove, and as soon as we got that crossed in the mode 4 region in the chart, I just assumed that we were there, but it would have been nice to have somebody call up and tell us we were.

SLAYTON — You and I weren't on that loop, unfortunately!

EISELE — It's in there; it's in the flight plan and checklist.

SCHIRRA — Yes, well, every time we've had a launch with Houston, we had a mode 4 call-out, and quite often, I'd hammer because he didn't come up with it. They got a little gitchy about giving us GO/NO-GO's or actually modes 4, but it's very important. Watch though, on the next family of boosters, you've got an S-IVB launch to abort to orbit case, and it's going to be a lot earlier than ours.

2.20 LET and BPC Jettison

SCHIRRA — Okay. The tower and the boost protector cover was very obvious to us, another noisy event, and I saw it go; a big ice cream cone just going out there and throwing off. And that event, I think, is what put a little bit of smoke on the number 2 and number 4 windows just about half an inch on the edges, as I described in the flight. That was there the whole flight.

REP — Did you see that early in flight?

EISELE — The smoke?

SCHIRRA — Yes.

EISELE — Where, down at the bottom?

SCHIRRA — No, no, it was up at the upper side there where I was sitting.

EISELE — Yes, well, along the edge.

SCHIRRA — Yes, along the edge - the biased edge along side of us, the 45 degree angle.

EISELE — Yes, you know, I didn't see a thing from that except a few particles of orange.

SCHIRRA — Yes, they're the only window that we could get it because they were in the plane at the thrust.

EISELE — I guess you could see it go away.

<u>2.21 Guidance Initiate</u>

SCHIRRA — Yes, I saw it. Guidance initiate, I made that point again on the 1 degree per second; I think it's very significant that you catch it there.

EISELE — That looked to me very much like the simulation we've seen, didn't it?

SCHIRRA — It was exactly the same as the simulations.

EISELE — It went off about the same CMS rates.

SCHIRRA — The CMS rates were good.

EISELE — It came back in.

SCHIRRA — It's so good that EMS velocity entry is exactly the way it worked with us.

END OF TAPE (Launch Debrief continues in Part Two)

<u>3.1.8 CSM Systems Checkout</u>

CUNNINGHAM — Yes, I'm in orbit. It's covering the first six REV's to get a GO/NO-GO for 17 01. Okay. This was done in various steps without really intending it necessarily to be that way. That's because we have certain items on the insertion checklist and in running through the insertion checklist and looking back at it, I guess I can say that everything was nominal as expected. All the items were performed, and I'm only going to mention things which seemed to be different or surprises.

We did the insertion checklist; we added an item to it which was not originally on our insertion checklist but should have been. That is the hatch gear boxes to NEUTRAL. We turned the hatch handle gear box to NEUTRAL and the hatch release itself to NEUTRAL and left the shear pin actuated, of course. At that same time, we took the bottle that was then on the line the nitrogen bottle for opening the hatch and we had had it pressurized with the handle in the OPEN position so that the bottle itself would all run out through the lines had we needed it on the pad. At this time, we returned that bottle handle to NEUTRAL. The pressure was up to what it had been at boost at that time, and we noticed very late in the flight it had degraded down to about half of that.

We did the caution warning systems checkout, SCS attitude reference and comparison check, Wally performed, and the two reference systems compared very favorably. I don't know if we have the numbers logged, or if we put it on tape at that point. Performed a service module RCS monitoring check which merely meant verifying the readings we had expected and they were, command module ECS monitoring checks, they were. We ran through all the EPS systems. Everything was nominal. ECS periodic verification tests consisted once more of just verifying the meter readings. Everything was what we expected.

SPS monitoring check was fine. We started off the flight with the helium pressure at 30, 400 and 2500 in each of the nitrogen bottles, and I probably have in my notes some place what it went to toward the end of the flight. We next ran through the ECS post insertion configuration. No big surprises there. We ran the post insertion checklist right down to and including the item of verifying the accumulator primary and secondary quantities between 30 and 70 percent. At that point, we held because we were in the couches and the follow-on items would require Donn getting out of the couch.

The first time we flowed the radiators, we went to glycol to radiator primary valve, we pulled to bypass, and we let it sit there. Inside of 3 or 4 minutes, we could see that the RAD OUT temperature was coming down, and we did not have to recheck this item. The RAD OUTs came down under the RAD IN, and the radiator flow was complete. When we did get a GO past 2-1, Donn got out of the couch and completed the rest of the ECS post insertion checklist. We did notice a mislabeled valve in the checklist. The waste stowage vent valve was supposed to be closed. We verified that. When we got down to the optics dust cover jettison procedure, I recall that Donn had some surprises. The telescope apparently - the telescope dust cover came off very quickly, and I guess for the sextant, he had to rotate quite a way around, at least farther than he had expected to before it finally came off. And it did come off; it came off nice and clear, and he was quite impressed with the sudden view he had out through the optics.

The next three configurations we did were after S-IVB SEP, which everything went as normal. Nothing to report, just as the checklist and flight plan called out. Prior to getting a GO for 17-1, we had to perform ECS redundancy component check, and that's about the only item left to comment on as far as the systems for the first six revs. The redundant component check itself was done in it's entirety as per the checklist. Later on, we made certain modifications to the redundant component check. I might say that this was the only time that

68-H-923

68-H-928

68-H-929

68-H-934

68-H-945

68-H-921

we flowed the secondary radiators with the exception of the secondary coolant loop test much later in the flight. It appeared to be working normally. I flipped the secondary heaters on and off, and I did get a transient each time even though we were above the 40 degree heater temperature. I interpreted this to mean that as I turned them on they temporarily flashed on, but the signal then turned the heater off because it was above the threshold. I'm not sure if this is correct or accurate, but at any rate, I felt like we definitely knew that the heaters did come on and off because I did get a transient at the time I threw the switch.

At this time, the checklist called for the evaporator water control secondary valve OFF; I believe we turned it off at this time. The first time the primary evaporator dried out, we turned that evaporator water control secondary valve to AUTO, and it remained at AUTO throughout the rest of the flight. Primary coolant loop deactivation was done per the checklist whenever it called for, and secondary coolant loop activation was done per the checklist whenever called for.

At this time, during the redundancy component check, I did notice that the glycol accumulator quantities were running towards the low end of the acceptable range, and I made a mental note to keep an eye on it. However, it never really changed throughout the flight. I wasn't concerned that it was low since all indications were that it was not changing much in volume because of temperature effects at all.

3.1.9 SXT Calibration Test

REP — We probably ought to make it clear that we've got an area in here that we've missed, in case someone is looking for that, and that will be coming up later. From guidance it goes through the sextant calibration tests. See?

REP — Yes.

EISELE — Well, the first surprise I got on the optics was when I went to get it from the optics cover. I was told that 20 degrees of shaft rotation would kick the covers off, and it took about 180 degrees before they let go. I had my heart in my mouth there for a few seconds until they finally went, because I could envision the thing not coming off and us having to do the whole rest of the mission with nothing but COAS alignment which we also hadn't verified at that time. However, they did pop off, and I could see the little pieces with sunlight reflected off them disappearing as they drifted away from the spacecraft.

Now the sextant calibration test I did using, I believe, it was Canopus and Regor. There were two stars in the southern hemisphere, and it just happened that this piece of sky that I ended up looking at for the test only had two Apollo stars in it, so I was not able to use a third star. But I did do the test for DTO, put the fixed line of sight on Canopus, and used the movable line of sight to bring, I believe it was Regor, into the super position. Then I made a mark, and I gather that was sufficient for the test because no one ever called up later on to ask for it to be done again.

The optics quality, in general, in the telescope, is not too good. It's about like the simulator; in fact, it is not quite as good as the simulator. You have to get dark adapted to use it, and that was another real shock. I put my eyeball on the telescope and didn't see a blooming thing for about 4 or 5 minutes. I got dark adapted and finally the brighter stars came first, of course, and then finally the dim ones came in. A great many of the dimmer stars that make up constellation patterns are very difficult to see; you don't see them right off. You can look in there, and you may see a handful of very bright stars, well known ones, ones that you would normally recognize from their constellation patterns, but you have to look at it for a long time before those dimmer ones come in and fill out.

For instance, Taurus, you can see Aldebaran pretty early. That's a nice bright star, but the other stars that make the V in Taurus don't show up right away. But if you just keep your eye on it long enough, for 5 or 10 minutes, you can see all of them that you need. The outer fringes of the telescope are distorted and blurred, and it is very difficult to recognize constellations when they are out on the edges of field of view. Of course, the field of view is movable, and you can take your optics switch and drive out there and put that part of your field of view in the center of the scope, and, you know, verify that whatever you thought it was really is the right star, or verify that it isn't in some cases. You can get faked out once in a while.

Mechanically, the telescope and sextant drive very smoothly in both direct and resolve and in all speeds. The manual aspect of tracking stars or landmarks or whatever is a very simple task to do, and you could get more than adequate training on that in the simulator. I would suggest for other crews that, after you have gotten your initial orientation on the celestial sphere in this planetarium, that you forget all about planetariums and stick to the simulator. It is a very faithful reproduction of what you are going to see in orbit with regard to the stars.

REP — Stars that you can see in the sextant? With the sextant I don't guess you had any problem?

EISELE — No, the sextant field of view, again, is very much like the simulator except that they do not simulate all the other dim stars that you'll see when you look through the real one. I didn't have any trouble any time recognizing the one that I was supposed to mark on because the Apollo stars are all bright enough, in relation to the little ones around them, that you don't have any trouble picking out the right one. And you can just pull

68-H-674

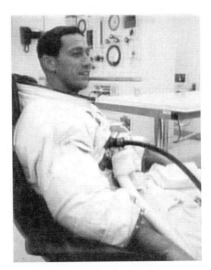

68-H-675

68-H-813

68-H-676

68-H-864

68-H-937

it in there and hit the MARK button. One little, kind of irritating thing is that you have to adjust the radical brightness when you go from sextant to telescope and back again, so you are continually rolling that thumb wheel up and down to get the right brightness setting. But you learn all these little things after a few times, and it's not a big deal.

3.1.10 COAS Calibration

EISELE — The COAS calibration worked out very well. I thought that it was a much easier task to do in orbit than it is in the simulator for two reasons. One is that the light loss through the COAS didn't seem to be quite as bad in orbit as it was in the simulator. Again, that's kind of a subjective thing, but I had the feeling that I could actually see stars better through the COAS in orbit than I could over here. Also, the simulator is a little jerky; when you put in a pulse it doesn't always take. In orbit it always does, and you can track that star very smoothly right through the center of that radical pattern, and you can't, you never freeze it. You can't ever stop motion - altogether, but you can get the rate such that the star will track very slowly right through the center, and when it gets to the center, you just hit the ENTER button, or whichever one it is you use to mark - the ENTER button. You get a sextant calibration that way, and it worked out very well. I found that the angles were about a degree off in shaft and trunnion from where they were supposed to be - that is according to, you know, where you expect the X-axis of the spacecraft to be, and we did another one later on in the flight. Wally did one, and I think they were still within about a tenth of a degree of that original reading, so the business of removing the COAS and then reinstalling it doesn't seem to change the orientation of the thing very much. It's very repeatable. I thought it was a very simple task to perform, and later on our results of using the COAS for alignments were quite satisfactory in rendezvous. IMU orientation and alignment...

3.1.11 S-IVB Ventilation

REP — Do you want to agree with that - any of the ventilation in these ice clouds of vapor, or - just leave that for...

EISELE — Oh - I don't know what that's all about; I didn't ever notice any ventilation or ice clouds or vapor around the S-IVB.

REP — These are some of the questions that they sent from Marshall out here.

EISELE — Why don't you just make a negative response and say I didn't see anything. You might ask Walt and Wally when they get back, because they had a better view of it actually than I did. I just caught a glimpse of it now and then out the hatch window, and once in a while I could peek out the others.

REP — I believe Wally said he thought he could see a little bit there once, little streamer, but not of any significance.

3.2 Rendezvous

3.2.1 IMU Orientation and Alignment

EISELE — Well, IMU orientations and alignments we did per checklist, before each of the burns. And I tried, at least particularly in the early part of the flight, to get a leg up on these alignments and not wait until just two revs before the burn. I even started three or four revs before on this one because I wanted to be darned sure that I had a good alignment. Of course, at this time, for these two SPS burns, we had had the IMU up continuously since lift off. So we had an orientation, and we could use AUTO optics and everything to tweak it in, and it worked out very satisfactorily. We did the, I think it was a nominal option 2, for the burns to bring it into some local vertical alignment at a particular time which is aimed to be TPI time. And I didn't have any particular problem using the computer or the optics for these alignments once I got used to the idea that the light transmission in the telescope wasn't as good as I hoped.

3.2.2 AUTO Maneuver-To-Burn Attitude

EISELE — On the maneuver-to-burn attitude, we didn't do much of an AUTO maneuver-to-burn attitude. What we usually did, or what we always did, was fly the thing manually to within a few degrees, and then put it in, say, wide deadband and SCS. Then as we finally got down to within a few minutes of the burn, say 10 to 20 minutes, you would tweak it in very tightly and then go to narrow deadband and then throw it to CMC AUTO and let the computer hold it. So about the only AUTO maneuvering we really did was the trim maneuver that we do just before the burn. We have a flashing 15-19 on the computer, and you hit the ENTER button, and the computer will then dis-autopilot within tweek of the spacecraft right into the attitude.

And so that's all we did, and the reason we didn't is that we found on the simulation if you have a large maneuver to perform the computer has a strong preference for maneuvering in yaw rather than pitch, and it'll drive you right through the gimbal lock region some times. So we just flew in flight like we trained and it seemed to work out okay.

3.2.3 SPS Burn I

EISELE — I am sure the other guys will have some comments on these burns too. As far as subjective impressions, particularly that first burn, we didn't know quite what to expect, but we got more than we expected. That thing really comes up in a hurry, and it's a real boot in the ass when it lights off; it's not a smooth thrust rise like you get off the larger booster engines. Man, it comes on all at once, and smacks you right in the tail, and just plasters you to the seat. It's pretty close to one g, and man, things are really going fast, and those numbers are clicking down on those counters, and valves are opening, and you watch the gimbal needles go up and down, and it's a real thrill, the first time particularly, to see it came out smooth as glass. We had some small residuals which Wally burned out very easily with the RCS system right after the burn.

SLAYTON — Is the shutdown as abrupt as the start, too?

68-H-1076

68-H-930

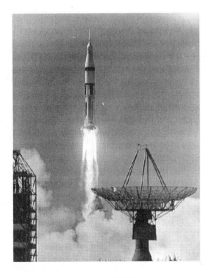

S68-48788

68-H-979

S68-50713

EISELE — Yes.

SLAYTON — Clean shutdown.

EISELE — It sure is. Bang, it's ON; and bang, it's OFF; it's very abrupt. Then we had a - I think I did the alignment between the burns. We did not have to do that intermediate MCC burn that they were talking about because the MCC-1 first burn was right on the money and came around; and I think I got an alignment in just before NSR there, but the tape will show it. It was just a P52 fine align.

I had noticed by this time that these gyro torquing angles were very small, even though the IMU had not been fine align for a period of several hours when you did it; the gyro torquing angles were way down in the hundredths of degrees in most cases. So I felt pretty good about the IMU; and, apparently, it was not even drifting anywhere near the allowed spec values.

3.2.4 SPS Burn 2

EISELE — SPS burn 2 was very similar to burn 1, the same sort of sensations; and it, too, was apparently right on the money. The targeting we got from the ground was just about letter perfect. Wally burned out the residuals to about one tenth of a foot per second with the RCS, and from then on, we were on our way. I wonder if I could just go through this in narrative rather than follow the exact check list because…

REP — Whatever makes sense to you.

EISELE — Why don't you turn off the tape a minute? I want to get my book.

After the first SPS burn, I did a little P20 tracking exercise, and I didn't actually do any MARK's, but I did ask Wally to maneuver in pitch to the point where I could get the S-IVB in the telescope field-of-view, called a P20, and found that the thing did in fact track the target, that I could see it in the sextant but not in the telescope; and I believe at this time, we were in daylight so that the S-IVB was visible with reflected light.

It came in loud and clear, and I did that mainly as a confidence factor, just to be sure I could see the thing; it worked out pretty nice.

After NSR, we called up P20 again, and I found that after the initial transients in attitude control and optics line-of-sight control that the computer settled down and tracked the target quite smoothly in auto optics. In the simulator, we had had some trouble with the thing being pretty jerky, and also in attitude control there were quite a lot of jets. After I made a few marks, the thing really settled in, and we had hardly any attitude maneuvers. Once in a great while, it would decide that it needed to correct its attitude, and all of a sudden, it would take off and move about 5 degrees and man, you'd think the thing was going wild, but if you just sat there and waited it out, it would settle back down and track the booster. There is a way of getting around that. You can actually do it manually if you want to, but procedurally it's much simpler just to let the computer track the thing and not worry about trying to fake it out. It doesn't use up that much fuel. The DELTA dot-R and DELTA-V updates were very small throughout the pre-TPI phase.

3.2.5 TPI Burn (RCS)

EISELE — One thing that was disconcerting was that when I recycled program 34 to get another TPI solution, the darned thing would quit tracking in auto optics. In fact, it didn't just stop it; it would just take the sextant and drive it completely off target somewhere, and since I could not yet see it in the telescope, I was sitting there flying blind as far as keeping the target in sight until it finally quit calculating its solution, and then it would pull the target back in.

Also, another surprise was that the TPI solutions took about 4 minutes, 4 to 5 minutes, whereas in the simulator I timed it, and I think the longest one I've even seen was about 3 minutes over there. So I elected to change our procedure slightly in that rather than waiting until TPI minus 5 minutes to get the final solution, I went ahead and took it around TPI minus 14 minutes to get all that done so it wouldn't interfere with our backup MARK's at 8 and 5 minutes.

At about TPI minus 9 or 10 minutes I believe it was, I took another VERB 85 plot (that's line-of-sight angle from the horizon to the target), and our procedure is that when you get the target centered in the sextant, you punch the VERB button and that freezes the display; then whoever is taking plots can write it down and get the data. I goofed and forgot to hit key RELEASE, so that when it got to 8 minutes, it was still locked up on the reading; it had been there 2 minutes ago. So I hit the key release, and we did a reading; I think it was about 30 seconds late. Just about then, for some reason - I'll never know why it did this - but for some reason, the computers - the optics drive started jumping around, and it finally went completely off the target, and I lost it, and it never would come back. This was about 7 minutes to TPI.

We scratched our heads for a while, and I compared the ground's solution with the computer's TPI solution and decided that it was close enough to go ahead and burn it on the computer because after I looked for the star - rather, for the target for a few minutes, and it wasn't there, I finally gave up on it, went on into P41 where you do get the DELTA-V components and local vertical coordinates, compared those to the ground, and they were right on the money. So I said, "well, the only thing we can do is go ahead and try the burn and burn what the computer said," and that's exactly what we did. We even did an auto maneuver to the burn attitude.

We were bellied up to at first... bellied up to the first, bellied up with the optics line-of-sight looking at it and went ahead and did an auto maneuver and just let the computer fly it back down to the burn attitude; it just tracked in nice as you please, just did a pitch maneuver, and the only thing I didn't like about it was the out-of-planes solution. We had about 10 degrees out-of-plane, and I felt that was too big, and I can't tell you why. It's just a Kentucky windage that we kind of picked up after running in the simulator some, plus the ground solution didn't call for that much out-of-plane either, so I suggested to Wally that he take about half of that out-of-plane angle out of it, and he did that. I don't know whether that was good or bad, but I know that we did end up coming up pretty much in plane at final breaking.

So that's the way we did TPI, and Wally couldn't see it in the front window, either. Apparently, those flashing lights aren't all that bright. They just don't show up until you get within 15 miles or so. They do in the sextant, but not through the telescope or the front window. We burned it blind without having the target in view; and then after TPI we went through the procedure and got back into P20 automatic tracking again, and it brought the target right back into the sextant; then we could do some more MARK's, and we went on. At that point, the image was so large in the sextant due to magnification that it was no longer point source. It was four discrete spots of light - you know, the four lights on the SLA panels - and they were flashing alternately and intermittently, and the booster was also tumbling. This made it a very erratic and difficult pattern to work with because you could never pick out exactly what the hell the center of it was to know where to MARK, so I was kind of going along guessing about where the center ought to be.

Apparently, it worked out because we got very good results on our DELTA-R and DELTA-V update, and we got a very good solution at first midcourse. The computer called for three and one half feet per second aft and a little bit down, and Walt got 1.7 on his charts, so I just suggested that we burn 2 feet aft. You don't like to take that energy out after you've put it in, so we just burned 2 feet per second aft, and I think just a couple of tenths down; and, apparently, it put us right on the slot because the second midcourse came up zero or less than 1 foot per second on the computer and less than 1 foot per second on the chart, so we didn't burn anything at the second midcourse; we didn't need to, and our polar plot showed us going right into the target. So that's the way the burns went.

All this time, of course, these lights were flashing in the sextant, and they were - the closer they got, why of course, the more erratic the P20 tracking became, and the harder it was to make MARK's because the target got bigger and bigger, although we were still in darkness and all you could see were these flashing lights, and it just looked like a bunch of flash bulbs popping out there.

The phasing was just about perfect because we broke into daylight and could actually see the booster in reflected sunlight, I guess, when we were 2 or 3 miles out. It was just about the time when the thing began to have some finite size in the COAS through the window, and from then on we used Wally's estimate of subtended angle and booster diameter plus charts to get a hack on our range in conjunction with the display on the computer. The computer solution of range and range rate was, as near as I could tell, pretty good all the way in to the final phase of breaking and line-of-sight control.

3.2.6 Thrust Monitor (LOS Control)

EISELE — The line-of-sight control - I'd better let Wally talk about that since he did most of it. As I recall, we had very little thrusting to do in the up and down, in the in-plane portion, and he did do some cross-plane thrusting, which I think had some out-of-plane components; we tend to want to bring that out-of-plane in so that you come in right on the bellyband. I know theoretically that's not most efficient; but, in practice, that's the easiest thing to do, so he will have some comments on that. I guess that's about all I have on rendezvous. I'd like to discuss the post-rendezvous tracking at 80, 160, and 320 miles. We could see the target.

REP — Before you get to that, would you like to make an overall summary that we can - conclusion about the ability to do this with one man?

EISELE — With one guy, it's a bitch; I'll say that. If I had two guys out there on the LM...

REP — I thought that was pretty wild.

EISELE — Well, I would hate to go and get somebody under these conditions. It's not so much the one-man time line, it's just that - you're never sure what the hell you got, because you don't have any radar. With one guy, particularly, you don't have time to do backup charts; you don't have time to deliberate and make these comparisons between ground and chart and your computer, and just about all you can do would be to work the computer, take the solution, burn it, take advantage of all the auto tracking and optics and all the auto maneuvers and everything else, and hope it came out right. That's all you could do. And I believe the rendezvous solution particularly is that you get a good - a nominal initial condition from the ground, on this first burn. You could probably get away with it, but it is not the kind of thing that you would want to hang your hat on for the purpose of rescuing people.

I felt very good about it being successful, but I felt very uncomfortable when I thought about it in terms of two guys being out there in the LM. There is just no way to go without radar. I've got some numbers and stuff, but that...

REP — You're talking about range rate information.

EISELE — Well, yes, without some kind of...

REP — That would be VHF ranging.

EISELE — Well, yes, that to me is radar, a measurement of some kind.

REP — Yes.

EISELE — Rather than computed in. Particularly at T-align, the tough part is the tail end of visual ranging; even though we got away with it on S-IVB, that's a big target. You've got a little dinky LM out there, and you don't have a subtended angle or a fixed reticle type of thing to really measure the optical range; you're really flying blind, I would imagine. Oh, I might discuss the braking schedule. We did use the computer in conjunction with Wally's estimates of booster size to get a hack on our distance and our closure rate.

Again, this is the kind of thing that you develop more by experience. We have certain gates where you're supposed to be a certain speed at a certain distance; but there is so much uncertainty as to whether you are really at these gates that it is difficult to judge. So we just developed enough coordination such that you can kind of tell by the way things are going, by what Wally says the size of the target is, and by what the DSKY is telling you that you can anticipate when you should do a certain amount of braking. I think we did it in two or three steps, and it came out just fine. If you kill-off too soon, you don't make it; and if you wait too long, you go whistling by it, but that's pretty much by the seat of your pants. The post-rendezvous tracking was kind of interesting. We found that you could, in fact, see that darn thing in the sextant at those distances. In fact, even at 320 miles, I could see it well enough to say that it was something besides just a point source, that it actually had some little bit of shape to it.

Okay. The subject is DELTA-V bookkeeping for rendezvous. We had a DELTA-V budget called up to us of 90 feet per second; and, of course, the problem onboard was to keep track in real time of DELTA-V expended. Since the fuel readout is not that accurate, the only way we can book-keep on RCS fuel is by keeping track of DELTA-V maneuvers.

There are two ways you can use NOUN 40 on the DSKY, or you can use this display in program 47. I started using the program 47 displays where you let the counter build up; then you recycle it to zero and write down the numbers. Toward the tail end of the thrusting maneuvers, recycling became rather rapid, and it's a little hard to always get it zeroed at the right time to get the next batch, so I went to the NOUN 40. The trouble with the NOUN 40 is that it integrates every single little pulse that comes out of the PIPA's, and they kind of have a tendency to go plus and minus, and they'll average out in the average "U" routines; but they do not average out in the NOUN 40, for some reason. We took a combination of what we knew we had burned at the midcourse and the TPI plus the NOUN 40, and I think it came out to something like 75 or 80 feet per second. I just arbitrarily in my own mind, at least, took off about 15 feet or so because the NOUN 40 counted UP to 50 feet per second, and I didn't think we burned that much after TPI.

CUNNINGHAM — Did you cover the burns that we did put in?

EISELE — Yes, I talked about the TPI burn, the midcourse.

CUNNINGHAM — How about the bookkeeping?

EISELE — The item of concern is the bookkeeping on the breaking log, and I got 11, 3, and 16 feet per second recorded in four and one half. I've got 14 left, about 16 right, and practically nothing up and down. The thing that puzzles me is the left and right in that if we had a large out-of-plane correction, which we might have had, you'd expect it to be mostly one way. I'm a little suspicious of my numbers. I do know that Wally did a considerable amount of inputs to null out his line-of-sight rates sideways. Whether or not our DELTA-V book-keeping is accurate and up to date, I don't know at this time. I think we will find out when we get the high bit rate data back.

CUNNINGHAM — Did you cover the TPI burn where I didn't get the high bit rate on?

EISELE — No, I didn't mention that. We did not get the high bit rate on for TPI. Consequently, we will probably not know precisely how much we burned. The computer solution was something on the order of 17.3, is that the number?

CUNNINGHAM — Yes.

EISELE — We burned the residuals to as close to zero as we could get. Of course, they pop around a good bit.

CUNNINGHAM — I think they add to about a tenth.

EISELE — Also, the DELTA-V counter was pretty close to that. So I would say that if you put down a number like 17.5, you would be within a half a foot per second of what you actually did burn at TPI.

CUNNINGHAM — Why don't we elaborate? Did you mention the confusion or consternation when we lost the target at TPI minus 5?

EISELE — I did.

CUNNINGHAM — Well, as a result of that - I have written on the top of my chart here all these things - high bit rate for all the burns when we were busy figuring out what we were going to do about the whole thing. We got down to deciding finally to burn the computer solution, and we were all ready at that time, and we burned, and I didn't get high bit rate on for that burn. But I had high bit rate on for the midcourse, and then we started braking. I had high bit rate on for the rest of the way, so it would all be on tape. All of these DELTA-V's should be on tape.

EISELE — Yes, it was a little spastic there on TPI because it's a good example of how operational problems pop up on you. The first thing that happened was that we lost the target. Well, that shook me up a little bit, and we were thrashing around, trying to figure out what to do. About that time, Wally was trying to look out the window and found he was being blinded by light reflection from the floodlight. We had forgotten to put up the floodlight screen. So I went scrambling into the stowage box to retrieve the screen, and when I did, my checklist floated away somewhere, so I didn't have a checklist for a while.

CUNNINGHAM — He handed me the screen, and I sat there trying to snap the screen on, and there are two other snaps that hold the cable. We had only seen that screen about a week or 10 days before the flight. We saw it once in the simulator, so I got wrestling around with pulling snaps off and putting the screen on. About that time, everybody decided to burn the onboard computer solution that was less than 3 feet in difference, according to ground. We went ahead and burned, and about the time we were getting over it, I remembered the high bit rate. We never did get to it. I finally got the screen up, but we didn't get high bit rate.

EISELE — That 5-minute period I think was about the fastest four-handed game I ever saw.

CUNNINGHAM — Six-handed game!

EISELE — That's enough on rendezvous. The post-rendezvous tracking went off very smoothly. We could see the target very easily up to 320 miles in the sextant. I never did see it in the telescope that far out. These were done during daylight passes so that we had reflected light. One time, I did see it at night. I think it was either 80 or 160, and the sextant - I could actually see the lights flashing. What was kind of interesting about that was that the lights stayed on a lot longer than the 7 hours they were supposed to. This was like 10 or 12 hours after rendezvous, and they were still flashing.

CUNNINGHAM — Did you cover the discrepancy between the computer solution and the backup solution at midcourse?

EISELE — Yes.

CUNNINGHAM — Okay.

EISELE — Basically, I think we burned the chart rather than the DSKY.

CUNNINGHAM — Yes, and not all the out-of-plane, not all the down.

EISELE — We burned about half the down.

CUNNINGHAM — Incidentally, on seeing the S-IVB visually later on that night - that night being local Cape time - Wally and I were still on watch; Donn was asleep; and we saw the S-IVB behind us. At that time, it was called out at a thousand miles.

EISELE — I think that was a day later, in fact.

CUNNINGHAM — Yes, it was a day later. It was very, very bright.

SCHIRRA — It was in reflected light just at sunrise.

CUNNINGHAM — We were already in the dark, and it was above the horizon. It was at a thousand feet (miles? Ed:) and was brighter than any star out there. I can't wait to see some of those pictures.

3.3 Post-rendezvous Through Deorbit Burn

3.3.1 S-IVB Post-rendezvous Tracking at 80, 160, and 320 NM

3.3.2 SCT Star Count Test

EISELE — We did the telescope star count test as per procedure, and I guess the people on the ground were happy with it because they said the star count went right in line with their predictions. The only reservation I have on this whole deal is that I don't want someone to reach the conclusion that doing daylight alignments

AS07-03-1531

AS07-03-1535

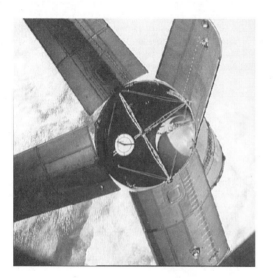

AS07-03-1538

AS07-03-1541

AS07-03-1545

S68-49301

with this rig is no sweat because, in general, that is not the case. It is very difficult to see anything useful in the telescope when there is any sort of daylight around. The sextant is different. If you already aligned properly and you do an auto optics maneuver to bring a star into the sextant field of view - you can see stars in the daylight through the sextant. You can see it right up to a relative sun angle of maybe 40 or 50 degrees. You still see bright stars in the sextant, but that's the only thing you can do with it. If you're not aligned or if you've drifted off such that you can't get the star to come into the sextant, you're out of luck.

EISELE — No, sir, except for a few minutes at sunrise, right at around sunrise or sunset. If your back end is at the sun so that you're looking out away from the sun into the dark sky, you can see stars for a few minutes either side of sunrise and sunset, but that is about the limit on daylight type realignments. I guess the application here for lunar flights is that this is the kind of situation you are going to have all the way to the moon and back where you've always got the sun out. What you're going to have to do is turn around and point the SPS engine at the sun and then hope that you're not looking at the earth through the telescope at the same time. My recommendation is that the Colossus and those other programs incorporate a feature to allow the use of the nearer bodies (the earth, the moon, and the sun) for approximate alignments sort of a course alignment.

REP — Are you sure you know how to run this one now?

<u>3.3.3 S005. S006</u>
<u>Photography</u>

CUNNINGHAM — The subject is item 3.3, subject 3 under - on the debriefing chart, S005 and S006 photography; there are various ways of covering this. I think you could talk about the cameras. We had one flight-modified Hasselblad camera on board. Our general feeling was that we could have benefited greatly by having two Hasselblads, for several reasons. One, in case one failed, and we did have problems with the single Hasselblad; and secondly, there were times when two people could both have been taking pictures. For example, the multispectral photography: one man could have had the green filter and another man had the red filter, and we could have done a much better job all the way down the line, but we didn't, I think, primarily because of the fact that the modified Hasselblad seemed to have problems that the unmodified commercial Hasselblads don't have.

Various modifications were made which allow you, in certain instances, to pull the trigger with the slide still in, and you can't tell. On the S005/S006, I just broke it down to a couple of categories. I'm going to tell you something about the cameras, and then about the film, and then maybe pictures. But on the cameras, to repeat myself, we felt like the modified Hasselblads brought in problems that don't exist in the commercial Hasselblads. One of these is the slider that goes in the back. The modified Hasselblad back has got a round knob that protrudes on the left hand side, and the slider, if you put it in facing one way, will go all the way down; if you put it in facing another way, it doesn't go far enough down to stop the shutter from throwing with the slider in. This is impossible with an unmodified back. Another thing that is missing off the modified back is the depth-of-field scale which can be useful in some cases for interior shots. I think on this flight, we got some very decent interior shots with the S0368. Still another one that would be nice to have, and preclude you from ever losing a frame accidentally, is the little dot on the back of the camera. You still get the dot on the camera when it is cocked, but the window is removed from the back; and in a commercial Hasselblad, when these two are the same color, white or red, you can put the thing on. It precludes you from putting a cocked one back on an uncocked camera and winding one slide through uselessly,

SCHIRRA — They really goofed a good camera, Deke.

CUNNINGHAM — Those are primarily the main criticisms; if something else comes up, we'll have to cover it later. The camera itself is still very, very useful for pictures. On some occasions, we used the ring sight; on others; we didn't. I think for my case, I would aim down the camera, line my eye up, and put it right down across the top of the camera, and have a good view of what I was shooting a picture of. The pictures themselves were taken with three different kinds of film, and this, too, introduced certain problems. We had S0368 on board which was to be taken with no filters; we had S0121 which was to be taken with the 2A filter. (Incidentally, the 2A filter was in no way, shape, or form marked 2A in stowage. We had to verify that with the ground.)

SCHIRRA — Sight, we assume, eliminated the problem, but we still wanted to be sure.

CUNNINGHAM — The Panatomic-X film was taken with a red filter and a green filter, each of which had different filter factors associated with it. Each of those three films, incidentally, had a different ASA number to be taken with. We ought to make note of the fact that all of our pictures were shot with a light meter, except the Panatomic-X film. For the Panatomic-X film, we used the gauge that was on the backs, and made an estimate of whether the sun was 30 degrees above the horizon or not and used the can solutions for exposures.

We had some problems in the fact that we generally had two kinds of film out to be available when we needed it to take pictures; and changing backs obviously entailed changing filters and ASA numbers on the light meter. There were times when we lost some pictures because of either not getting a red filter off when you took the Panatomic-X back and put it on, or vice versa. We took one whole roll of S0121 without the 2A filter on, primarily because we were also taking S0368 at the same time (this was during the S-IVB turnaround and SEP maneuver and that time frame), and we did not want to be messing with the filter coming on and off. This was also labeled on the back. We also took that same roll of S0121 at an ASA of sixty-four instead of the recommended forty-five to fifty, which we did on all the rest of the backs. That was to preclude having to reset the light meter. There were a very few frames, maybe two or three throughout the flight, that were lost because of refocusing the camera from 3 feet to infinity.

SCHIRRA — That's a high risk.

CUNNINGHAM — That is; that's a high risk. It's a procedural type error, but it is something that you can very easily get suckered into when you are changing backs, ASA numbers, filter factors, and focus distances on the camera at the same time.

SCHIRRA — I wasn't listening completely, but I would like to add a point.

CUNNINGHAM — Go ahead.

SCHIRRA — The Hasselblad as a designed camera is a good foolproof camera.

CUNNINGHAM — I didn't cover that item by item.

SCHIRRA — We've made it for idiots, now, and I think it's wrong because it is not idiot-proof, now; it's too simple.

CUNNINGHAM — You might repeat your comment about your own Hasselblad.

SCHIRRA — I never have goofed with a picture with my own Hasselblad. I've missed a picture because the slider was in; that's much better than blowing a whole bunch of them with the slide in. I've never goofed on shutter setting; I've never goofed on focus because I have reflex action; and there is no reason not to have reflex action; there's lots of room in there.

CUNNINGHAM — You could also use the little eyepiece.

SCHIRRA — There is a reflex eyepiece, so you don't have to look over the top (you see photographers using that), and I would recommend rather than have it close up - because then, inside the cockpit with it, you know, it has to be set at 3 feet, the guy's out of focus - you look out the window, and it has to be in.

CUNNINGHAM — We feel that we have room in this spacecraft to get up to the windows like that.

SCHIRRA — Lots-of room - fantastic room.

CUNNINGHAM — I think every one of us, at least once, took pictures with the slide in - attempted to, I should say.

SCHIRRA — You could see a filter on there if you had it on. For S0368 I blew two of those.

CUNNINGHAM — Stop it a minute. I don't think we can...

SCHIRRA — I recommend - we haven't really brought this up till right now - that we get this forward looking...

CUNNINGHAM — It's called a prism viewfinder.

SCHIRRA — Yes, that's a stock Hasselblad item for precise photography of the LM, of lunar landmarks, of earth landmarks. You can look right through it; you can tell then whether you have the window cutting out your picture or not, as well; and it's real good.

CUNNINGHAM — Also, you don't get a ring sight then if you look right through the lens.

SCHIRRA — We lost the ring sight one time, and all of a sudden, it came cruising by - "Ah, there it is."

CUNNINGHAM — Getting back to the films...

SCHIRRA — You said one other thing; I'd like to correct you. Walt is not a fan of the ring sight; I am. I would rather correct it. That's an opinion. I feel the ring sight is required for a precise picture of a precise area.

CUNNINGHAM — We did use it sometimes.

SCHIRRA — Yes, I know, but you inferred that it wasn't a requirement; I think it is.

CUNNINGHAM — I don't mean to imply that you shouldn't fly the ring sight because I used it lots of times. For example, I used it on the S-IVB picture; I used it in cases where I felt that I had to be more precise, where I had a narrower field to take a picture of...

SCHIRRA — If you were going over the Cape and you wanted the Cape and not just Florida in general, you would know that you could get Florida in general, but to get the Cape in the middle of the picture, you would have to use the ring sight.

CUNNINGHAM — Yes. There's one other thing to add to this. In my training with the Hasselblad over the last couple of years down here for example, I did it both with and without the ring sight, and I concentrated when I didn't have the ring sight. I'd take a whole roll of pictures and come back and find out that I was aiming the camera always a little low. I corrected it to the point that when I took my pictures without a ring sight, I was being able to center the thing pretty good. Now that's merely a personal preference, and I think the ring sight is a good thing to have; I really do. I would never recommend that you don't have the ring sight along.

SCHIRRA — I would dispense with the ring sight and go through the prism reflex. The real reason there is that you are always worried about spacecraft structure knocking out some of your picture, and with this, you don't. You know what you're looking at.

CUNNINGHAM — Yes, I definitely felt that, too. When we have taken the 16mm pictures, you got the camera sitting up there, and it's trying to look down the X-axis, and you always have a little bit of a problem with that camera getting a little...

SCHIRRA — One of my problems on that stripping: I guess I was the one who really got the multispectral stripping, and it turned out that way because he unfortunately had the slider in. When we came across South America, we had a long strip of this with the red filter on, and the object was to overlap, so I stripped with the Hasselblad, and I couldn't remember every time what I was looking at. With the sighting on the top of the camera trying to pick the same target and move the target enough so I would overlap it, there's a lot of pictures. If you could look through the lens, you would know that you weren't goofing it.

CUNNINGHAM — Yes, I agree.

SCHIRRA — This is going to be true with that four-camera system in the event you should have a sight like a tube sight, not just a little ring sight.

CUNNINGHAM — On the various kinds of film on board, I don't think we can overstate the fact that pairing mixed-up film loads does create operational problems. We always run the risk of having the kind of interchanges of filters and filter factors, ASA numbers and backs, and it's not insurmountable, but it does create bookkeeping problems.

SCHIRRA — You know that green strip up there? That was the most fun we had in the flight with pictures. Walt was on the right with the movie cameras stripping; Donn was doing landmarks; I was on the left with multispec with southwest US, and I had the red filter, green filter, and each one had a different f stop, and we just did what it said on the back. We didn't have time for spot meters for stills. One of the things we've talked about since the flight is that we have color film, have some kind of color on the back so you know it's color. For the black and white, have the back black, and you know it's black and white.

CUNNINGHAM — While we are talking about those backs, they had a piece of tape on it to write what was taken, et cetera. The tape that was there was not very compatible with the zero g pens that we had. It was very difficult to write on them, and I think we ought to have something a little better than that to write on.

SCHIRRA — In the old days, Deke, we had a - I know it was plastic, but it wasn't - I gathered it didn't pass the fire board. I remember it was that rubbed fuzzy plastic, and you could write on it with pencil. We used pencils, but ink would go on it as well. The tape was very hard to write on; and we - of course, in the old days, we wrote with the pentel, and it would go on. But the ball point doesn't hit that fiber; that was the problem.

CUNNINGHAM — Moving on to the pictures themselves: we took many, many pictures, probably on the order of 115 or 120 pictures on the S0368, and 400 plus on the S0121. During that time, there was an attempt to make, on several occasions, the same area with both kinds of film as a comparison, and I was thinking primarily of subjective evaluation of looking at the two, at which really looks like the nicer picture. I also feel that during that time, we probably accidentally got some comparisons, too, in certain areas, such as up around the Red Sea where we had S0368 early in the flight, and later on maybe taken the same kind of area with S0121.

SCHIRRA — You have a point there. It's something I brought up. If you look at our board up there, you see the strip on southwest US, and the strip coming down through Africa; that was with multispectral stuff. That was asked for because of 502's pictures. That was one damned rev that 502 made; we made all these revs, we could do the same thing over again each pass because we hit that same pass in Africa every 24 hours. This meant that we could go over it one day with 368, which is the way the protocol should have been; another day with 121; and another day with black and white Panatomic-X. That's the way it should be done, rather than have us try to pick up a whole shaft that another flight had.

CUNNINGHAM — That is why I wanted to go to Panatomic-X that last day for some of those ground pictures, because we had enough information on board to make the same kind of comparisons as they were shooting for on those specific spots. Those specific spots, incidentally, were not easy to hit. I happened to notice the pass that I blew over Africa; I happened to notice that we were going to go right down it. Nobody had told us we were; in fact, I noticed, before the flight, I was going to say, "Well, it would be very fortunate if we happen to make that pass."

SCHIRRA — We didn't think we'd have a chance at those; just remote odds. The orbital map on board went to worms because it was a thirty-two and a half inclination. We were at 30; the modes went all cockeyed, all over the place. We just started pulling up program 21 and all that stuff, and finally faked it, but later in the mission, the last day, we asked for updates, and for something like that, I think we probably pushed them off a little too hard; they were turned off by us. They might have said, "This next pass, if you are in position, is ideal for DTO block" that's all; they don't have to give you anything more. That's not pushing; that's just saying.

CUNNINGHAM — Another thing that some of this photography suffered from, was the intent from the beginning, that we use a minimum of RCS fuel. On a couple of different occasions, we managed to use a small amount of RCS fuel. Wally would be able to plan ahead a half a rev or so and pulse it in - half way around the world - then you could end up looking down, and with four windows for photography, there was a pretty good chance you could get a picture of the area.

3.3.3 S005. S006 Photography

CUNNINGHAM — There's no question about it - we could have gotten more pictures had we not been constrained on fuel. Going back to the actual hardware itself, there's a problem with the Hasselblad sticking up, and we found dry lube in it, for one thing, and we think that maybe the trigger was a little bit bent. Wally worked with it for some time. This all happened about the third day, and it looked like we were going to have the Hasselblad out and not get any more pictures because it was - we were waiting sometimes a couple of minutes between shots before everything would recycle back. We used the nose cream to lubricate a couple of the joints; Wally bent the trigger a little straighter, and I think that was really the key, Wally.

SCHIRRA — Yes. The little rod that comes through into the magazine - that little flat rod in the back.

CUNNINGHAM — We had very little trouble the rest of the way.

SCHIRRA — Yes, all of a sudden it started working like a dream from then on.

CUNNINGHAM — The other thing about the packs is that the people that stow those things very carefully stowed every single camera pack with the slider end out. You know, down in the blocks?

SCHIRRA — You're worried about fogging the frame is what he's getting at.

CUNNINGHAM — Yes. When I restowed them I very carefully stowed them all back again. But it should be a standard procedure when you stow those things to make it foolproof for the guy in a hurry, that he doesn't reach down there and end up pulling on the slider to try to pull it out… the other. And you also ought to…

CUNNINGHAM — The last one's got a hot frame. Another comment on those backs: well, let me finish up with this stowing these with the slider end in. There also ought to be a piece of tape to write on that's on the end that would be out; in that case, you could see that it had an X on it. The tape is on the side that's hidden, and in order to see if you had a used pack stowed, you had to pull the pack out. It's a small item, but it should be taken care of. The other thing on those packs is that you don't know when you're through, to the last frame. The one with 165 frames on it, the large pack, Donn took another ten pictures past it and finally called the ground and asked about it. It was reading a hundred and…

SCHIRRA — Tell you why, you don't feel torque. On a ground camera you feel the film go on the spool, and it goes into the used side. Here, you can just feel the same all the time. There's no mass or inertia. It's subtle enough on the ground; you can feel it; you can't in flight. The movie camera - you can hear the magazine quit as the load comes off the motor, and it goes ticka- ticka-ticka.

CUNNINGHAM — It should have either a definite stop on the thing, or else we should…

SCHIRRA — Have a flag come up. And you also ought to mention Dean Edmonds wasn't aware of the fact that we were going to tape those slide backs. There's a hot frame behind that slide. I'll tell you what the Hasselblad does. Very simply, in the magazine, they have a little window that shows you when you wind, and if you don't wind, it stays red… that's how you know you're out of film, because you don't pop the magazine anymore.

EISELE — Another thing that we really ought to bring out here is that we were film constrained on our S005 and S006. We ended up - sure we shot rather freely at the early part of the flight as compared to the latter part of the flight, but for the last 4 days, we started taking film counts and cutting back on what we were taking.

SCHIRRA — Just like a survival mode, you start budgeting.

CUNNINGHAM — I was going to bring in that there were several items on there that we felt like we had so much that we would rather have had a couple of film packs. We had the rotation hand controller pack, at which I wasted something. We had extra mirrors sitting on my side; at one time, they were intended to look down the X-axis for some reason, but you could look down the X-axis anyway, without the mirrors. We had the fecal canisters scar weight left in. There were various items that were carried on board that we would have traded for just one more pack.

SCHIRRA — We could have thrown away about 15 pounds in there. That's all you needed really.

CUNNINGHAM — But at any rate, we felt very strongly that since this flight was about the last one in which we probably would have the freedom to be drifting and taking pictures of the earth, a couple more packs would have been fabulous.

SCHIRRA — We got hung up on that.

CUNNINGHAM — Donn went through a night pass when he went all the way down the coast of New Guinea; we were on our film saving phase at that time, and it wasn't one of those areas that was blocked out on the map.

SCHIRRA — If we took the pictures, they would have wanted more.

CUNNINGHAM — So he didn't take it, and we never got back to take it again. Wally brought out a good point about that map. Seems like the areas that are outlined to take more pictures are just that, the ones they already have some pictures of. I guess I wasn't as strong an advocate of this until I flew with you, Wally, but any pictures, any good interface land, water, coastlines, interesting geology inland, anything...

SCHIRRA — If it gets our interest, take a picture; that's the point.

CUNNINGHAM — That's right. I guess we probably could have covered the flight adequately with two more packs.

SCHIRRA — Color packs, 121 or 368.

CUNNINGHAM — The other thing is that we haven't seen the 121 and 368 and all that yet, so maybe the 121 turns out nice pictures; we really don't know, but we have taken comparisons. We also think that everybody ought to look through the films and compare, take a look at all the areas we took with the 121 and several areas we took with the Panatomic-X and see if they can't do some of the multispectral stuff with that. Another thing we ought to make a note of is that since we had the Panatomic-X and had poor likelihood of going over the required multispectral areas and/or getting enough fuel to orient to tape multispectral discrete spots, we suggested and started using the Panatomic-X with the red filter for cloud cover. Essentially, for the first part of the flight, we didn't concern ourselves too much with cloud pictures. We took several interesting ones that Wally had spotted, or we took discrete pictures like of hurricane Gladys...

SCHIRRA — I would like to bring this up, a real surprise. We saw hurricane Gladys, but the big surprise to me was the cyclonic effect on top of the thunderstorms. I never even saw it before in the earlier flights, and no one else has reported it, but particularly on our South American runs, every thunderhead had a reverse coriolis effect which you'd expect... and typical sea shell coriolis vortex, and it was brought to my attention from having looked at Gladys and then here that the thunderstorms all had it, and it was wild because we had a whole string of them coming down across the A of Brazil up there on that map. I wanted to take pictures of it; I took just a couple, but if I had really been going at it and been more prepared for it, I could have taken a lot of them. I'm sure we will see it, and it's going to shake up the meteorologists.

Then I saw it in the northern hemisphere after I was prepared to look for it. I never even heard of it before; I don't think you had either, and it really surprised me, but that's why you need spot meters. Almost all our pictures were with spot meters (that's why you need a large selection of film), but on the same ASA so you don't blow your spot meter setting, so you just set it. That same problem came up, and while I sat there working like a madman to find a sixty-four, the spot meter was wrong; it had fifty and then two increments to one hundred.

CUNNINGHAM — I know, and it drives me bats every time. I always sit back and look at that log scale and say now if I'm going up, the numbers get closer together. Does that mean I stay closer to 50 or closer to the next number? I go through that every single time.

SCHIRRA — Yes, the thousands bug me. I said years ago, put a little mark on there for 64, a little mark on there for a thousand where you have the spot meter calibrated.

CUNNINGHAM — That's a good recommendation. We ought to have that; we ought to have a mark on there for each ASA that you've got on board.

SCHIRRA — Forget the other numbers; they're academic.

EISELE — That's right.

SCHIRRA — And for gods sake give us back a depth of field; we know what that is. Give us the exposure index number so we can flick around and play the game. You saw my pictures at Indianapolis; not a one of them was a goof; they're all exquisite because I use a light meter, and I use reflex, and I use exposure variable and plain depth of field.

CUNNINGHAM — We got a lot of good work together. When Wally and I were both awake, for example, we were always involved in one guy taking the exposure readings, the other guy taking the picture.

SCHIRRA — That is why we want them to call them the Apollo 7 crew pictures because everybody was involved. It was either mark planning and attitude way back in China for South America or spot meters. The camera was back and forth, and I'd rather not go through and research the thing on who took it other than for the rendezvous.

CUNNINGHAM — Yes, we told them that everything except the rendezvous or the S-IVB pictures were...

SCHIRRA — ...group pictures.

CUNNINGHAM — If possible, Deke, I think we'd like to see all three names on them. They all go out - you know, NASA has that stamp on the back. We think we covered the world pretty well, and it was only because Donn was getting areas that we weren't; we were planning ahead, and I'll tell you, I was glad to hear some of those pictures turned out good because we really put effort into those.

SCHIRRA — When the camera jammed, we didn't know whether it was working right, you know, as far as shutters and all that stuff.

CUNNINGHAM — Also, we made a great effort to be geographers.

SCHIRRA — We'd call up the names of places.

CUNNINGHAM — We had a good time. After about 4 or 5 days, Donn finally asked us how we knew where in the hell we were.

SCHIRRA — Yes, when I described a city in South America, he said "How the hell did you know I was down there?"

CUNNINGHAM — I've been interested in geography for a long time, so we were sitting there discussing historical locations, you know, just like I took that picture of the upper Nile. I took the picture of the upper Nile because I had one art appreciation course at college.

SCHIRRA — On some of the cloud shots that were intriguing, I think the experimenters like Ken Maynard should realize that we had gone through enough education in meteorology to realize an interesting cloud formation much like this cyclonic effect which is a new thing, and we're going to be piqued by it, and we don't have to be told to shoot it. There's no reason to have that briefing about what to take pictures of. Those blocks on that and the blocks on our map are sufficient; those are interest areas. I don't think you even need that unless, for example, you come over a certain area where there's a landmark, and we don't have a photograph of it; that should be brought out if it's a lunar Apollo landmark. We ended up doing that on some occasions. We took pictures of landmarks that didn't have photographs. One landmark Walt was trying to mark on was wrong. We took a picture of it; there was a bridge across where there was supposed to be a channel.

CUNNINGHAM — Everybody was looking for it.

SCHIRRA — Donn and I were looking out the windows - I said, "That can't be it; it's a solid line." It was; they put a bridge in in the last 3 months. So we took a picture and that landmark is now updated. That's the kind of stuff that photographs are going to help us on. That briefing we had that late evening really was a waste of time. I think the crew, if they're interested - and they all are; you see guys carrying cameras all the time - are interested in photography, they know about weather; they know about geography; and if you have quiet time, you're going to take those pictures.

CUNNINGHAM — The only possible thing you might have on there, really, I think if you see a good picture, take it. If there are some areas that are saturated, you might...

4.0 RE-ENTRY

4.1 CM/SM Separation

EISELE — It really looked funny out that hatch window because we were to do a roll. I've seen these rolls, and in fact, it was mostly yaw from my reference. It looked like the whole thing was catty wampus. It looked like it was yawing out of plane or something. The first time it rolled I thought, "What's it doing?" Well I felt kind of funny. I sat over there saying "Look at that fireball!" Didn't you see it?

CUNNINGHAM — I could see a nice vortex down there.

EISELE — Oh, I couldn't see that.

CUNNINGHAM — Oh yes. Looking right out the window.

EISELE — All I could see was a streamer going past the windows. A... streamer, right?

CUNNINGHAM — No, it was a nice vortex and it lasted a lot longer than I expected. It got pink earlier than I expected it, too. Very early.

EISELE — Wally, wasn't it about 25 feet? Just a little fast for a burn like that.

SCHIRRA — I couldn't see it.

EISELE — And another thing. The whole re-entry was kind of an up-phase I felt. A lot longer than the simulator. It went all the way down to like 65 or 50 000 ft. I felt like things were really going on. The spacecraft was flying itself like mad back and forth.

REP — In other words, you could feel it.

EISELE — I don't know when it ever really quit being red or out.

REP — Orangey red? Orangey red, yes.

SCHIRRA — Orangey red, yes.

EISELE — I don't know either; I didn't look at it too much because I was watching the screen. And you know one thing I saw, and I guess I mentioned it. I think that I'm sure it was the service module. I don't know what else it would be...

CUNNINGHAM — Oh yes, out that window, even though it was bright inside and dark outside, you could see this whirl of orange lights going around, and I don't know - apparently, after we separated, I think the back was 45 out of plane. Wally must have been rolling and yawing back at the same time. That's the only way I can figure that that window would ever get around to where I could see that thing. But I swear I saw it going by the window.

SCHIRRA — You probably did.

EISELE — I mean quite a ways up back.

REP — The service module?

SCHIRRA — I was planning on looking for it.

CUNNINGHAM — Well, the first thing that was anything different than regular timeline was on the EMS de-orbit test. They gave you a NO-GO.

(Everyone talking)

4.2 Reentry Parameters

SCHIRRA — That was a NO-GO, and the reason for that is and it's not data that can be supported. The...

CUNNINGHAM — Range zero. It failed to test.

EISELE — Well, the range zero...

SCHIRRA — Yes, I'm trying to get you the - scroll is the word I'm searching for - the scroll had plus or minus point 2 feet per second, and I had minus or plus.

CUNNINGHAM — Minus.

SCHIRRA — ...minus 2.2 feet per second for big - spread.

CUNNINGHAM — You mean the counter and not the scroll. The scroll gives you a number, which is .2 feet per second.

REP — In the range zero position.

EISELE — Oh yes, in the range zero position, we had a minus 2.2.

SCHIRRA — And as a matter of fact, it was as we all saw, the darned thing wasn't working on the flight.

EISELE — Just like the simulator.

SCHIRRA — Yes. (Laughter)

EISELE — It may mean that there was something wrong with that - I just wondered.

SCHIRRA — Well obviously that must be it. Those guys might have to use it. It's obvious that that thing failed.

EISELE — That's right, it really failed.

SCHIRRA — We've got to get that on an OPEN.

CUNNINGHAM — It's a fact.

SCHIRRA — We've got to get more of the details. And as soon as we set up do you remember I said it's a NO-GO?

CUNNINGHAM — That's right, I've got it written down a NO-GO.

SCHIRRA — It means to me that we have an OPEN for the next mission. Yes...

(Garbled conversation)

CUNNINGHAM — Yes, that's right. The other problem, you know, that's going to come up, they are going to say, "well, are you in essence a NO-GO before lifting off?" But I think we should treat this both crew and otherwise, as maybe a separate anomaly. I don't know if it is a separate thing or not. Boy that scroll - I gave up watching it because it was so bad. I saw...

REP — I think that's the same kind of thing that's happened to it before.

EISELE — I saw minus 300 miles or something like that. The scroll went off into the next blank, into the next... scroll. It was up around 29 000 feet the last time... It should have been my second time around. I'd been all the way through once. I went through one scroll, through two test patterns, and the next scroll...

SCHIRRA — It was a dismal failure.

CUNNINGHAM — Yes.

SCHIRRA — Which is good in the sense that it vindicated our judgement prior to the next mission. But of course, that's the big one.

CUNNINGHAM — There's a minor anomaly that I mentioned over the air with the DELTA V counter. You set the DELTA V counter.

SCHIRRA — Okay. I saw the same ninety thousandths on it when I tried to get the test 1 position; it did it four times.

CUNNINGHAM — I'm glad you mentioned the same manner of problem. I don't think it was covered any place else.

SCHIRRA — I did; I wrote it up in the log. Okay.

CUNNINGHAM — Okay. I don't understand TM. I do want to make note of the fact that I went to test 1 for re-entry. I got ninety thousandths about three times; I finally cycled back so I could go into zero. Why it went ninety thousandths, that I don't know. That's new to me.

SCHIRRA — I don't know.

CUNNINGHAM — Of course, it was shortly before lift off.

EISELE — Well, the thing that scared me was the time it came up spontaneously; there was no reading on the panel...

REP — I have it all written up in the log.

CUNNINGHAM — Yes. This was the new ninety thousandths.

EISELE — That was the other day, anyhow on the EMS for the tail off? 19-8.

SCHIRRA — That's for 19-7.

EISELE — True. Yes, and it clicked one over for you. But wait, in 38 seconds it'll clock up. Right is three, but anyway - the problem I mentioned over the loop was, someplace there we have to close the gap. The difference between the computer's DELTA-V and the DELTA-V that was set does not equal what they gave us on the entry up date as the DELTA-V at tail off.

SCHIRRA — We asked that, and that's an open question that they'll have to answer for.

EISELE — It was awful close, though. It came out 19...

CUNNINGHAM — Yes, but a conservation rejection...

EISELE — But that was when we burned off late, it was very small, about 1 foot in X.

(Everyone talking)

SCHIRRA — I thought two in g, and one in X.

EISELE — I was amazed I got three ones for the error. I couldn't believe it. One third...

CUNNINGHAM — There's one thing about it, you see, on this DELTA V tail off, I was told to tape an update for the chart using 19 feet per second...

SCHIRRA — I understand that. We have that in real time, too.

REP — Oh, you were talking with reference to your charts?

EISELE — Yes. Walt made that point clear before retro and the DELTA-Vc was what it was supposed to be.

SCHIRRA — Yes.

REP — Okay. That's a good point. The retro burn, I'd say, was just about a perfect getaway.

EISELE — How about covering the - I'd like to mention things that we didn't do per checklist of our configuration.

REP — Did not do?

EISELE — Yes. We left the suit return air valve open because we had the suits open.

CUNNINGHAM — Correct.

REP — Oh, yes.

EISELE — The emergency cabin pressure valve we left on instead of off.

SCHIRRA — Right.

EISELE — And we had the direct O2 which I did not play with later.

EISELE — Right. And we ought to - we might mention the configuration we did have with the towels - towel bags folded.

REP — Okay. Let's go over that. That's very good.

EISELE — I think we ought to cover the full details of how we were set up for the landing.

SCHIRRA — Well, let's lay that on the - Walt's idea of putting the food bags on the headrests worked out perfectly for all of us; we taped them on. We should have photos of that to document that configuration.

EISELE — They kept getting pretty...

SCHIRRA — One of two towels in our towel bag and fit those underneath our necks and by our Adam's apple.

EISELE — I guess we tried to figure out every way we could turn our neck or head with those helmets off, and the only thing we could see was perhaps banging our chin on the front of the neck ring. We built these towel things and laid the course...

SCHIRRA — And vindicate my decision; it was a group decision.

CUNNINGHAM — That's right.

SCHIRRA — ...coming in without a helmet.

CUNNINGHAM — The thing that was exciting was - we took care of...

EISELE — We didn't discuss this over the air because it is too big a magilla to discuss. It is the pains that we did take this morning to check out: we put the suits on, we tried the helmets on, and we strapped all the way down.

CUNNINGHAM — We had more head clearance than we can afford to have.

EISELE — That's right. We found out we could possibly get the helmets off, possibly get our nose cleared, but you would never be able to get the helmet back on; you'd have to stow it and have straps all over you. Okay, I'll say one thing, speaking of crew equipment related things: those couch foot pans were a great disappointment to me because North American type guys sort of promised that they would fix those latches on the lids, and they never did. You latched my one side. Yours latched on one side, I think yours latched on one side, and mine did initially...

SCHIRRA — But then your foot got caught in it.

EISELE — Well, the dog-bone got caught down when I went to the 96 degree position, so Walt got out of his, and we got mine squared away. After that, somehow, the foot band was no longer locked.

CUNNINGHAM — Give us the first problem you had though, Donn. The first problem you had was it didn't lock down; it kept folding. Could we go back to one more step?

SCHIRRA — We changed the foot pans because we were worried about a land landing. Now, all of a sudden, in real time in flight, a water landing is the crisis.

CUNNINGHAM — That's right.

SCHIRRA — That's why I'm left holding the bag and, I just don't like that.

CUNNINGHAM — Well, I tell you - I think we all agree - mission rules were written which indicated...

SCHIRRA — Were violated...

EISELE — Yes. Which under certain cases, you would make a re-entry unsuited and then we end up - well, we did put the suits on; we did try the foot pans, and let's say we did have some problems. Now you locked up on one side.

SCHIRRA — I fixed that. I pulled the pan...

CUNNINGHAM — Would your pan bend with your ankle?

SCHIRRA — I couldn't tell.

EISELE — No, I fixed his so that he had one pin in but not the other, and initially I reached down and fixed mine, but he couldn't wait.

SCHIRRA — He couldn't get to the outboard one on my left foot.

EISELE — But the point is, none of the three of them latched in completely the way they should have; mine was - had neither latch in, and it was just flopping around on reentry.

CUNNINGHAM — Right.

SCHIRRA — The real problem that I see is they were added to the spacecraft so late we didn't have a chance to really fully evaluate those things in the spacecraft. We had one brief visit down there; I'm sure we could have asked for more. Like any other thing, you are pushed to the limit to get ready, and we didn't really psyche out these foot pans as we have in the past.

CUNNINGHAM — We uncovered this problem when those foot pans came back from Downey after the fuel restraint mod, and we put them in the simulator, but they weren't fixed. Donn had two problems; one is if it wouldn't lock up the foldable mechanism, he got down, got it locked up. Then he couldn't get his left foot out. He had to readjust - in order to get the dog-bone out, he had to get his left foot out. He couldn't get his left foot unlocked.

SCHIRRA — He technically couldn't get his foot out?

CUNNINGHAM — That's right. So that's when I got unstrapped. This was after we all were supposed to be strapped in.

SCHIRRA — T-32 minutes.

CUNNINGHAM — That's right: T-32 minutes.

SCHIRRA — Right about, right close to retro.

CUNNINGHAM — I got unstrapped, and I had to really tug his feet; I tugged his heel and got it out.

SCHIRRA — I was almost ready to cancel that retro.

CUNNINGHAM — I gave it thought, but I figured I could get back in.

SCHIRRA — I was watching for that, and you made it. I was going to give it another 5 minutes and then I was going to cancel that retro. I didn't tell you that until just now; I admit.

CUNNINGHAM — I was too. We were off our time line.

SCHIRRA — Everything was good but the damn couches with the new mod were not right.

CUNNINGHAM — Well, after I did get Donn's feet loose, we did get the dog-bone unfastened; we did get strapped in - I think we ought to mention that when we were fat, the couches worked so much easier than I had even anticipated in zero g, very easy handling.

SCHIRRA — Off nominal will blow you right out of the seat.

CUNNINGHAM — Right. And as soon as Donn got strapped in again his foot pan did not lock down.

SCHIRRA — He was stuck with a high risk, and yet here we were putting on our suits for a system that wasn't even going to wear a helmet.

CUNNINGHAM — Well, my foot pan apparently was the only one that held. I mean it was firm; it wouldn't go like this.

SCHIRRA — Mine held firm; I can say that.

CUNNINGHAM — Yours were firm, but only one side was locked up; I think yours was the same way.

EISELE — I could slide my feet in and out.

CUNNINGHAM — When mine were in tight, I kicked my boots off.

EISELE — The point is that it was a late mod, and they didn't fix it the way they should have in the flight check.

SCHIRRA — We judged that you were in good shape for knee clearance in the center couch. If it had been Walt or myself, I'm sure we would have scrubbed the retro. But you mentioned the fact that you felt good, that you were safe, that your legs were - it was a high risk, just like that elevator down, like everything else. We went way out on a limb on everything on this flight.

EISELE — I'm glad we did it that way. It worked out fine.

SCHIRRA — But we lucked out on these high risk areas. Land landing for take off, no doubt; elevator out of commission.

EISELE — There's something else I don't mind stressing right here. Uppermost in my mind in that whole re-entry as far as risk, and as far as I thought my neck was hanging out, was that whole business they told us about a land landing.

SCHIRRA — Oh, prior to lift off?

EISELE — No, excuse me. I don't mean land landing; I mean the hard landing on the water.

SCHIRRA — The water landing was predominant on our minds all the way through the last day.

EISELE — That's right. From the time they started giving us that - the problems with water landing, I kind of quit worrying about the chutes opening and the drogues opening.

SCHIRRA — Well, the oddest thing - and I can recall this very strongly in Mercury and in Gemini - we were so upset about the chutes coming out and then POW! No problem. The chutes came out just great; I got chutes; now I really got to worry.

EISELE — That's kind of what I felt, too.

SCHIRRA — That is absolutely ridiculous to put a crew in that kind of frame of mind, ridiculous. I think we really ought to go hit it - get on record with the fact that we were not recklessly coming in with our helmets off. We considered all the possibilities; we picked all the precautions we thought were reasonably good, and as a matter of fact all three of us felt damn secure. I really felt like I was every bit as secure, in fact, I felt more secure than I would have with the helmet with my head possibly bouncing around, as opposed to 8g landing.

REP — You would have had your head secure.

CUNNINGHAM — That's right, I had my head secure with a COMM carrier squeezed between my two-day-old meals sitting there, and I think that the worst possible configuration we could have been in for the landing would be with the helmet unfastened on our head.

SCHIRRA — At least as described to us.

CUNNINGHAM — That's right; it is as described to us. As it turns out, that landing was so soft that it wouldn't have made any difference. Now you might want to argue that point.

SCHIRRA — I'll pick that up for you. Our update was that this landing would have twice the severity of a Gemini, which had a little bit more, I might add, than my Mercury, because Mercury had this flotation bag, air bag, underneath it to really soften the blow, and you were in a form-fitted couch. This was the softest landing I've ever had in a vehicle like that. It made Gemini look like I got hit by a barn door before.

CUNNINGHAM — You've ridden through some mighty good P-38 with me that were worse than that.

SCHIRRA — In fact, I've had harder landings on a carrier landing. If you ever watch a guy land in a Demon, for example, his head goes bla-lah-lah lah-lah-lah as he rolls out on the flight deck. It's that bad. I didn't feel any discomfort whatsoever. I had the doctors check me completely.

EISELE — You know, the thing about it is they came in and wanted a good solid whoof, and that's all there was to it. It didn't roll, or twist or do anything.

CUNNINGHAM — It turned over immediately.

EISELE — Except turn over. You know when the doc, or somebody wanted to get an actual time of landing, we were all sitting there.

CUNNINGHAM — Scared to death.

EISELE — Scared to death, hanging onto our shoulder straps, heads tucked in, and just waiting for the worst possible happening.

SCHIRRA — They were just wondering where all the blood and gore would go. I'd like to say that after retro it was just like any other burn, other than the fact we knew we were coming home.

CUNNINGHAM — Yes, you see one SPS burn, you've seen 'em all.

4.4 Attitude
Control Mode

SCHIRRA — Right. We cut the residuals down; one was left, I guess. But I felt from where I was sitting that I wasn't ahead by any means. I was with the time line and had a little slop left in it, but I didn't by any means have what I would call a casual time frame where I could sort of sit back and say, "Okay, let's check out the command module RCS thrusters."

EISELE — I remember very distinctly looking at my watch and saying something. I said, "Is it really retro plus

8 minutes already?" Because it just - hardly anything had happened, and we were already 8 minutes into it.

SCHIRRA — We were just taking our time going through the checklist and making sure we were doing right and verifying.

CUNNINGHAM — Yes, checking it off.

SCHIRRA — I really don't think we have time to do that much of a checklist. You might rush into it and frantically do it.

CUNNINGHAM — The only thing we took time to do was for about a minute you let me tweak the stick just to see how it flew.

SCHIRRA — That was after SEP.

CUNNINGHAM — We had 16 minutes to .05g, and it's a little bit earlier than that for 400 000.

SCHIRRA — Okay. Let me go back now; I'd like to describe that C&SM SEP which is a new newey.

EISELE — Boy, was that a beaut.

CUNNINGHAM — The pyrovoltage just didn't go down.

SCHIRRA — The C&SM SEP?

CUNNINGHAM — No, we did that at 40 minutes, and we weren't in ground contact, and the tape wasn't running, and we had 36.8 volts and 36.8 volts.

SCHIRRA — But we stayed up.

CUNNINGHAM — Yes.

SCHIRRA — You talking about post- SEP?

CUNNINGHAM — No, this is at T minus 40 minutes; we were out of ground contact.

SCHIRRA — Oh, oh, okay.

CUNNINGHAM — We armed the pyro up, and we had 36.8 volts on the bus.

SCHIRRA — Well, when they called back on that, they gave us the GO for it; they never gave us the voltage, did they?

CUNNINGHAM — That's right; they didn't.

SCHIRRA — What's the point, Walt?

CUNNINGHAM — The pyro battery voltage was still up.

SCHIRRA — Yes; right.

CUNNINGHAM — And they didn't have any telemetry on the same time. Maybe they got it later.

SCHIRRA — I thought you meant you were expecting them to be changed.

CUNNINGHAM — No, no.

SCHIRRA — Okay. Let's back up to where I yawed left and you waited until I said, "GO" for attitude which is per standard procedures. Then I said to Donn, "ACCEPT", and that was a real powerful blow.

CUNNINGHAM — It was a POW.

SCHIRRA — Boy, was that a crack. I didn't have any attitude problems, by the way. I was in RATE COMMAND.

CUNNINGHAM — No, I didn't feel any transient.

SCHIRRA — I was still worried about that

CUNNINGHAM — I didn't hear a bunch of jets firing.

SCHIRRA — So, I was willing to expend the energy in RATE COMMAND and have that thing lay in there tight. I just didn't want any problems with it. I know, it was just making these swoosh-woosh woosh wobbles a bit.

CUNNINGHAM — The first thing you said after that was, "Boy, it's a beautiful control system."

SCHIRRA — That's right. It worked just right.

CUNNINGHAM — The point while they were recalculating real time, but we had only 3600 psi.

SCHIRRA — It came up to about 37 or 38 at one time. Remember I said something; it looked like it might warm up. I think it was probably speed loaders you all said were real time.

CUNNINGHAM — Yes.

SCHIRRA — Okay. Then after SEP, of course, you were yawed back to zero degrees and...

CUNNINGHAM — That's about the time I saw that service module whizzing its way through this hatch window.

SCHIRRA — Yes. As I was yawing in and rolling in. So I guess, in fact, I started the roll and then you saw it. Didn't I roll from 180?

EISELE — Yes. You had to roll 180.

SCHIRRA — I'd like to add, too, maybe it's just me, but I definitely was left with confusion about what attitude to be in for a retro roll and for re entry roll. Don't ask me why; I think it was because I didn't have that damn ORDEAL ball working. That's the reason.

REP — That's right, Walt. You see, if we follow the time lapse, as the note I have here, at T minus 12 minutes, it's just a convention, there's no ORDEAL.

SCHIRRA — They ask and what's - Donn saw the program alarm prior to retro as the sextant started roll, roll attitude, and then for re-entry I kept thinking, "Heck, you know something must be wrong." Then I said, "I've gotta roll 180." So that's a real sneaky one that I think the other command pilot should be - or the command pilot should be aware of depending upon how they want to fly. You can really get a circuit play in that roll.

CUNNINGHAM — A little out of sequence, but there was something else that was mentioned here; that difference in the way we spinned it all the time. The first time they came up we said that we were going to have to hit COMMAND RESET to get our tapes in the high bit rate data.

SCHIRRA — Typical of the range. We have new rules.

CUNNINGHAM — That's right.

SCHIRRA — They seem to make up rules as they go along.

CUNNINGHAM — Well, you try not to have that happen, but I had a contingency entry in here nearly all along that, you know, in case the tape wasn't running I'd go ahead and do that, but I don't think it mattered. Oh, yes, the tape was running. But command - high bit rate, COMMAND RESET, and, incidentally, the tape ran out just prior to landing.

SCHIRRA — ...second over burn, there's a whole new picture to me. I wasn't really ready for it.

CUNNINGHAM — Okay.

SCHIRRA — In that short of notice, but that range was good. Okay. I think my biggest shock was to see those batteries down after SEP. I almost had a heart attack right there on the spot, and I'm glad we didn't have EKG because I would have blown the tracer right off my back.

EISELE — Let me elaborate a little bit on this point, the reason that the main buses were down. I had thrown battery C on as per program, battery C; battery A, B, and C were all on. The state of charge on those batteries was something like 26 volts apiece on A and B, 39 volts on battery C; this was a lot less than we had expected to have at this time. It was less than we would have had by the agreement as to what kind of charging we would do on the battery. And when we SEP'd, we immediately got main bus A, main bus B undervoltage. We were reading about twenty five to twenty five and a half volts. It was the lowest voltage we'd seen on the main buses all the time. The only reason that I had some confidence that we hadn't glicked anything was I had watched it. I just happened to be watching that when we SEP'd, and it creates quite a bit of consternation.

SCHIRRA — Well, it shook me to the core because I was convinced we had a beautiful alignment; we had a beautiful retro burn.

EISELE — We did.

SCHIRRA — Everything was very exquisite, really exquisite; and then this silly thing coming here...

EISELE — That's why I told you that we had everything we had available, that we just had to write it in that way.

SCHIRRA — As a result, Donn rode a long time before he...

EISELE — I was worried about the guidance system and that low voltage.

SCHIRRA — The EMS was bombed out, and we knew that anyway. The only confidence I had...

CUNNINGHAM — The result of inadequate charging during the...

SCHIRRA — Yes, it changed the...

CUNNINGHAM — There are two things there that we have to be fair about in here. It was inadequate charging because they are worried about blowing a battery, which had not been blown with less than five charges on it, and the battery charger did not measure up to snuff.

SCHIRRA — I don't think we can blame the range on that. They were informed, and they didn't want to charge the batteries. I'm sure a lot of people were involved, and we'll probably hear more about this subject.

EISELE — The only reason we charged battery B a second time, I got the impression, was to check the battery charger electrical system.

SCHIRRA — Rather than the battery.

EISELE — That's right. If we had not charged battery B a second time, we would have been even lower.

SCHIRRA — Well, B didn't go up very much, though.

EISELE — Well, C was on both buses then. C shared on both buses, A on A, and B on B.

REP — What kind of amperage amp hours did you have on B at that time?

EISELE — B had 26 and a half after the last charge and A...

SCHIRRA — Was that after the last - that's the number they called up to me one time. You mean they didn't charge it after that?

EISELE — No.

SCHIRRA — You're right.

EISELE — A was 29, and B was 26, and he never charged it after that.

CUNNINGHAM — Battery A at the end of the last burn was something on the order of 25 - my data is gone now and 26 on B.

SCHIRRA — We're going to have a lot of fun finding out where we really landed.

EISELE — We did have a shock on the undervoltage. We continued on from there. This is where we were going very methodically through a checklist, as far as that goes. We ate up the time that surprised us. He went ahead and configured for ring A the way we had normally done it.

SCHIRRA — That's after reentry attitude.

EISELE — That's right.

SCHIRRA — In the ring A pulse, we called out rate high; and, of course, in pulse it didn't bother me. We set up exactly as we'd always done. The only part of it was I had to let Donn fly it, and how beautiful that control system is. It is much better than the simulator. Real nice. We could hear every pulse very clearly.

EISELE — Really clear.

CUNNINGHAM — The controls where you take your pulse were far less in the spacecraft than in the simulator, which made it very easy to...

EISELE — If we could write in whatever our attitude was...

SCHIRRA — I don't think we ought to worry about flying that thing in direct.

EISELE — No. I got very jealous.

SCHIRRA — Beautiful. That spacecraft should go into the Smithsonian. It's beautiful; it deserves it.

CUNNINGHAM — I guess we'll have to go out and give Healey one big plug.

EISELE — Oh, we really will.

CUNNINGHAM — Back tracking just slightly: Since we did burn the residuals out, it turns out that the post retro update was not as necessary as it's been. Every time we've sent it now, we start burning the residuals out. We go with a pre-burn update, which simplifies a lot of problems, and if we always burn the residuals out, we don't have to worry about getting that post burn update. It came pretty close - the post burn update comes awful close to blackout.

SCHIRRA — I caught my fourth channel without you calling it. I don't know whether you noticed it or not.

CUNNINGHAM — Yes, I know; I called it anyway.

SCHIRRA — In reference to the fourth channel, we go into any SPS burn with one roll channel disabled. After the retro burn or any of the rendezvous SPS burns, we started to take out the residuals, and I need that fourth channel. I got it this time, after goofing that last simulation.

<u>4.6 Visual Sighting and Oscillation</u>

CUNNINGHAM — Did we mention that, Donn? Donn does think he saw the service module when we went back in...

EISELE —... back in on the yes.

CUNNINGHAM — I had planned on looking for it. At one time, we even discussed taking pictures of it. I'm glad we didn't even plan on it. I was so busy reading the checklist and putting checks on it that I didn't see a thing out the window.

SCHIRRA — Let's go back to what we did see out the window, which I thought was new.

EISELE — You're talking about...

SCHIRRA — ...pretty spectacular. It was that pink cloud.

EISELE — Yes, wasn't that pretty?

SCHIRRA — It was the most delightful light pink I've never seen in Mercury or Gemini.

EISELE — It was early and high up.

SCHIRRA — Very high, way up, long before I was still in...

EISELE — It was a beautiful pink. In fact, I can't help but think we must have been heating a little.

SCHIRRA — Oh, we were; we had a little energy going for us.

EISELE — Very strange.

REP — Do you think it was off the spacecraft or...

ALL — Oh, yes, yes, it was. It really was.

SCHIRRA —... looking for, and I looked.

CUNNINGHAM — I'll tell you something else that was - It was very high and before you start getting

EISELE — A light pink like a pink sherbert. It was very pastel. It was really a very definite contrast between that and what I saw later. Actually, the impression is that it was something external to the spacecraft, just back around the side...

SCHIRRA — I couldn't believe...

CUNNINGHAM — We were in sunrise right there, and I'm kind of wondering if sunrise might have something to do with it.

SCHIRRA — We were - I never saw the horizon, by the way, ever, on the re-entry.

EISELE — I was a little worried about that.

CUNNINGHAM — I did. I saw it in the hatch window.

SCHIRRA — Did you?

CUNNINGHAM — I remember I made the remark about how well the window marks line up.

SCHIRRA — Of course, we'd made up our minds we were going IFR anyway.

CUNNINGHAM — That's right, and we turned all the lights up. We blocked the sextant star.

SCHIRRA — I think you've got to make up your mind that when you can't go outside, you check if you buy the star sighting.

CUNNINGHAM — I had a little bit more time from here on down to rubberneck. That's when you and Donn are sitting here discussing buying...

SCHIRRA — You said rubberneck. They look out more; I'm busy.

CUNNINGHAM — Well, I was sitting there, and I...

SCHIRRA — Why don't you describe the lighting phenomenon?

CUNNINGHAM — Yes, I was watching a lot out of the window, and I know I called you guys' attention to it one time. There was little, well not very little, sometimes...

SCHIRRA — - It was blobs...

CUNNINGHAM — It was big blobs coming off. I thought it was some of the ablative area breaking away. Looking at the spacecraft, there aren't too many big blobs missing out there. You could definitely see a vortex behind it. I was looking out that window and watching.

SCHIRRA — It was a tube; I saw that.

CUNNINGHAM — It was a tube, and it was twisting.

SCHIRRA — In contrast, in Mercury and Gemini, we had copper beryllium up topside.

CUNNINGHAM — Yes.

SCHIRRA — Were there any green rings?

CUNNINGHAM — No, no green ring at all. And it got lighter as it went back, but I could see the vortex; it was actually twisting up.

SCHIRRA — It was a hot ride to... Well, let's come up to the one that shook the hell out of me. The one that scared the hell out of us was when some thing on my side went Pow!

EISELE — That's right, and when I saw it...

SCHIRRA — Donn said we lost pitch and Walt said "What was that!", and I'm trying like a madman to bring all the thrusters back on the line.

EISELE — We nearly went back to two rings, using everything we could get. But what happened there: we'd been pulsing pretty heavy in pitch and yaw, you see, cycling fairly well...

SCHIRRA — We were rotating, reversing bank.

EISELE — Yes, and the system was fighting all these moments that was going on. All of a sudden, this big hunk of whatever it was went POW. I was looking out the hatch window, and this big hunk of yellow...

SCHIRRA — When I looked out my window, I thought the window - the outer pane of the window had blown out.

EISELE — You must have seen the same thing and all of a sudden. At that time, the thing seemed to stop firing. I said "Good grief, I've blown a pitch thruster."

CUNNINGHAM — Wally had a hard time getting over there. It was just like zap, they're all in.

EISELE — Apparently, what happened is that one or more chunks of the ablator came off rather explosively. I don't know how it happened. They just blew off. At the same time, we were into the atmosphere far enough that we had aerodynamic standing and didn't need the tip because you looked at the way the rate meters were moving. They really weren't going very far at this point. I think that's what happened, and we got faked out.

CUNNINGHAM — Was this before or after we bought the computer?

EISELE — Oh, this was after that.

SCHIRRA — This was after we had reversed back.

CUNNINGHAM — Okay. It was after we bought the computer.

SCHIRRA — Let's go back to buying the computer now, and that was your job. No, I had already written off the EMS. That was a flop. I want to give you a big fat plus for hitting the mark on the philosophy of EMS. That was something I wasn't even ready to do. I was looking at it very disappointed. It just wasn't working right at all.

EISELE — He made a comment to us that you're not allowed on the loop.

SCHIRRA — I would like to have you analyze how you bought the computer, if I may.

EISELE — Well, we were just following our standard rule which said we would not believe the computer to the extent of doing the CMC AUTO until it did something smart with its bank angles. It just took this one forever to deduct and command a bank angle other than zero. I think part of it is that you maneuvered to a 55 degree bank; it started over-anticipating a little early.

SCHIRRA — No, you gave me the .2g, and then I went for it. I didn't go any earlier then that.

EISELE — I think you did.

SCHIRRA — Negative. In fact, I was behind you. Because at that point you said "Is that .2," and I said, "No, 67." You said "Roger," and then I started over. In fact, I didn't come over fast enough; I was real slow.

CUNNINGHAM — Here's the thing that got me about it. I was listening to you...

SCHIRRA — It's supposed to be 20 degrees per second going over there, and I didn't go like that.

CUNNINGHAM — Well, I was listening to your conversation over there, and we were anxious to buy the computer to get the guided reentry.

SCHIRRA — Well, I wanted that.

CUNNINGHAM — Wally was pumping Donn about...

SCHIRRA — Well, I had a good feeling...

CUNNINGHAM — ...is it okay, and Donn was holding off to the last minute. You know the last minute is funny. The last minute seemed like a long time, but it is the same place he always buys a computer, after the downrange area gets down to less than about 10 miles.

EISELE — The downrange area has to go down to about 9 miles before that thing will command the bank angle other than either zero or 55.

CUNNINGHAM — That's right.

SCHIRRA — I'm sitting there saying, "Oh, Donn, please buy it. Well, we have to wait till the downrange area got down there, and all of a sudden...

CUNNINGHAM — I tell you, I think that's in our minds. I was sitting here doing the same thing. We knew that computer was consistently giving us - you know, a hundredth of a degree in both...

SCHIRRA — We saw it in sections - all the way through the mission, every inch of the way. If we had to go that dinky old 55 degree bank for re-entry and go somewhere in the Atlantic - that's all I can give you - I would have cried; I really would.

CUNNINGHAM — When he finally did buy it, I think we bought it at the right time, and it was kind of a nominal time.

SCHIRRA — You notice how he gave it to us? Voom! He flew it right in for us, and she flew. We were watching him like a hawk.

CUNNINGHAM — You know from that time on, I was impressed by the way that really blasted across to the other side.

SCHIRRA — That machine is built to do the 20 degrees per second.

CUNNINGHAM — I know, but boy, I'd look out the window...

SCHIRRA — ...goof this little machine by not rolling fast enough.

EISELE — Yes, Wally flew in a normal, smooth way, I think, but when that thing got in reverse...

SCHIRRA — That thing was wild the way it reversed. It even did one around the bottom which I got a big kick out of. It was smart enough to do that, and I wasn't smart.

EISELE — I didn't even notice it.

SCHIRRA — Yes, it went around the bottom.

CUNNINGHAM — That was late, that was after we had already killed off most of the error. Oh, yes, there was a lot of - it got down there where there was a lot of... It would just go swish, swish, swish. Well, it had to swap sides to take out cross range that it still had...

SCHIRRA — By the way, I want to go on record the leather elbow, pipe smoking boys did very well on this mission. You've got to hand them that, and I retract all my snide remarks except for the fact that gimbal lock still terrorizes me.

CUNNINGHAM — So the next surprise I had was after drogues. We started steaming up.

SCHIRRA — Oh, that's the windows. Yes, the windows occluded due to cloud moisture.

EISELE — Yes. They were cold like a T-38 will steam up...

SCHIRRA — That's right, and then it just started clouding up, and I said "we have an IFR clearance straight in, no delay expected."

CUNNINGHAM — There's one other thing to mention that the guys might be surprised about. There were fumes in that cockpit.

SCHIRRA — Yes.

CUNNINGHAM — I didn't know whether they were ingested fumes from the RCS or whether they were pyros. Donn said they smelled like pyros.

SCHIRRA — No, that wasn't RCS, that was pyro. It was detectable sometime after drogue since we hadn't really brought up the cabin yet. It was after drogues, some time between drogues and mains.

CUNNINGHAM — I think it was also the same kind of area where we...

**4.7 Drogue Chute
Deployment**

SCHIRRA — Let's get back to drogues. By the way, the drogues didn't squirm; I didn't feel this bumpy road stuff that I did in the Mercury and Gemini. Very steady, very solid. You could see the drogues working, but they weren't squirming, a real vibrant ride. I looked and said "gee, it's not doing very much", but the spacecraft was stable on drogue. Very stable.

CUNNINGHAM — Oh, yes. And I will tell you one thing that helped Donn and I, not having been through this before; Wally told us to stand by for the dereefing and that the drogues were really going to be a shock. I really wouldn't have expected the drogues to be a shock, and there wasn't a terrible pulse, but I wouldn't have been braced at all if he hadn't said so.

SCHIRRA — I expected more than we got, frankly.

CUNNINGHAM — And I had one brief flutter in my heart when the cover came off the drogues.

SCHIRRA — No, that was the pilot chute that went out with the apex cover.

CUNNINGHAM — Yes, and it kept right on going. Well, I'll tell you my thought at that time. My thought at that time was "well, we've got another drogue."

4.8 Main Chute Deployment

SCHIRRA — Well, that's not true. What went through my mind was - "okay, we've got to get down to 5000 feet, and the card says 7000, and I've got to start getting RCS logic back on, ELS manual, all that good stuff. So I can fly the... down to 7000 indicated to get the mains out. And all of a sudden click, click, click". I looked at that water, and the chutes went out.

CUNNINGHAM — I'm sitting here helpless over on the right side, and all I could think was, "well, we've still got another drogue," and I remember thinking "gee, that first one failed, that second one might fail too"

SCHIRRA — You know, I've seen movies of the drogue, and yet they didn't look like those movies, and those beautiful mains when they came out...

CUNNINGHAM — Well, in between there, incidentally, the cabin pressure started increasing sooner than the simulator. I think right after drogues I started seeing cabin pressure coming up.

SCHIRRA — You had me go to dump.

EISELE — Well, the thing about going to dump there was that I wanted to get rid of that Delta P across the cabin lower. They'd like to have us go to dump, down about 3500 feet, and I didn't know what we would be doing at 3500 feet. We had gone to dump a lot of times... It's a good idea to get that Delta P out if you can.

SCHIRRA — That Delta P light? Yes, you always put that out, if you can.

EISELE — So anyhow, we've got about 50 seconds between drogues and mains. Many times in the simulator, we've gone to dump because the cabin pressure wasn't increasing, and it seemed like a good place to do it. We went to dump, which did speed up cabin pressurization, and we left it in dump until we closed them below 1000. You know the thing that struck me about both drogues and mains, the reef, and disreef, were that the opening shocks were very mild, more so than I expected. I looked up, and they just quietly opened. There wasn't any delta g at all. We were bracing ourselves. We had discussed the procedures for reentry, incidentally, like grabbing hold and clasping your arms together and holding your shoulder harness. I did that each time Wally had told us to expect a shock, and it turned out that the shock wasn't that bad.

SCHIRRA — Everything was less, which was great. Before I forget, the max reentry g I saw was 3.2. I might shade it to 3.3. That's all.

EISELE — Well, it seemed to drive up to some level like 3 plus and then just hold for a long period of time. Yes, I looked over there a couple of times; it was almost a constant g.

CUNNINGHAM — There was a long period of constant g, and it seemed to me that there was more going on at re-entry, for a longer period of time than we were used to in the simulator. All the way down to 65 000, I felt like there was a lot going on; and in the simulator, I always get the impression that for some period up above 100 000, we're just waiting for 65.

SCHIRRA — I felt we were just with the time line all the way down, maybe on, 30 seconds to a minute and a half ahead but never comfortably ahead where you could sort of sit back, other than the times that the darn...

EISELE — We had about 4 minutes to .05 g with nothing else to do.

SCHIRRA — Now the other thing we always worried about which we simulated failures with was the altimeter. Now that beauty was on! The drogues came out right on the little tick mark which is exactly 24,000.

EISELE — An anomaly showed up here. We did go to dump at 17,000 or some place around there, and it wasn't because the cabin pressure wasn't increasing. It was to take care of any excess Delta P down lower. The cabin pressure did increase, and the mains came out. They were beautiful, but we were in an overcast, and it wasn't the same as looking at it against the blue sky. We were IFR, and we started to fog up inside. At this time, I was sitting there thinking "well, we'll break out at 2000."

SCHIRRA — Wasn't that wild, the way the wind reports changed? Hours before retro, it was CAVU; then it started closing in and closing in; the winds went up; the clouds came up; next thing you know...

CUNNINGHAM — Well, quite frankly, we recovered in weather that I didn't think they recovered in manned spaceflight.

EISELE — Apparently, they do. I think we have a new parachute.

4.9 Communications

CUNNINGHAM — At any rate, I was sitting there expecting to break out of the overcast at 2000 feet; and at 10,000 feet, we went through the checklist items. I turned the VHF A simplex and the beacon ON.

SCHIRRA — You did turn the beacon ON? This is a big problem.

CUNNINGHAM — Yes, I turned them both on. We were transmitting and receiving. Apparently, the beacon was not putting out until they got a cut on it just before landing.

SCHIRRA — Yes.

CUNNINGHAM — Donn made a voice report which apparently wasn't received, incidentally. We went through the normal checklist items, just like it's called out, and they didn't get a beacon until after we had uprighted after landing.

SCHIRRA — No, that was the beacon light, which was on me per checklist. That was why I was confused with you? Air Boss said he could not see the light. I didn't turn them on, and I wouldn't turn it on in daylight, normally. This wasn't really something on my mind, but I did goof on the - we got into stable II and of course I was worried about the fan. Donn was getting kind of queasy.

EISELE — Queasy, hell! I got dog sick after about 5 minutes of that.

4.10 ECS

SCHIRRA — Let's get back to rate of descent. It looked very good. I was timing it. Then I noticed our windows started occluding due to the moisture condensing on the windows, and I just don't know. I don't think I ever called out altitude as often as I did today with you fellows.

CUNNINGHAM — Oh, yes, in fact, this is funny. This is the only real one that I've been on, but we did everything much more thoroughly than we ever have in the simulator.

SCHIRRA — I was terrorized about the landing, so I kept calling at 1000 feet. I wasn't sure 1000 feet was good, so I wanted to be in position myself; and I said "okay, I'm on the sticks," remember?

REP — I might mention that you said the mains came out at 11,000.

SCHIRRA — About 10,500, almost 11,000. We never got that far away. Remember, I never got an altimeter error call up. We'd rehearsed that with Houston, but I never heard it.

CUNNINGHAM — You got an out-of-date setting.

SCHIRRA — I wanted a setting very badly. I wanted a number on which I would deploy the mains. I never heard that number for the recovery area. I should have asked for it, but I think they're supposed to remember that more than I am since they're going to play the role of adviser instead of commander. Whenever the mains did come out, about 10.5M - 10.6M they looked great. I called out altitudes to Donn. He was interested in lock up, and I locked up and kept calling hundreds of feet.

CUNNINGHAM — I heard 600 and 400.

5.0 LANDING AND RECOVERY

SCHIRRA — I called 300, and then I said, "I'm not going to talk any more. I want to hold on."

5.1 Impact on Touchdown

CUNNINGHAM — I turned off the main buses between 600 and 800 feet, so it actually read 100 feet. We were still airborne, and then zero feet - splash. Nice quiet little drop in. We slotted, and immediately we were stable II.

EISELE — The chute took us; I'm sure we landed downwind rather than upwind of the chute. The chutes went right over us and flipped us into stable II. We went through our normal egress procedures.

5.2 Postlanding Checklist

CUNNINGHAM — I was surprised at how fast we got the suits off.

SCHIRRA — That was great.

CUNNINGHAM — You had your two switches. I hit the circuit breakers, and they were off immediately, but we were already stable II.

SCHIRRA — When I looked out my window, I could see the chutes sinking.

EISELE — I didn't notice it till later. They were underneath us.

SCHIRRA — I could see the dye marker coming out. I was very surprised because I hadn't thrown the switch, but there was the dye marker.

EISELE — Well, they explained to us later here that apparently the dye marker leaked a little bit.

CUNNINGHAM — Well, I don't know that it should leak, but I guess it did.

EISELE — Well, it's still undeployed on the upper deck.

CUNNINGHAM — I was a little concerned about the swimmers - deploying. It was sure hell about that. I didn't want to get them all green.

SCHIRRA — So then in stable II, we elected to light off the compressors for the prefloat bags, so we kind of cluttered up on wave action, and it didn't work. But we ought to mention that we were in stable II and went through our post landing checklist. We knew there was a 10 minute cooling period in stable II. Donn started feeling kind of bad at about...

EISELE — I wish I hadn't thrown up...

SCHIRRA — Four minutes, and I wish he had said he was feeling bad, but you know what he said? He said "any of you guys feeling sick?"

EISELE — I was looking for company.

CUNNINGHAM — I don't know if we mentioned it earlier; I don't think the Range knew it, but Donn and I at least had both taken nausea pills.

EISELE — Marzine is what it was. Wally did not, being an old salt.

SCHIRRA — What's that again?

CUNNINGHAM — I felt like I was carrying it fairly good, but I was not all that confident that I wouldn't get sick if we had not, you know, stayed in the spacecraft a little bit longer.

SCHIRRA — I didn't think that Marzine was very effective.

CUNNINGHAM — In fact, Donn was telling me...

EISELE — That was what I tasted when I was gagging; it was the bitter taste of the Marzine pill coming back up.

5.4 Spacecraft Status   SCHIRRA — We had to use the flotation bag to bring us up. We tried to press the circuit breakers and brought them all on.

CUNNINGHAM — The post flight bus circuit breakers and the post landing circuit breakers. I tried to find the suit decompression circuit breakers.

SCHIRRA — What surprised us was that we did not see the flotation bag as we did in the water egress Training in both the Gulf and in the tank. Incidentally, the cooling period was supposed to be in 10 minutes, and we were timing it out. Donn had gotten out of the couch; he really looked like he was suffering. At 8 minutes, we turned on the compressors and started uprighting. We figured it was a bit of hedge in there.

EISELE — I felt very green, but not with envy.

SCHIRRA — He looked white. He was carrying on admirably. I know he pulled the pyro circuit breakers down there when I thought he was going to die, but instead he was going to throw up.

EISELE — My last heroic effort before I could finally pull those circuit breakers.

CUNNINGHAM — When he got it all over himself, he was a scientist then. When Donn finally gave up and admitted he was going to get sick, you should have seen the wrestling we did around there to try and get him a bag in a hurry.

SCHIRRA — We wanted to help because we all realized if one guy gets sick, the other guys probably will. We had some very great sound effects. I wished you could have recorded those.

CUNNINGHAM — Oh, yes.

EISELE — Oh, no!

CUNNINGHAM — While we were in stable II, I thought that we had contact; recovery I spotted us, and then recovery 3 was over there in a hurry.

SCHIRRA — No.

CUNNINGHAM — You were talking to him, I think.

SCHIRRA — No, I wasn't talking in stable II.

CUNNINGHAM — I heard you tell somebody we were in stable II. We were all ready in contact, I think.

SCHIRRA — You might think that I did, but I doubt that anybody heard me. There is no way. My window wasn't clear. The window was fogged.

EISELE — The windows were filling with water, and he was saying shipping water, which is very bad form.

SCHIRRA — When I say shipping, you interpret as meaning coming inside the spacecraft.

EISELE — That's what shipping means.

SCHIRRA — I meant shipping it into the interspace between the windows.

CUNNINGHAM — There are two panes between us and the water.

SCHIRRA — I don't believe the spacecraft took on any water.

CUNNINGHAM — No.

SCHIRRA — Okay. Let's make that clear. The fact that the water came inside up the two panes away from it washed out all of those problems we had on the windows. There was nothing there. It's what happens on every flight.

EISELE — And it's funny too, the water seemed to drain out before we ever started uprighting.

CUNNINGHAM — I think it's going into the insulation.

EISELE — They've probably got a lot of water sitting out there in it.

CUNNINGHAM — Remember, we flipped over into stable I about 4 minutes after we started inflation?

SCHIRRA — It took about four and a half minutes after inflation, and we kept the float bags running for a set 2 minutes; and since we hadn't used the full seven for uprighting, I left them running about for 4 minutes. I never saw a float bag.

CUNNINGHAM — I never did either, till I got out.

SCHIRRA — They weren't fully inflated by the way.

CUNNINGHAM — No, we probably could have run them for 7 minutes plus 2 minutes, 9 minutes all together, something like that.

CUNNINGHAM — In the egress training, they were tight as a drum. We heard both compressors which cycle effect the heat... revolving systems in the heat band.

EISELE — Incidentally, while we were in the water, I turned the VHF and the beacon off because we inverted. I was actually just following the checklist by rote down here.

SCHIRRA — What was the goof on coming up, Donn? When we got back up on stable I? I looked down at the post landing vent control, and it was normal. I put it in open, nothing happened; I put it back to normal, nothing happened.

EISELE — But it seems I forgot all about the power switch from low to high; that's why we didn't get venting.

CUNNINGHAM — I don't know if you heard me; I called high.

EISELE — That never got through. We had this going on.

CUNNINGHAM — Well, this was afterwards. It was after you had gone through all that, and I read this checklist again, but I couldn't hear - Donn was doing his bull bellow out there. We felt we couldn't hear what was going on.

EISELE — Of course, I had a goof right here, too. I had left the switch. I thought I was monitoring batt bus, but I had left it on main bus.

CUNNINGHAM — I got down here and said if the battery voltage is less than twenty seven and a half, take one of the batteries - take two of the batteries off the line, and I was reading zero.

SCHIRRA — Oh, swell.

CUNNINGHAM — And I thought, "well, I'm not going to take these batteries off the line until we're up anyway." Then I remembered battery bus; we were reading about 29 volts on each battery bus - something like that - between 29 and 30 volts.

SCHIRRA — Why don't we take a break here? I think Donn has a couple of questions that need just Donn talking. Go ahead.

CUNNINGHAM — Yes, Donn has mentioned that they had some kind of an anomalous behavior with the beacon. They never did receive the SARAH beacon or received it only very briefly before splash down. I would estimate that it was probably about 9,000 feet when I turned the VHF AM to simplex A, the beacon ON. And then when we went to stable II, I turned both of them OFF. Then when I got down the checklist, it called to turn them OFF, and I had already hit them both OFF. When we uprighted, I turned them both ON again. No, when we uprighted, I first turned the beacon ON, and I didn't have the simplex A ON yet. I had beacon ON for a while before I went back and turned simplex A ON. Yes, I think you tried to transmit, and it didn't get out.

It would seem to me that a possible problem here was a kind of slow deployment of that recovery antenna. There's two separate recovery antennas, and I think they've had problems before. Donn mentioned test articles. They had a little trouble with those antennas deploying.

SCHIRRA — That's how they gave up so-called VHF, because it didn't deploy.

CUNNINGHAM — Oh, okay.

SCHIRRA — That's what you're thinking about. They call it an HF. We're using UHF which we call VHF, and we're using VHF which they call HF, by inspection.

CUNNINGHAM — Well, at any rate

EISELE — It finally gave up a radio set to recovery.

CUNNINGHAM — We got down to the point right here where we had done everything we could. You were in radio contact.

SCHIRRA — Yes, I talked to Air Boss.

CUNNINGHAM — The next thing I would have had to hit on the checklist would have been low powered check list. I could see no reason to do it since we were in contact.

EISELE — I could see him. Remember, I said that?

SCHIRRA — Remember, I asked Donn and he said he saw him? I asked him one thing. Now, what was that? Oh, I know. I didn't ask him. I asked him to give me the word on whether I was aboard the grappling hook or not. He said the last we heard, we had some 20 odd knots of wind, which was going to blow us downwind.

EISELE — I'd like to take a couple of minutes just to mention the suggested, but mainly the things we heard. We've already talked about the SEP which was a big surprise and a hell of a bang. The next thing that happened, and actually before then, was about three-quarters retro when we pressurized the command module.

SCHIRRA — Oh, yes, the mode A.

EISELE — We proved the regulator sounded just like hydraulic chatter in a T33.

CUNNINGHAM — I immediately felt like it was a valve chatter. It was hit with some pressure all of a sudden and then backfired.

EISELE — When I heard this gurgling, I hit the pressure switch. That's when I switched. Then I turned the propellant isolation valve on, and we heard all this gurgling noise.

SCHIRRA — I'm glad you brought that up because I was convinced that it was a waste of time to check it out, regardless if it was good.

CUNNINGHAM — I might mention that as soon as he did that I said, "Look, I can hear it going down the lines." You could hear it run through the lines.

SCHIRRA — I am convinced it is a waste of time to check out those RCS. You still.... Everybody else hesitates. All the other guys say "oh, you should check it out." And I said, "What are you going to do on a lunar mission?" Well, you could hear the squibs go; you could hear lines gurgling.

CUNNINGHAM — There's no lack of confidence. We heard the whole thing right down the line. You don't have to get the chatter, incidentally, to know you have pressurization. The pressure does come up.

EISELE — I was not aware of any particular aerodynamic noise during retro.

6.5 Electrical Power

6.5.1 Fuel Cells

CUNNINGHAM — Another thing that was performed at this time was venting the batteries; and in venting the batteries, I noticed that the pressure was initially about 1.4 mm, excuse me, it wasn't 1.4 mm. The voltage on systems test meter for 4A position was 1.4 volts. When we vented it, it went down to about .6 and seemed throughout the flight to tend to maybe outgas a little bit more; and in doing our battery venting from then on, it worked its way on down to as low as .25 volts at one time.

New subject. This time, we're covering electrical power for the orbital phase of the flight. It's paragraph 6.4 in the debriefing guide. Number 1 is fuel cells, and I'll cover these item by item.

The PH high indicator - PH high indicator had shown no changes throughout the flight.

Fuel cell radiator temperature low, never made any change from its gray bar state throughout the flight. Fuel cell flow and the module - Okay. Starting over again on the subject of fuel cell flow and the module temperature indicators: the fuel cell flow, the H2 and the O2 flow, always appeared to run very, very close to what you would expect for the loads that the fuel cells were under. The module temperature indicators, however, did show anomalies.

The skin temp was consistent with the performance of the fuel cell. However, the condenser exhaust temperature does show anomalies. It looks like we have some kind of possible control problems in the bypass valves on the - probably the primary coolant loop in the fuel cell. The fuel cell 2 started showing high indications on the condenser exhaust temperature at approximately 162 hours into the flight. This was a slow increase; the ground apparently noticed the trend a little earlier than we did. We were watching it, however, and standing by for a master alarm should it reach the trigger value of 175. It turns out that the fuel cell did continue to climb.

(BREAK)

...triggered off, it was rather annoying, in that the temperature was not constant up there, and it triggered on and off for some time before it maintained steady above it, and we had a lot of master alarm activity for fuel cell 2. From that time on in the flight, the standard position of the fuel cell, time shared meter was for fuel cell 2.

The temperature continued to climb; we opened the circuit of the fuel cell, and it dropped very rapidly back down to its normal range, but we started seeing an anomalous behavior in fuel cell 1 at this time. It appeared to be a sympathetic reaction in that the fuel cell 1 condenser exhaust temperature began to climb when fuel cell 1 was called upon to take more of the load. This is the only time throughout the flight when we open-circuited fuel cell 2 that we saw this behavior. However, it leads you to believe there is something maybe slightly squirrelly in these glycol coolant loops.

This ties in with the fact that a little bit in fact very late in the flight, the condenser exhaust temperature on fuel cell 3 dropped down low enough to trigger off a condenser exhaust flow light. But the real problem - there was little or nothing in the control loops for fuel cell 1 and 3 as compared to fuel cell 2. Fuel cell 2 continued to go up and down throughout the flight depending on whether it was under load or not. On the drifting flight configuration, fuel cell 2 came down and carried its share of the load just fine. Fuel cell 2 was the one that was shared on both buses, for example. It seemed to run just about 2 amps higher in current but not enough to make any difference. As soon as you powered up the SCS and G&N, fuel cell 2 continued to climb. On one particular burn, I was a little bit concerned about hitting the 200 degree limit, just prior to the burn and just after the burn; it apparently peaked out at 195 and started down again right after, when we started powering the loads down again.

Apparently, there was much discussion on the ground about what this limit really was; we weren't aware of that, and as far as we were concerned, our onboard consideration was to keep it below 200 degrees. This was what prompted my concern for the deorbit burn; I wanted to bring the power up a little bit earlier before deorbit. Donn was going to be up by himself for awhile, and he could get a one rev jump on getting the alignments and getting suited so Wally and I would have a free run of the lower equipment bay when we got up. He did get powered up, and the fuel cell temperature started to come up. I had asked the night before to power it up like that but then open fuel cell circuit 2, so that we could save it and let that temperature increase occur much closer to the burn. The ground apparently felt that we could go ahead and leave it on the line and power it up very late; they had decided to open-circuit fuel cell 2 also. So we ended up open-circuiting fuel cell 2 late in the flight, also. I might comment that the first time we open-circuited fuel cell 2, it was open-circuited at 163 hours, stayed open-circuited for several hours, and at 163 hours and 45 minutes with fuel cell 2 off the line, we had a transient main A and main B undervoltage. This was probably due to some cyclic load triggering the fuel cell down below the twenty-six and a quarter for the main buses. It's the only problem we really had, undervoltage; we had fuel cell 2 off the line until late in the flight when we open-circuited it again. At 232 hours and 45 minutes, fuel cell 3 showed a low condenser exhaust temperature. It was apparently anomalous; it came back in and worked fine since. I don't know if that is one of your items on the open anomalies.

SCHIRRA — Walt, that happened on my watch there just before entry, and I asked him if we had a cold one and a hot one if we could swap the loads around, and they said they were considering that, but they never came back with any statement one way or the other, so I just let them run the way they were. Number 2 didn't really get all that hot right then, but it did later on after you guys were awake. Got up to about 180 or so, right around there.

CUNNINGHAM — At the end of the flight, it turns out that we brought it on the line - about 5 hours prior to deorbit, I believe - and at 257 hours and 52 minutes, the ground concurred. At that time, the total load was about 70 amps, and fuel cell 2 condenser exhaust temperature was 185, and we had about an hour and a half to go before deorbit, and fuel cell 2 was open-circuited. It dropped very rapidly and nicely down to within limits, or almost down to within limits again. At 257 hours and 54 minutes, main A and main B undervoltage lights came on; this was associated with activating the secondary coolant loop. When we turn the secondary coolant loop pump on, we put it on AC 1, but because of the bi-loads and all, both buses pulled down momentarily under the trigger level, and we had main A and main B undervoltage lights. We reset both the buses, and it was all okay. I believe that covers in fairly decent detail the fuel cell 2 problem.

I consider it an open anomaly. It's nothing I wouldn't go ahead and fly with; I think that it would have been very nice had we gotten the fuel cell 2 back. It seemed to be behaving in a manner which was rather strange. I think it's associated with the glycol loops in the fuel cells themselves. However, we could have gone for a long period of time open-circuiting the fuel cell at high condenser exhaust and putting it back on load when the skin temperature got down to 375. It's an anomaly. It would be well worth looking into to see if we can't handle the problem one way or another.

That is worth a little bit of laveration because from a crew point of view, after you're flying those late changes just don't sit too well with you in flight; and in this particular case, I worked with the fuel cells for a long time before I was on the Apollo flight. I worked with the malfunction procedures. I worked with the North American engineers on it, and they were adamant in the malfunction procedures that 200 degrees was the place to open-circuit those fuel cells. It's my understanding that when it looked like we were going to hit 200 degrees, we had a letter come from North American saying that 220 degrees was good for 50 hours or some period of time and even later, 250 degrees. Now, we felt like we got smarter in flight about the systems; maybe North American felt they did, too, but you have to look, I believe if you're familiar with the situation and have worked with it some time prior to that, you have to look with a jaundiced eye at limitations which come through as a result of the system not working right. You should make every effort to have the real limits before flight and not change them to conform during flight. We all recognize that if it had been a case of just trying to limp along long enough that certainly we'd run as high as you have to.

(BREAK)

CUNNINGHAM — ...that had it hit 200, I wasn't going to be concerned about it. At that point in the game, I would have let it run right on as high as it could have before deorbit. That fairly well covers the condenser exhaust situation, I think. The fuel cell indicator switch - as I say, we checked it back and forth generally in conjunction with checking the fuel cell performance with, again with the current EPS. The indicator switch itself, whenever we had a problem we've got, we were faced with the ganged inputs to the master alarm once more. We used to have nine inputs to the fuel cell lights; now we have five, but at any rate, when one parameter triggers the fuel cell light, you are not going to get a second caution and warning light coming on for fuel cells. Therefore, the standard procedure is to monitor the one that has the indication. We were fortunate; we never had more than one fuel cell that required this. We monitored fuel cell 2 almost continuously and not from any undue concern as much as just from the fact that that was the only way we could really verify fuel cell 2 after the light was triggered.

Purging is an interesting topic for discussion here because purging was changed in real time in the flight plan. I think this is the way to do it. There is a nominal purging time line that you can have for a spec purity of the reactants. It turns out that for oxygen it's not too terribly flexible; but for hydrogen, it's a very strong function of the purity of the hydrogen that you're getting. Since we had apparently much better hydrogen than the spec, we were able to relax the purging of the hydrogen. It's also very worthwhile because apparently it was expected that we would have about 6 percent remaining on the hydrogen, and we really ended up with about 14 percent, I think. Donn, I wrote that down some place. It looks like about 14 percent.

EISELE — It's either 12 or 14 percent on the meter.

CUNNINGHAM — Yes.

EISELE — It's right in that region. We had plenty.

CUNNINGHAM — Hydrogen is always going to be probably the most critical of the reactants. We finished up with 14 percent of hydrogen, and so it's well that we did schedule hydrogen purges in real time.

The purges themselves are a nuisance in one way, and it's the same thing that has bearing on other things that go on on the flight. There's a lot of things going on at the same time. These are relatively time-critical, and you're supposed to purge hydrogen, for example 80 seconds, and you want to purge one fuel cell at a time. You go ahead, and you purge fuel cell 1. You check the clock before you get the time to turn fuel cell 1 off. If something else has interfered, you're taking an update. When you get through with the update, you look back. Fuel cell 1 has already been running more than 80 seconds, and you turn it off, and you get fuel cell 2 on.

It takes a lot of concentration and ignoring anything else that is going on in order to keep these things coming out right. I would bet that there weren't a half a dozen purges that went on on this flight that lasted the spec time, and some of them you know were only a few seconds over.

Early in the flight, I felt very bad about it when it looked like we were going to be close on hydrogen. I felt very bad about it if I ended up taking - instead of 4 minutes for our purge cell, ended up taking six for example. I felt like I had wasted 2 minutes of hydrogen. So it is a problem; and for oxygen, it's not too critical because of the consumables, but you purge those for 2 minutes which allows you a little bit longer time to get distracted.

I couldn't stress more that when you get down to this part of the systems work, it's well to let a guy go to work on that problem, and just don't bother him at all until the thing is over. Another thing that would be very useful is a timer. I had suggested this prior to the flight. We tried it out in the simulator, and because the simulation is not quite like flight in these respects, you never do purge fuel cells because the performance never did degrade. The simulator is not realistic enough here as far as keeping you moving along with this kind of a time line. We found that we weren't using the timer in the simulator. In flight, my general impression was we could have used it. What do you think?

EISELE — It would have been very helpful.

CUNNINGHAM — Yes.

EISELE — Because there are so many little things that you do not only purges, but little things that you may start and then want to come back to and monitor a few minutes later. But you'll forget to come back a few minutes later because you'll in the meantime get engrossed in something else.

REP — Are you talking about a digital type event timer?

EISELE — No, an alarm clock.

CUNNINGHAM — This was like a cooking thing.

EISELE — Something you can wind for a few minutes and let it climb down and ring a bell and let it remind you that you better go look at your gimbal angles or your fuel cell purge or whatever.

CUNNINGHAM — The one that I had Pete King bought from Joske's or something for four bucks. It was a little round one like a pocket watch and very flat, and it was accurate to within about 2 minutes over 30 minutes which is pretty useful. You just crank it up and wait for it, and it would buzz when you got through. I really think we could have used it in flight. You mentioned a digital timer, Deke, and I really feel like in the right couch - I think, I covered that in the room with you one time - a DET would really be good someplace there where the guy on the right couch could see it. I felt like - you might expand on this, Donn - we didn't really make much use of the DET and MET in the lower equipment bay.

EISELE — No, the only time they used the DET was during rendezvous. We were down there most of the time. I used the MET quite frequently in the day passes because the bright sunlight would obliterate the one on the MDC. When I wanted to know what time it was, I would lean over and look at the one on the LEB which was not blanked out.

CUNNINGHAM — We used that one also to check the accuracy of the one on the MDC because that one seemed to run right on; MDC would lose a couple of seconds.

EISELE — You'd lose a little time now and then.

CUNNINGHAM — Okay.

EISELE — Well, I think the MET down there is valuable; I'm not sure about the...

CUNNINGHAM — At any rate, purging is no problem. You could definitely see an improvement in the fuel cell performance immediately after; almost during it, you can see it come up a little bit. The hydrogen purge naturally always triggered the master alarm. The oxygen purge when you were in drifting flight configuration generally would not trigger it. When you were powered up, the oxygen purge would trigger the master alarm just as expected. The reactants, switches, and indicators - the CRYO's themselves: I might comment that the hydrogen pressures and the oxygen pressures seem to hang in the lower half of the green areas throughout. Now this was expected because of a marked difference between actual pressures and what we were reading on our meters. It seems that we are living here with meters that are less accurate than I would like to have, and in some cases, this inaccuracy even runs into contradictions or complications with the caution and warning limits.

In some cases, the nominal range of operation gets you closer or even possibly exceeds caution and warning trigger limit as for example, the CRYO tank venting. At one time, flight operations director was much concerned with the CRYO tank venting, and it turns out that the master alarms for the CRYO tank high pressures doesn't even trigger until after you exceed by a very slight amount the venting pressures. We had one very definite problem associated with the reactants switches, and that was the oxygen fans. Early in the flight, we had an AC bus 1 fail. I reset it; it went into the log as an anomaly. Sometime later, we had an AC bus 1 and an AC bus 2 fail simultaneously, and this was an anomaly for a while. I can't say too much about the way the ground took care of this one and troubleshot it. In real fast time, we were somewhat concerned about it, naturally.

The ground took a look at all the data and correlated very nicely the oxygen fans in their AUTO position. They both kicked off at the same time, triggered by a pressure switch, and it turned out that this transient load loss on the AC bus was allowing the AC buses to hit an overvoltage of above 130, and it kicked the inverters off the bus, and we had a bad situation staring us in the face. The procedure they recommended to get around this worked successfully throughout the flight. That was that we went to O2 1 fans to the AUTO position and the O2 tank 2 fans to the OFF position; and at specified times, in real time, we would turn the fans to the ON position in tank 2 and allow the mixing to go on. This was aimed not so much at never having the glitch occur again as it was at making sure that if the glitch did occur, it would only affect one bus, and I think that is probably a good head. As it turns out, we never got the transient any more. There was a time when we would have both fans ON, but one was in the ON position, and if the AUTO position on tank 1 had kicked off, we still wouldn't have gotten probably the transient. During burns, both fans were in the OFF position.

(END OF PART ONE OF TECHNICAL DEBRIEFING)

68-H-1059

CONFIDENTIAL

SPACE ADMINISTRATION

NOTICE: This document may be exempt from public disclosure under the Freedom of Information Act (5 U.S.C. 552). Requests for its release to persons outside the U.S. Government should be handled under the provisions of NASA Policy Directive 1382.2.

CLASSIFICATION CHANGED TO
U
BY AUTHORITY OF _memo,_
Gene R. Bui _____ Dick.,
DATE 1/15/71
Sally O Gates - 10/6/75

APOLLO VII
TECHNICAL DEBRIEFING
Part II
(U)

PREPARED BY

MISSION OPERATIONS BRANCH
FLIGHT CREW SUPPORT DIVISION

GROUP 4
Downgraded at 3 year
intervals; declassified
after 12 years.

CLASSIFIED DOCUMENT - TITLE UNCLASSIFIED

This material contains information affecting the national defense of the United States within the meaning of the espionage laws, Title 18, U.S.C., Secs. 793 and 794, the transmission or revelation of which in any manner to an unauthorized person is prohibited by law.

MANNED SPACECRAFT CENTER
HOUSTON, TEXAS
OCTOBER 27, 1968

DATE   OPR   #   T PGM SUBJECT   SIGNATOR LOC

CONFIDENTIAL

SCHIRRA — ...Yes.

2.24 SECO

SCHIRRA — SECO was nominal as far as I could tell from the time line; that's nothing to worry about.

2.25 Orbital GO/NO-GO

SCHIRRA — We got orbital GO/NO-GO quite fast, and the most satisfying thing was S-IVB safing information, safe for destruction.

EISELE — Very quickly.

2.26 Communications

SCHIRRA — We had all the COMM that we needed. COMM was sufficient but for the lack of mode 4 call out. That would have been critical if we had had an early SECO and we didn't know it. When you get down to it, we had very little complication for orbital insertion. That COMM must be straightened out. That's a big anomaly which is the kind of thing that we should have on the blackboard. Insertion COMM was not GO.

EISELE — To have COMM, all you have to do is turn your S-band up.

SCHIRRA — I knew I had it up. It says so in the log.

EISELE — When did you get your S-band up?

SCHIRRA — When I couldn't hear them. I didn't hear "Roger" for a couple of calls, so I turned the S-band up. They heard me say S-band up.

EISELE — When we talk of listing things up there, I personally don't think that this is a constraint on Apollo 8, on the C' mission.

SCHIRRA — I very much do. The communications at SECO is necessary. If you don't hear a SECO, it is hairy. You have got to have a GO/NO-GO for mode 4.

EISELE — That's just during the launch period.

SCHIRRA — That is true. It's a constraint for another launch, and the next one happens to be Apollo 8.

EISELE — Not necessarily for C'; that's what I'm getting at.

SCHIRRA — Yes, the next Apollo launch should have communications into orbit.

EISELE — That's right.

CUNNINGHAM — The next Apollo launch is either the C' mission or the C mission again.

SCHIRRA — Then it's a constraint. Communications were not satisfactory during boost. That's what I'm trying to say. Maybe there was a procedural error. The call after we acknowledged by selecting the appropriate control made — it may be we're unearthing a problem.

CUNNINGHAM — We have always been concerned about the flame pattern affecting the antenna characteristic.

SCHIRRA — Why didn't that happen in the Mercury and Gemini?

CUNNINGHAM — I don't know. They had pretty small flame patterns compared to this.

SCHIRRA — Not at SECO. It was enough to covert the whole sky from down range. I'm not about to testify to the size of the flame pattern, that communications had better be improved. We can't afford not to have communications through SECO. I guess that's my error rather than yours, Walt.

CUNNINGHAM — Do you want to write that up here?

SCHIRRA — Yes. I think you ought to write EMS up there also while you are standing at the board. That was a constraint, and everybody knows it.

2.27 Control and Displays

SCHIRRA — Controls and displays were satisfactory.

2.28 Crew Comfort

SCHIRRA — Crew comfort was satisfactory.

SCHIRRA — That was a rush, rush, and we lucked out.

EISELE — Yes, we somehow got off the time line there, and we had to kind of squeeze it in there.

SCHIRRA — We had a gimbal lock. The first time through, we changed seats.

EISELE — Burn number 3 was a ditty.

SCHIRRA — Burn number 3 came up down the road from that test, and we had lots of things going wrong.

REP — Is that what went wrong?

SCHIRRA — Yes.

REP — Okay.

SCHIRRA — We had a gimbal lock, and we changed back to our original couch configuration.

EISELE — We had to hustle.

SCHIRRA — I wanted you down in the LEB doing the sighting. Not that I felt Walt couldn't do it yet, but you had had more experience down there than Walt for two burns. We briefed that if we ever got in trouble, we would go back to our original seat configuration. No one was offended; we raced right through it. Walt was more experienced in racing us through the checklist, and I knew what I wanted to do in my seat. As it was, we checked out and made it. That was the one place where we came close to blowing the time line.

EISELE — Yes, that was pretty rough.

SCHIRRA — We had given up on the White Sands rendezvous radar test, but the ground said go ahead and try it anyway. We had to throw it into attitude. I remember I was flying around pretty fast there.

CUNNINGHAM — In fact, it was on the real time flight plan we put in on the next rev. It wasn't intended to be there until the next trip.

SCHIRRA — That was when we were getting a little speedy.

EISELE — There was a change in the flight plan; they moved that in, sandwiched it into somewhere else. And that is what threw us a little behind, that plus the gimbal lock. But we did make it and got a good test. All is well that ends well. They did very well.

SCHIRRA — I would like to say one thing I didn't say in real time. I feel like I did in Gemini VI with that rendezvous radar done for that next crew, like Gordo and Pete did for us on Gemini VI.

3.0 ORBITAL OPERATIONS

SCHIRRA — CSM/S-IVB orbital operations went exactly as predicted.

3.1 Insertion Through COAS Calibration

EISELE — I think the time line and the procedures we followed - the sequence of doing things - went almost identically to what we rehearsed in the mockup and simulators.

3.1.1 CSM/S-IVB Orbital Operations

CUNNINGHAM — We followed very closely the detailed first six revs checklist.

SCHIRRA — One thing we should get into is this little deal here. We followed this religiously. We smuggled it on board as part of the checklist.

CUNNINGHAM — Yes.

SCHIRRA — He passed it to me, and I had it over here on my side all the time to keep track of any glitches. It was very detailed, like what you unstow, when and other things like that.

CUNNINGHAM — It should have been part of the flight plan.

SCHIRRA — Here are all the cameras you have to have up here. There are some numbers I recorded on the launch vehicle propellant pressures. I gave these to the ground, and I don't know if they should be recorded again. They're in this thing in case they need them. That was for four different times. They change. I was surprised. Fuel pressure went up, and the O2 pressure went up. Before I go on, we were scheduled for a debriefing on the S-IVB time line real late in the game. We have been over that many times. I really don't think you need all these booster briefings.

REP — I think the Marshall people requested it.

3.1.2 S-IVB Safing

SCHIRRA — We did mention on yesterday's tape that I was very much concerned about GO/NO-GO on S-IVB safing. That was a very warm feeling, knowing that it was safe. I perspire at the thought of going one more rev with that thing. It was one less thing hanging on my mind on the first rev.

3.1.3 S-IVB Take-Over
Demonstration

SCHIRRA — Demonstration was exactly as we planned it, and I appreciated the rapid response of everybody cutting that time line in half because it was too long the first time we did it. That's one of the few rapid responses we had with DTO. They responded to that almost immediately in Huntsville. The S-IVB flew better than in simulation. I prefer it to go that way than I would the other way.

3.1.4 Return to S-IVB
Auto Control

SCHIRRA — Return S-IVB automatic control, no problem.

3.1.5 Separation
Transposition and
Simulated Docking

SCHIRRA — This was a whole new world to me, and I guess that was one of the big things we discussed and lost. I talked to almost all the command pilots out there on the horn. We really concentrated on getting on that Langley simulator. That's the only device that I know of that will do that. I suggest that they don't try to pitch around, particularly if they get faster than 5 degrees per second. I think that's a big mistake.

EISELE — There's no big rush about getting around.

SCHIRRA — I opened at 1 foot per second, and then I descended to one tenth of a foot per second. Then I pitched between two and half and 3 degrees per second. It's still fast, but you get kind of anxious to see what is going on back there. Donn saw it right away and started saying "WOW, what a sight!" You don't know what's going on. I didn't know if it was going to come down on my back like a big train. When I looked out, all I could see was S-IVB all over the place. That one panel was in the way, which discouraged me from going in too close. That was the panel that I couldn't see when I came in. I aligned to the docking target, and we came in close, as the film will show.

CUNNINGHAM — I took that picture, and I didn't know we were that close.

SCHIRRA — We were in there. I was afraid I was losing sight of that one SLA panel. It was catty wampus. I think it is a good decision to have the SLA panels go; that's the only way to do it. Get rid of those things.

EISELE — They have got to go out 30 degrees before they go.

CUNNINGHAM — I wouldn't guarantee that that was 30 degrees.

EISELE — Maybe 20 or 25 degrees.

SCHIRRA — Those pictures are invaluable on that basis. That is a problem. I really didn't feel comfortable with this machine. It felt like a big, big truck. Another analogy I've used, was first time I had a boat, a trailer, or a house trailer behind my car. I was really scared to back that car up. I had to back the car up countless times before it never bothered me. That's the kind of analogy you get when you first see that S-IVB out there. It's awful big, and it is very difficult to maneuver the command module that precisely. We have a light command service module compared to the rest of the missions. I can only recommend the device we have at Langley for training crews. I wish I had gone up there. I would have known more about it.

3.1.6 SLA
Photography

SCHIRRA — SLA photography is evident. We don't need to talk about that now. I see we've got our pictures back.

CUNNINGHAM — It turns out that the SLA photography was slightly hampered by the window view.

SCHIRRA — One thing that bothered me was the field of view in that window.

CUNNINGHAM — I think you were up a little high on that maneuver in relation to your window.

EISELE — Yes, you're right.

SCHIRRA — I needed to roll in order to line up.

EISELE — Yes, that's right.

SCHIRRA — I needed to roll to get both windows lined up in the same place.

CUNNINGHAM — That's right. The sequence camera, when it's mounted in the bracket is pointing out a nice unused hole down there in the rendezvous window. It did not tend to line up if you moved off a little.

SCHIRRA — I would like to go back to that transposition. The mode I used was PULSE in roll and yaw and ACCEL COMMAND in pitch. I think everybody should use that one. Rather than RATE COMMAND in yaw and roll and whatever in pitch. That's the cheapest way to get around. Once you get around, you can start tightening up as you start getting ready to translate; then you might want to use RATE COMMAND for the three attitudes. I do think you need something to stabilize attitude when you translate. You could use DAP pulsively. Jet priority logic on subsequent SC may help the problem.

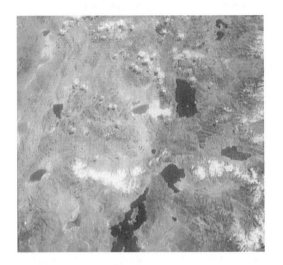

AS07-05-1617

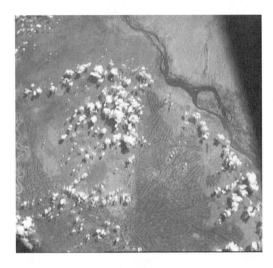

AS07-06-1718

AS07-07-1748

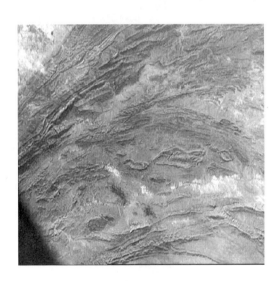

6AS07-07-1832

AS07-11-2008

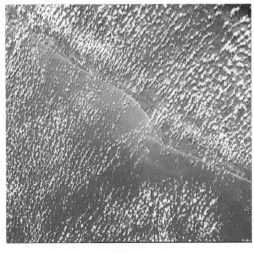

AS07-11-2038

3.1.7 RCS Phasing SCHIRRA — We did the RCS phasing with the service module RCS separation. That thing was less than 10 feet per second. It was a simple maneuver, and it went off quite well. We took residuals out, didn't we?

EISELE — We didn't have any.

CUNNINGHAM — You were burning 7 feet. You burned 7 feet on the P47, didn't you?

SCHIRRA — We used P47 for venting, too, and it worked out quite well.

CUNNINGHAM — It was significant. I was surprised. We built up how much? 25?

SCHIRRA — 26 feet per second on the DELTA-V counter. That had a bias that is calibrated and has been reported over a period of time.

3.1.8 CSM Systems Checkout EISELE — You were out of here when we did that, Walt. We have already gone through that.

3.1.9 Sextant Calibration Test REP — Donn's got a NAV COAS calibration.

3.1.11 S-IVB Ventilation EISELE — We noted that when I came in close at the point where the S-IVB was stable, I could see little vent pipes I never even knew about up there in one of the SLA panels. The one just south of the target adapter was squirting stuff.

CUNNINGHAM — Yes. I want to make note of the fact that we did see trash inside there. It looked like part of that charge stuff there. There were bits and pieces of that floating around. There was a lot of it. There's nothing really to talk about on ventilation, ice clouds, and vapors. They were just there. That wouldn't deter me from pulling in to take the LM. I definitely wouldn't want the S-IVB to start moving around. The CSM isn't that spry of a vehicle that you could go in there and fight some other system and try to fly as well if the S-IVB were moving.

3.2 Rendezvous SCHIRRA — Line of sight control was very good on this particular flight. We had real good luck with it. I was a little worried about the fact that we had what I would call a hidden TPI. We didn't see the target. I had no confidence in the rendezvous because of that. Everything worked nominally. The plot was beautiful; time was good. Everything looked like it was good. The midcourses justified the solutions. We did have to take one backup that Walt had to justify the midcourse.

CUNNINGHAM — We essentially burned the backup.

EISELE — We burned the backup rather than the G&N because I felt the G&N was too big a number.

SCHIRRA — We had - out of plane if I remember right.

CUNNINGHAM — A little less than half out of plane.

EISELE — We did all maneuvers to the burn attitude for TPI, and I suggested taking out half of the out of plane which we did...

SCHIRRA — I'd say the whole run worked well, but in real time I was scared to death.

EISELE — I just had the feeling that we could go ahead and do the TPI on faith basically, and we would know later whether we were going to make it or not. I figured we'd see the target sooner or later as we got up close; then we would know whether we were going to hack it.

SCHIRRA — The real threat was when I finally did acquire the target visually. (It was after midcourse.) We saw the lights blinking, and that's a nice feeling. I hadn't seen it before because I wasn't aimed.

EISELE — The next crisis was whether or not we were going to come into daylight before we got to it.

SCHIRRA — Yes.

EISELE — We figured we did.

SCHIRRA — The line-of-sight control was no great task. I didn't do much dittering because I was afraid to ditter with this big boat. It's too expensive when you set up a rate and have to take it back out again. I remember I made one remark that I was happy about the fact that we had a theta of about 130 or 135 degrees, and I said "that's perfect." Right on the mark.

3.2.7 Braking SCHIRRA — Braking was a complete nightmare with no ranging whatsoever. To judge the diameter of the S-IVB, all you can use is a good number. Anything else is arbitrary. The length of it, the SLA's diameter are not good. It was so bright that you get overtones of light across the COAS, and you're not sure if it's 1 degree. I believe I called out 1 degree, and it was something like eight tenths of a degree. We braked a little bit early, all the way in. This is an awesome target.

CUNNINGHAM — It looked about right from my side.

EISELE — I didn't have any...

SCHIRRA — You didn't have an index, but you could feel it.

EISELE — It felt like we were coming in pretty good, a little slow in the end.

SCHIRRA — The interesting part of this was that this is a very big target. You take a little LM up there with only an ascent stage; that's a very small target. My point is that we have got to validate a ranging device for braking, because the LM is awfully small. You have to have a tool on board to range that LM for braking. You have the VHF ranging, and you have the LM radar. These are still available and shouldn't necessarily fail. My anticipation is that if command module active rendezvous is required because of running low on fuel in the LM rather than because of a PGNS radar failure, then you can use the LM's radar as a ranging device. This helps fantastically on braking.

3.2.8 Rendezvous Navigation

SCHIRRA — You covered rendezvous with navigation, didn't you, Donn?

EISELE — Yes, I covered that. I don't recall the exact number of marks. All that should be on the tape. Generally, DELTA-R and DELTA-V were small and appropriate because we had such a fine set up to begin with. Phil Shaffer and the flight controllers were right down the slot on that.

SCHIRRA — It was really good.

EISELE — We had a very good state vector there. It was in the same condition all the way.

SCHIRRA — It really meant that the onboard computer agreed with the ground solution.

EISELE — The auto optics tracking of the target became a little spastic there as we got in closer to the target after TPI.

SCHIRRA — I would like to go back to braking again. We asked for a ranging device like a stadimeter. It fell down the crack because people thought their visual optics system was good enough. There was one in work, and I recommend that that be reopened, particularly for a small target the size of a LM. There is a device in the shop that can be made usable for the LM, not the one that was unsolicited from the Coast Guard. This one was like the sextant I used in Gemini VI with Tom Stafford. It is big and bulky, but it's good. For example, in Houston we worked with a rendezvous device. The darn target had an apparent size of 10,000 feet. We tried that 10,000 foot mark, and I made every rendezvous with just one range reading. You get super confident in that onboard system. The other thing we made note of yesterday that disturbed me no end, was earlier Donn was not able to train on checking the state vector data display against the sextant display of the horizon en route to TPI. I feel that should be done. It fell out of my time line because there was no way you could practice doing it. I did ask you to do it a long time ago, and that was something you could rehearse doing. I think that's more important than any backup data point because you have to validate that statement somehow.

EISELE — I know I got it put back in the update form, and we got it from that. It worked just the way I thought it would. Since we had not trained to do it, we would not get on doing it.

SCHIRRA — It was too late before I discovered you weren't doing it. We discovered this in one of the SIMs. I was surprised it fell down in the crack. I didn't get with you enough earlier to explain to you how important that was. I didn't take advantage of my experience there. That was a goof on my part.

3.2.9 Formation

SCHIRRA — Formation flight is just about the same as transition and docking. It's an expensive mode in the command module. I have heard people talk about the command module doing the docking with the LM. I think you will find it is much easier to use the LM for docking with the command module. It was just too big to move around. You still have a big load on that command module, but if that is a requirement again, I say spend a lot of time at Langley. We're not lacking for the tools to practice. We don't have a tool in Houston to fly command module active, but we have a tool for flying LM active. That is the only tip I would like to pass on.

3.2.10 Final Separation Burn

SCHIRRA — Final separation burn is the big burn. I guess that is what we're talking about here.

EISELE — One foot per second.

SCHIRRA — Oh, this is back in rendezvous. That did concern me initially because I didn't want to be in a position where I might close in again on the target. As it turned out, we had effected the rendezvous from below and stayed below it inertially. We got to the point where we were going to separate. We separated from below it - minus - as we backed away from it which is what we're supposed to do. The rendezvous was completed with a so-called whifferdil. We went around the thing up at the top and then had to go by the thing and then do the separation burn. As it turned out, we were in the right place. You definitely don't want to burn towards the vehicle zone.

3.2.11 S-IVB Activity

SCHIRRA — It was moving at rather high rates, and that was logged on the film.

3.3 Post-rendezvous Through Deorbit

SCHIRRA — We went through the first three items up to the WSMR. I think that one is self-explanatory; it went off very well. It felt real good to know that thing tracked out, and I think I ought to bring that up during the press conference; we felt very warm about it, and we had asked for that test to be done. It was almost dropped, but people responded and got the gear ready for us, and we worked it.

3.3.5 Sextant Tracking

EISELE — We tracked landmarks and stars and everything went fine. Later on, we talk about the mid course NAV.

3.3.6 SPS Burn Number 3

SCHIRRA — Burn number 3 was just like burn number 1 and 2; it was very nominal. No problems whatsoever with it.

EISELE — I'd like to mention that burn 3 was an SCS burn with G&N monitoring, and the residuals were very small. I came away with the feeling that for anything except an extremely long curve burn such as lunar orbit insertion, that you're probably just as well off to do them in SCS because it is right down the wire. Cutoff was just within a couple feet a second.

SCHIRRA — Cuts off better than the G&C does.

EISELE — Errors were very small also.

3.3.7 Slosh Damping Test

SCHIRRA — There is no problem with slosh damping. After each major burn, we found a big puddle of water on the aft bulkhead, and it stayed there. It didn't go all over the cockpit; that is the best slosh damping test we ever had. And there is the answer to slosh damping. There is no problem.

CUNNINGHAM — We never saw any evidence of any kind of motion you could attribute to fuel sloshing around after any SPS burn or RCS maneuver.

EISELE — This puddle of water didn't even move. There was only one area that it came from.

CUNNINGHAM — Yes, I think so, too. We did the tests that were in our burn schedule and flight plans, and we never noticed a thing from it.

3.3.8 ECS Radiator Test

CUNNINGHAM — Let's see, the next one is the SCS radiator test. I think it was a big surprise there initially. Donn started the thing out and found out that we were in minimum deadband - the 4 degree deadband, and the machine was kicking off thrusters like mad. Wally had already seen that we hadn't pegged what we call perigee torque yet.

SCHIRRA — I remember you sitting in there for a while, and you were getting real worried saying, "My flight control technique, it's terrible, what is this?"

CUNNINGHAM — When Donn got out, I relieved him. Donn had eventually come to the conclusion that we were better off doing it in pulse in all three axes, instead of holding pitch and yaw and rate command. I got in there, and we were holding it in pulse. I must have gotten in there just as we started through perigee, and we were supposed to be holding within 5 degrees, and we ended up 10 degrees off.

EISELE — I said, "This is your crazy DTO, you better fly it."

CUNNINGHAM — That's right; he washed his hands of it; he did.

EISELE — I got out, got out, got out of there, went down in the LEB and blew my nose for a couple of hours. I was flying along and found out that the pulse was better than the attitude hold, and I was tweaking it in, holding within a couple of degrees, you know, just going along just fine, and then Walt got in. Apparently, right about then was when we started getting perigee because Walt started hollering about the thing wouldn't stay where it was supposed to. I looked, and he was 10 degrees off.

CUNNINGHAM — In pitch and yaw.

EISELE — I wondered what has he been doing wrong, so I got in and tried it again. After a while, it was doing the same thing. It seemed to be intermittent.

CUNNINGHAM — We were 90 degrees out of plane for the test.

EISELE — Yes, which is the worst case for the perigee torque business. And we were trying to maintain an ORB rate roll, which meant that we were coupling up between pitch and yaw all the time. I guess we got that comment on tape about how many pulses it was taking when you were in attitude hold.

CUNNINGHAM — Yes, we counted them, and it was a fierce number per minute in attitude hold.

SCHIRRA — That is where we became concerned about these tight control modes.

EISELE — And then we went to all pulse modes, manual pulse mode, and the number dropped by a factor of ten, at least.

CUNNINGHAM — We finally finished the test, and it was a four and one half hour test. It turned out we were on the nominal amount of fuel which had been allotted for it, which was a lot more than Donn and I had figured we could do it for.

SCHIRRA — I remember. You all got concerned about it, and I did take over towards the end because I wanted to find out what the control problem was.

CUNNINGHAM — Yes, you did relieve us for about an hour there.

SCHIRRA — That is when we discovered the perigee kick, because I started calling up 82 and 83 to find out what kind of perigee we had. 83 wasn't any good since we were out of plane, so we called up 82, and I found out we were going through perigee when all these problems came up.

CUNNINGHAM — One other thing, we did do the coarse align. - because of a misleading on the DAP load. I loaded the DAP load into P30 the first time through. It looked like we were about ready to blow the thing on that rev, and Donn came to our rescue and coarse aligned us. He went through P30 and loaded it right and did a coarse align to the right attitude.

EISELE — Yes, we didn't have a night pass to do a fine align, so we just bought the coarse align. We really lucked out on that because later on, when we coarse aligned to the subsequent…

3.3.9 Midcourse Navigation

SCHIRRA — We are now on the area of course NAV.

EISELE — I was thinking it was some point over Guaymas, I don't remember what it was now.

SCHIRRA — What's this mid-course NAV consist of?

EISELE — This is P23.

SCHIRRA — The one on the DTO.

EISELE — The midcourse NAV program was set up to do marks using a star and earth horizon technique. And we found on the first and only attempt at this, that it didn't work very well. The main reason is that the earth horizon is a fuzzy kind of a thing; it does not appear as if there's any precise lines or delineation that you could use reliably as an index for a mark. This is true when you look at it in the sextant because of the magnification. When you look at the air glow or the earth horizon at certain times, such as near sunset and sunrise, you do see some very distinct banding if you are looking at it through the window or through the telescope. Again, that only happens at certain times of the day, at sunset and sunrise, and only in the area that is pretty close to where the sun is going to be coming through the horizon. At other times, such as at night, the horizon is just kind of a muddy brown and fuzzy looking. During the day, if you look off away from the horizon toward the sun you don't see much of a well-defined horizon. So this test did not work out at all. I just could not pick out anything in the airglow. I could not pick out what looked like a horizon at all. And, also, it turned out that the stars - this was a daylight type of thing - had given us an attitude to fly some shaft and trunnion angles. I put in the optics and no star appeared in the sextant, so apparently the angles were a little bit off. I didn't know how in the world I was ever going to get that star in there.

I thought about it later, and perhaps if I had enough hands and was swift enough, I might be able to do a P52 and pull the star in with AUTO optics. Then I would have to hold it there manually while I reselected the P23 program. It didn't seem like it was worthwhile because we had a horizon problem. We reported this to the ground, and they apparently agreed because there was no more mention of the star-to-horizon technique. Later on in the flight we did a P23 using a lunar landmark and a star, that worked out quite well I thought. It was very easy to do. The moon was in a phase where it was getting close to the sun; that is, the final phase of the moon. We picked up landmark 5 very readily because of the low sun angle on that part of the moon. We were able to use lunar landmark 5 and I don't remember what star it was, but, we pulled one star in there and I got a couple of marks on it. I think only one of them got down on the data, and I did hear that they were satisfied with the results.

CUNNINGHAM — We might mention that the three of us took a look at it, and it was a very easy control task. I had never tried anything like that before.

EISELE — Yes. Also, we spent considerable time at various periods examining that air glow and the earth horizon out the window and through the optics. None of us could make any sense of it, as far as being able to pick out anything repeatable to use as a reference.

CUNNINGHAM — The only way that you could possibly get a fix was to watch a star occult as it went through.

EISELE — It was pretty hard to tell exactly where it occulted.

CUNNINGHAM — Yes, it started blinking right down at the bottom. You were never really sure when it disappeared.

EISELE — Well, I think the problem is that P23 has applications to the translunar flight. Normally you would not be using it anyway until you were several thousand miles from the earth. I am sure at that distance that the horizon, the earth horizon, or the earth landmarks would appear quite different from what they do at 100 miles UP.

CUNNINGHAM — Does that handle mid-course now?

EISELE — Yes, I think so.

3.3.10 Cryogenic Stratification Test

CUNNINGHAM — Okay, the next item of discussion is a cryogenic stratification test. This was a test we performed at three different quantities in the hydrogen and the oxygen tanks during the flight. We did end up performing it three times with the hydrogen and only twice with the oxygen. The results are in the DTO book, and they will be passed on. I did update the procedure in flight with the pressures at which the hydrogen tanks were really cycling back and forth. Hydrogen tank 1 was running between 228 to 248 psi, and hydrogen tank 2 between 237 and 255. I modified the procedure to reflect these numbers. The data showed little or no stratification. in the first hydrogen test the pressure may have changed after the heaters were turned off and the fans were turned on. On the oxygen stratification test there was a very definite decrease in pressure when the fans were turned on, which I would have interpreted as having stratification present. The second time the test was run the results indicated to me no stratification in either oxygen or hydrogen. This was nominally at the 60 percent level. At one time, on the last day of the flight, or during the night preceding the last day of the flight, the hydrogen stratification test was run. It showed results similar to the earlier test, essentially no stratification.

3.3.11 SPS Burn 4

CUNNINGHAM — SPS burn 4, I will only say that the system worked as planned. On this minimum impulse burn, though, we did use, I believe, our first 2-jet ullage. We ullaged for 20 seconds and selected the quads for ullage appropriately after being advised from the ground which quads were most desirable to reduce the fuel in. The engine worked normally, and the burn time was about .54 seconds, maybe 17 feet per second, something like that. We were still impressed by the fact that the engine, even though it was burning only half a second, came up and slapped you in the back just like all the other starts; and it was over immediately. Ball valves, all four of them flipped, had time enough to flip completely open and closed again. Essentially, I don't feel like there is anything significant to report other than it was a normal SPS burn.

3.3.12 SPS Cold Soak

CUNNINGHAM — The SPS cold soak test was the one where we were to monitor the oxidizer distribution line temperatures and the fuel distribution line temperatures. We monitored SPS propellant tank temperatures as they were labeled on MDC 3 and did the cold soak attitude for 3 hours. The cold soak attitude was then taken up. The procedure involved turning the heaters on at 45 degrees F and off at 65 degrees F. The temperature never changed, we never activated the switch, and, as a matter of fact, the propellant tank temperatures ran between 68 and 70 the entire flight. I never felt like the heaters were necessary for controlling the line temperature. On ground request they were turned on several times, based on another SPS temperature which was down by the injector valves or something. The ground did have another temperature that they were interested in. When we turned the heaters on, apparently it satisfied them that the temperature in concern rose. There was one other time, later in the flight, when the heaters were tested just for operation. I had proposed we do this early, and the ground had some reservations about it. Later on we operated for 2 hours and ran a 6-hour test, 2 hours with line heater in position A, and then another 4 hours with it in A/B, and to my knowledge the temperature never changed. It was finished up on Donn's watch.

EISELE — Yes, I think it got up to 72 degrees and just sat there. I guess the point is, the SPS propellant and line temperatures seemed to be very stable and always stayed within the normal range. We never, at any time during the whole flight, had to turn on those heaters to keep it within that range. There was never any problem at all, and the so-called cold soak test really didn't get it very cold at all. It still was above the minimum.

CUNNINGHAM — The significant point is that we never required them.

EISELE — No problem.

CUNNINGHAM — I know where I got off. Bill Pogue labeled it cold soak.

3.3.13 SPS Burn #5

SCHIRRA — All attitudes were great. We started off the burn as a G&N burn, and at 30 seconds, we were scheduled to flip into GDC. The only variable that came up was a new way of doing burn 5, and that was a big mistake. The mistake was that the ground's way of doing burn 5 was to add 100 feet per second so we could shut off the burn with a hundred feet per second to go on the DELTA-V counter, with the thrust normal switches A and B OFF. This is to check the ball valves OFF and terminate the burn that way. We should have had simulated burn 5 with Houston on the simulator; we didn't do it that way. I'd never heard about it prior to this event. I negotiated them down to 50 feet per second, and Walt was trying to talk me into going down to 20 feet per second on top of the scheduled burn. The surprise was that the burn itself was perfectly normal. The rate needles were never 5.5; the error needles were never displaced more than a degree. It was easy to control; it would often roll about 4 or 5 degrees, but that's nothing; that's typical. It's just that there is no real roll control in MTVC, just the stick, rather the hand controller. You don't fight that; it is like the old retros in Gemini or Mercury.

If you don't fight roll, pitch and yaw, they start to give you a little trouble. It didn't cup up; I just took out pitch and yaw, then I flipped roll in once in a while to bring it right back on. I was starting to watch the DELTA-V window, and I couldn't see it. The sun had started shafting in as we burned, and extinguished in that sense. Because of the bright light, I couldn't see anything on the DELTA-V counter. I started to reach up to kill it with my left hand; by that time the DELTA-V counter would normally cut it off. We overburned it by 50 feet per second; that's all there was to it. I heard it was an out-of-plane error, something like 15 feet per second. I don't remember that number showing up on the DSKY. The DSKY was running all the time to monitor the DELTA-V we got, not that I used it; this is to bookkeep. Also, the state vectors were up to date. We didn't see a number like that. I remember a very small number being out of plane. I think Dave Scott was telling me he saw a big number and wondered if I'd diverged a little bit in yaw, so that number has got to be checked again. As I recall, residuals were very small in out-of-plane and up/down. The in-plane was 50 feet - well, wait a minute, the in-plane was in X-axis and was 48 feet per second, which was about 50 feet in actual burn direction. I can only say that you don't change a classic burn like that that late. It was changed right at the last minute.

In the flight plan I had, maybe it does say the burn will be terminated by the A & B switches. That isn't the way we did it in simulation, and I did lots of burn 5's in simulation. Here it is right here, Deke; it says G&N ON plus switch OFF.

SLAYTON — That's right; that's the way all flight plans had it. That's the way it is in the DTO.

SCHIRRA — Yes, but I did these things, and no one caught me doing it the wrong way in all the simulations. I did it with Houston, and I didn't add a hundred feet per second to it when we did burn 5 with Houston. Then all of a sudden, someone gets... That's why nobody agreed with it. It was a new thing.

SLAYTON — I don't know how long it's been in the flight plan, but...

SCHIRRA — That is not new, but adding a hundred feet per second to the burn was new.

SLAYTON — I see.

SCHIRRA — And then having me cut off a hundred feet per second error, that's the point. I understood what they were driving at, but I'd never done it that way. What got me was that I was prepared to do it that way, and I - we'd talked about it; we had enough lead time, but when I couldn't see the DELTA-V counter, evidently they didn't know I didn't know what velocity was left. If I'd known this, if it would've been brought to my attention by simulating it - which is how you learn all these things - I would have known then that I couldn't do it that way. You see my point. It was a surprise, and surprises are almost lethal. It could be lethal if that went off in the wrong direction. We always said if a burn wasn't going right, we'd stop a burn, except an abort-to-orbit and a retroburn. So this broke that rule by putting in more than you're going to. We did this simulation without adding DELTA-V, that's what I am trying to get at.

Regardless of the surprise on burn 5, it didn't hurt us so because all it did was knock off another 50 feet per second. That just drove us a little bit further in - back. We tilted the line of axes so that we had a little less than 30 degrees inclination, a smidgen less. I think it was called 30.08 less. Maybe we had 30.07. Since that was a very small error, it didn't hurt us one bit. But that was the one thing where a new technique, even though it was called for in the flight plan, disturbed the whole system. That's why I was objecting to it, because I'd never done it that way. I'd never terminated burn 5 by turning the switches OFF. Yet it was there. I just never caught it in simulation; no one caught me doing it wrong in simulation. With the instructors, we did burn 5's any number of times just here at KSC. They didn't catch me. And when I did it with Houston simulations - every burn we had here, by the way, was done with Houston - they didn't catch it. They didn't throw in another extra DELTA-V, so that was why I was surprised. If I hadn't done burn 5 with them, then I wouldn't have argued with you. So they were thinking on their time that I didn't know about it, and that's the kind of stuff I don't want to have happen, that you shouldn't have happen.

In the same light (I have to say this) we shouldn't be that iron bound to a burn, but the technique was - I'd never shut a burn off that way. All our mode 4's I could shut off within 2 or 3 feet per second with those same switches; I trained for that. That's the way you shut off mode 4's because when you got 3000 feet up there, you could go from a hundred feet per second to 2300 feet per second. We were cutting those off right on the money. It's a technique we knew how to do in simulation, but not that burn; that's the whole point. I guess we'll just have to give the crew a briefing on that stuff.

SCHIRRA — It worked, I'm not making it a major crisis; it wasn't. Okay. Did you talk about window photography?

REP — Right. We've gone over that.

SCHIRRA — I'm very concerned about those windows, I might add: I talked to Kennedy, and I talked to Healy about that today.

3.3.14 Passive Thermal Control Test

CUNNINGHAM — The passive thermal control test was the one which was run twice with slight variations. I guess what accounted for the 101 percent, among other things, was the fact that we did the pitch attitude.

EISELE — This was a test aimed at seeing what kind of cross coupling, or coning, you could get if you tried to set up a small roll rate with absolute zero rates in pitch and yaw. It was also to see how long it takes for that attitude to diverge in pitch and yaw in a coupling and whatever torques there were on the spacecraft. It seemed to cone out pretty rapidly during this test. I really think that's because we are in an earth orbit, and even though you are up a couple of hundred miles you're still getting some torquing and some interference from the atmosphere.

CUNNINGHAM — I show that the coning angle went out to about 4 or 5 degrees, didn't it?

EISELE — Yes, in the course of that 20 minutes or so, it was about 4 or 5 degrees. The part of it we were concerned with and discussing was the fact that the test required a period of about 20 minutes in tight deadband prior to the time that you initiated this slow roll and went to free in pitch and yaw. The intent of this period, primarily, was to damp out the pitch and yaw rates. We had found out earlier in the flight, that the best way to damp out the rates was to use the manual pulse mode rather than rate damping. The tight deadband served no purpose other than to eat into the RCS fuel budget, and generate small rates in pitch and yaw, which we never did zero out. We tried to explain that to ground controllers and apparently it never was fully understood by the people responsible for this DTO. So we went ahead and did it as programmed and found that the coning was significant.

CUNNINGHAM — I have a suggestion for the procedure. I think that one of the things they did was that they attempted to free the attitude hold just as they hit 200 miles going up.

EISELE — Yes.

CUNNINGHAM — And it would seem to me that after we made the suggestion, especially after the worry about perigee torquing, they would have attempted to have the test finished at 200 miles coming down.

EISELE — Coming down, yes, and that would get you away from having to do a tight maneuver near perigee.

CUNNINGHAM — That's right, they would have had better data, and less complications by outside torques.

EISELE — Yes. Well, in retrospect, I don't think it was all that significant. It would have optimized the test a little more, but we did accomplish several things. We found there was some coning. I think it remains to be seen on translunar flights, where this maneuver might apply, whether or not you really do get any significant coning over that period.

CUNNINGHAM — Yes, certainly.

EISELE — The other aspect of the test, and they added on another part to it, was to do a slow pitch maneuver rather than a roll maneuver. We performed that in the same manner with the tight deadband for 20 minutes, and then went to free to do the pitch. I don't know if that turned out any better. I don't believe it did; we still had some crossed coupling in the other two axes.

3.3.15 Window Photography

CUNNINGHAM — On the window photography, we took stills through the window, before S-IVB SEP. We took still shots of the window post-S-IVB SEP. I believe I focused on the window using S0368 film. We also took two shots during the disrupt time when Wally and I went to bed the night before deorbit. These are part of the data that's already in the photo lab. We took many pictures through the window focused at infinity in our normal course of events, so we made no special pictures to fill that part of the DTO. They wanted films of the window coating and degradation where we pitched 180, rolled 90, yawed 180; we declined to do them. It was a rather purist approach to the thing. We believe we had significant data on the window degradation. We made many visual reports and tracked the degradation of the windows throughout the flight. The degradation could have been studied a lot better had we not resulted in being in stable II after landing. The windows, except for the rendezvous windows, were vented between the panes, and we ended up with sea water getting in there and washing the panes.

EISELE — In general, the rendezvous windows stayed essentially pure throughout the flight. The side windows degraded slowly, and the hatch window was the worst of all. It got a lot of condensation in it.

CUNNINGHAM — I think we should make a point of the fact that there was a significant difference in window 1 and window 5. Window 1 was located next to the urine dump, and we were continually having little crystals settling on it.

EISELE — It had a lot of crud on the outside of it - particles.

CUNNINGHAM — In addition to having any other degradation on the window, we had these particles settling on it. I never did have any of those particles on my windows.

EISELE — It never got over to window 5.

3.3.16 ECS Secondary Coolant Loop Test

EISELE — The secondary coolant loop test was conducted at 183 hours and 40 minutes into the flight. We initiated the secondary coolant loop operation, checked on the primary coolant loop and ran for 3 hours at an essentially drifting flight power load. The secondary coolant loop operated absolutely as smoothly as possible throughout the entire test duration. At the end of 3 hours we powered up enough equipment to add about 400 watts to the load. We continued to let the temperature stabilize for an hour and a half and then ran another 3 hours, and it operated every bit as well. During that entire time I believe we utilized about 3 to 5 pounds of water in the waste water tank. Glycol evaporator OUT temperatures, the secondary loop, were maintained between 40 to 48 degrees Fahrenheit. The radiator OUT temperature was generally between 40 and a little over 40 degrees and slightly over 50 degrees. I guess the key thing here is the fact that I felt the secondary coolant loop operated absolutely faultlessly. I would not like to lead to any false conclusions here, because the secondary evaporator did not dry out during this 7 and one half hour run. We should not imply that it was any better or any worse than the primary evaporator. The primary evaporator ran on numerous occasions for longer than 7 and one half hours without drying out and yet would still end up drying out at some time. So I don't know what kind of problem we had there with the drying out of the primary evaporator; we don't know for sure that the secondary evaporator isn't subject to the same thing. The DTO required a comment on the condition of the secondary cabin temperature valves. The secondary cabin temperature valves did stay in the MAX cool position throughout the test. Smooth test.

EISELE — I thought you might make mention of the fact that we still don't think this is a very good system to fly with by itself. For example, if you were having to make a long flight back from the moon or to the moon, the G&N system would not be cooled by it.

CUNNINGHAM — No, that's a significant point. The G&N system is not on it, but I stand considerably higher in my regards for the secondary coolant loop test.

EISELE — Yes, it does quite an adequate job of cooling everything else.

CUNNINGHAM — That's right, we operated it during the redundant component checks at one time; it operated for a period of about 15 minutes to an hour. During that period of time the primary radiator outlet temperature, which was operating also, went down from about 50 degrees all the way down to 10 degrees. It does a lot of cooling. We also utilized the secondary coolant loop for reentry. It was very satisfactory.

EISELE — It bypassed the radiators and used the water boiler in the secondary loop for entry.

3.3.17 SCS Backup Align

EISELE — The first surprise on this one was that the south set of stars were not sufficient. We found out that the south set stars were only visible during the night pass for about 6 or 8 minutes, and we didn't think that was long enough to permit us to do a proper assessment of these backup alignment techniques. So we consulted with the ground; they came up with the north set of stars, Navi and Polaris. So we used those, and the test of them worked out very well. Wally maneuvered the spacecraft around to the approximate attitude on the IMU ball, and then I took over in the G&N station with the impulse controller. It was a rather difficult and tedious task to try to align the thing very precisely because you have to control all three axes simultaneously. What I attempted to do first was to take the key star, which was Navi, and put it on the 50 degree mark of the telescope's crosshair, and then go to attitude hold in pitch and roll. I figured that would hold it on the spot. Then I did a pure yaw maneuver to bring the other star on the line. Well, when I did that, I forgot that the SPS lets go of the attitude hold in all three axes anytime you break the hand controller out of the détente. So it didn't hold on that 50 degree mark, and I ended up going back to pure pulse for all three axes.

After numerous attempts to get both stars in exactly the right position, I finally settled for a condition where I had Polaris right on the line and Navi very close, but not quite right on that 50 degree mark. I tried it several times and finally settled for what I thought was the best feasible thing to do, so we coarse aligned the CDG at that time. Actually, Wally was holding the GDC align button and he released it when I said, "Mark." We took that as our alignment. We then flew back to the 0-0-0 angles on the GDC ball and made the comparison with the IMU which was also aligned for that purpose. We found that the error was on the order of a quarter of a degree, which I thought was pretty fantastic. I'm not sure whether we just lucked out or whether it's really that good. The point is, it's tedious and time consuming and uses some amount of RCS fuel, but it does work, and it works very well. I would not hesitate at all to use that for either an IMU or an SCS backup alignment if I had to.

3.3.18 SPS Burns 6 and 7

EISELE — I can cover burn 6 because that's one I did in the left seat. That was another SCS control burn with the G&N monitor, and again we found that the SCS results were quite comparable to the G&N burns. Everything went nominal, and we cut off on the DELTA-V counter with very good results. I'm sorry, burn number 6 was a G&N minimum impulse burn, which was just like burn 4, also very nominal. Burn 7 was the SCS burn. Both of them went as planned and were quite nominal in all respects. No problems.

3.3.20 SXT Calibration

EISELE — The sextant calibration, I think we already discussed this earlier. We only did one sextant calibration test. It was called for a second time in the flight plan, but we were advised to delete it from the flight plan. Apparently they felt the first one was good enough, or else they weren't getting anything out of it. I don't know which, but we did not do the second one.

3.3.21 PIPA Bias and EMS Bias Test

EISELE — I did it twice during the flight, once very early in the mission, and once later on but I don't remember when during the latter days of the flight. The PIPA bias hardly shifted at all during the entire mission. The PIPA bias compensation values that were loaded in prior to launch were quite adequate for the whole flight. The difference between what I measured with the test and what was loaded in was on the order of .01, whatever the units are. (I don't know what they are.) But it was a very small difference, and it was quite stable. It was interesting to note that the Y PIPA had absolutely zero bias in it. The thing was perfect, as near as we were able to measure. The first time I did it, I was quite concerned. I thought perhaps the Y PIPA wasn't working at all because it got no bias whatsoever for 4 minutes. The ground had the same reservation, and we actually went as far as doing a small thrusting maneuver with the RCS sideways and then back to see if the PIPA's really worked, and it turned out that it did. It measured the velocity very nicely. The EMS Bias Test. Wally performed the EMS bias test at various times in the flight, usually before a burn. We'd check it out, and we would simply go to DELTA-V in AUTO and watch the DELTA-V counter count. Usually, we got one tenth or two tenths of a foot per second over a minute or two. Very small bias.

SCHIRRA — On the EMS bias test, I tested the EMS as it would be used. I didn't feel that there was any reason to test it any other way. We did run it for one long period of time about 5 minutes, I guess, but the real valid test of that is the 30 seconds that it is ON prior to the burn plus the burn time. This should be done prior to the burn, so you will know what the residuals are from it. As an example, we had a 36-second one; it was a 6 second burn. The bias was one tenth of a foot per second. I think that is all that needs to be said on that EMS bias test. The other interesting thing I might make note of is that there was nothing on the EMS, nothing on it.

SCHIRRA — I'd like to make this statement because I've spoken about it during the flight readiness review about having a hardline go across the LEB, so you won't have to make and break. I still think it would be the way to do it. You have got to have that hose in there anyway for urine management when you're in the suits to dump from the couch. You do that; we did when we first started out because there is no way to get all three guys down as you get ready to unsuit. So you do have to bring that hose up from the urine nozzle to a man in the suit.

EISELE — I guess on water management, the only management we did was to dump the waste water periodically. When it got up to 95 percent, we dumped it down to about 20 percent.

SCHIRRA — We did it one time voluntarily and they never called us on it.

CUNNINGHAM — There are two points I think ought to be clarified. One is the fact that you can't open B8 which has got about eight or ten cans of 16mm film in it, in our case. You can't open B8 with that little valve hooked on there. You should have a shorter valve or one coming out at an angle if you are going to have something protrude at all.

3.4.17 SPS Propellant Thermal Control

CUNNINGHAM — I would like to make sure that it is well understood that apparently no thermal control was required for the SPS propellant tanks temperature. The only time that any work was done with it was for ground request and to verify heater operation.

3.4.18 Auxiliary Propellant Gauging System

CUNNINGHAM — We used the auxiliary gauging system for the long burn, 66 seconds, and that was in order for the ground to be able to collect comparative data. The primary system worked as advertised. It was interesting to me that after the first two burns we showed more oxidizer than propellant left; but by the time we finished up, we were showing more in the other ratio. I would assume this was down within the accuracy of the meter. My personal feeling was that I had that meter quantity reading to probably about plus or minus -5 percent at best.

SCHIRRA — There's the answer. Reduce O2 tank fan cycles, and that is it.

CUNNINGHAM — Yes.

3.4.26 SCS Backup
Alignment Procedure

CUNNINGHAM — Have you already discussed SCS backup alignment procedures, Donn?

EISELE — Yes.

3.4.29 Launch Vehicle
Propellant Pressure
Displays

CUNNINGHAM — Did you want to say anything about those?

SCHIRRA — I called all those numbers down.

CUNNINGHAM — Yes. Easy to read, no vibration during boost, etc.

SCHIRRA — Let's compare my numbers that I called down with the ground readout, and if they're good, let's get those back to prime. They weren't evaluated prior to that. That's why I didn't want them to be prime. Do you get my argument on that? Remember, we called down when we were venting? I wrote them in the log. Let's correlate those with time, and if the instruments are good, let's bring it back to prime. When it's onboard.

SLAYTON — But it was neither prime onboard nor prime on the ground by the time you flew. It was no longer a consideration.

SCHIRRA — Agreed. But there's an MTS case, and there is also a leak case.

SLAYTON — Okay. The MTS case we threw out.

SCHIRRA — I would like to get the instruments back to prime if they checked out. If they just read the same thing I did, then I would go by the instruments. We've had a flight test on it.

3.4.30 Window
Deposits

CUNNINGHAM — I believe we described this in real time very adequately.

SCHIRRA — We have that on tape.

EISELE — We have that on tape, too.

3.4.31 Manual Retro
Attitude Orientation

CUNNINGHAM — Did you hit that or not, Wally?

SLAYTON — You commented on all of them. I think we have all of them.

SCHIRRA — We got that in real time; I didn't have any problem with that. The ground goofed on that first one. They gave me the wrong angles, and we got that straightened out in real time.

3.4.33 CSM ARIA
Communications

CUNNINGHAM — I would like to add a comment under Item 33. CSM ARIA communications were not really all that great. It turned out that S-band through ARIA was definitely clearer on board the spacecraft than the VHF was. To my knowledge, that was about the only time I noticed a significant difference between VHF and S-band. For the non-ARIA contacts, the difference was negligible as far as I was concerned. It was nice to have ARIA communications, but I don't know that we ever utilized them for anything other than standing by. On the communications, it was nice to know that you had the contact. We did not have these in the flight plan. It was always passed up real time from the CAP COMM so we would have it.

3.4.34 CSM Structural
Performance

CUNNINGHAM — I can't think of any comments we might make on CSM structural performance.

EISELE — Yes, I do have one. I looked at the MET after landing, and that can still be looked at, the MET glass. The failures we were seeing in that and the cracks didn't change before I exited the spacecraft. Remember, we had the little crack on one side that has been described pretty carefully? We didn't remember to tape it there.

CUNNINGHAM — No we didn't.

EISELE — But it did not change as a result of landing.

SCHIRRA — What you mean is that the crack we got from the burn is worse then the landing.

EISELE — That is the way I would academically put it. That should be looked at and documented.

SCHIRRA — A hole was put in the spacecraft after landing by someone inside, on board the ship. A Hasselblad camera lens (not ours) was dropped right where my feet were in the aft bulkhead. I am not sure whether that data has been recorded back here, but I'm sure that was taken up... The only other thing that we had as a surprise structurally was this loud, loud noise during entry that caused me to switch rings. That's a big opening in my mind. I don't know whether it was structural or thruster or what, but it was a very loud audible noise on my side of the spacecraft. We all went into some degree of shock at that point; whatever that was, I don't think it could have been transitory, much too high for supersonic or hypersonic effects. This was way up there. The time that best documents this event - I would say the event occurred probably 4 or 5 seconds before I started pushing circuit breakers in. Not much more. It was an awfully fast response. Reaction time was almost instantaneous because we were hair-triggered anyway. Those circuit breakers were going on awful fast. As soon as Donn said something about pitch, of sixteen circuit breakers (only three of which were in originally), all were in.

CUNNINGHAM — Another item that comes under structural performance is that of vibration and resonances, and I didn't notice any resonances in the spacecraft in orbit.

3.4.35 Crew Activities

EISELE — I think I've evaluated and discussed practically every activity.

5.0 LANDING RECOVERY

SCHIRRA — We took our time aboard ship. Knowing we were going to stay overnight, we didn't rush through the medical area. I think the doctors were very cooperative on our request, giving us a little quiet time. One of the errors made was about the three pair of sneakers; two were size 9, and the other was size 11. I assumed that they would know our sizes. We did have our own blue coveralls here; that's what we came home in; and they had flight suits available for us, so that was covered very well. However, they didn't have the right size skivvies.

EISELE — I thought the operation after we got aboard the carrier ran about as smooth as could be expected.

SCHIRRA — I think you ought to let the crew have one good night off the ship, at least. We felt so good the next day that I just couldn't believe it.

CUNNINGHAM — I don't think that either Donn or I really realized until after it was over just how much benefit it was.

5.1 Impact on Touchdown

SCHIRRA — In the flight plan, I wrote down, "Apollo landing is a crash," and by no means is it; it was the softest landing I've had in the history of this business. Not to make a Monday morning quarterback, it really was. I'm not trying to sell anything to anybody or justify my decision by what resulted in the landing; it was a very soft landing. I've had harder landings on a runway in an airplane. To add to that, it was - I'd say, the waves were at least 4 to 5 feet high.

CUNNINGHAM — It looked like about 4 foot waves on top of some pretty healthy swells...

SCHIRRA — We had winds up in the area of over 18, maybe 20, 21 knots. I know those numbers because when I sail, I know when I have 18 knots.

CUNNINGHAM — Yes, there was a squall there.

SCHIRRA — I would have taken my main down and run on the jib, which means it is over 20. I've been in the same kind of water on a real rough day off Galveston, so go get your things and get that kind of water for egress training. It wasn't a wild sea; it wasn't a wild sea.

CUNNINGHAM — No, but I'll tell you, I think it was similar to the sea we had for our egress training on 101 in the Gulf.

SCHIRRA — Except for the froth on the top of the waves, the white caps, you know.

CUNNINGHAM — You're right, it was.

SCHIRRA — The sensation I had - we were really braced in that thing - gosh, you just can't imagine how tight we were in there. Such a surprise, it just plopped. Plopped, not a POW. Much less of a surprise, for example, than the SPS burn. How does that grab you for surprises?

SCHIRRA — We didn't expect the SPS to do that, that's one. We expected horrors on landing; that's probably why I can say that very safely. The spacecraft did not tumble. That is very important to make that point clear, and we said it on the tape on the ship, I know. It rested, and we looked at each other and said, "My gosh," and I looked out the window and saw we were going over because the chutes were falling down as you would expect. It torqued us over, and we were just about X-axis horizontal. We got the chutes off, and then I could see them going down in the water as we moved along overtaking them because they stopped once they were released, went over and beyond them; even in stable II, we were moving.

CUNNINGHAM — The thing that impressed me about the thing right there, Wally, is how very quickly we were upside down. We started covering the postlanding checklist in orbit; Wally had looked at it the night before; I reviewed it again before entry. All I had to do was put two circuit breakers in; and Wally had to turn two switches off. I was pleased that we hit the water; we looked, hit the vent, and the chute was off in a couple of seconds.

S68-49661

S68-49539

S68-49529

68-H-990

68-H-988

68-H-993

SCHIRRA — I don't know how we got off it took me 14 seconds.

CUNNINGHAM — You did turn the ELS AUTO off?

SCHIRRA — Yes. The cover guard on the ELS logic switch has points on it; I didn't want that out for landing. I've been trained long ago; I wanted that off again for landing so I didn't get my knee in it in case I did come up. So that was down. You know what the other possibility is? It is that maybe it didn't come disconnected; it just collapsed. It didn't come disconnected in 14 seconds, and that is part of the reason we ended up over.

SCHIRRA — We were being blown over, I knew that. We could see the chutes up.

CUNNINGHAM — We were kind of going, yes, but you know the chutes were still there sometime later because I didn't see them for a long time.

EISELE — I had the feeling it took several seconds before we actually got over in stable II.

SCHIRRA — I disagree with you on our very hurriedly getting in II. You guys hit the switches very quickly, but you are right, the chutes may not have come off at that particular time.

CUNNINGHAM — What I am getting at is that I was surprised. We hadn't really gone through this part of our checklist in training very often - you know, the postlanding part, but it went click, click, click, and they were off. It was faster than I expected, and the 14 seconds…

SCHIRRA — I don't think they were off; that's the point.

CUNNINGHAM — That's right.

SCHIRRA — They collapsed, and we cruised along with the wind over the chutes which were in the water. We had relative motion. I remember looking at the chutes out of the left window and seeing the lines and this big squid down there. I was reminded of that poor scuba diver in Mercury days who leaped back up on the life raft when he saw that monster down there.

EISELE — What was it, the chutes?

SCHIRRA — Yes. Poor guy was white all the next day.

5.2 Postlanding
Checklist

CUNNINGHAM — There are some differences here on the postlanding checklist, incidentally.

SCHIRRA — Somebody on Recovery I called for the beacon lights on, and I had no reason to turn them on in daylight. So I turned them on and verified that they worked.

CUNNINGHAM — I think - I am not sure if they - yes, they were calling for the beacon lights. When they kept calling, I first thought they were calling for the beacon radar.

SCHIRRA — Air Boss said, "No, beacon lights." I went "click." and I said, "Are there beacon lights now?" And they said, "Wait a minute and we'll see. Roger. You have beacon lights," and I turned them back off again.

CUNNINGHAM — Maybe it was because it was such poor weather.

SCHIRRA — You shouldn't have to use them in daylight is my point.

CUNNINGHAM — On the checklist itself, we ran through the test down stabilization portion. We got down to the part about cooling for 10 minutes and then filling float bags for 7 minutes. We cooled for about 8 minutes and turned them on. It took about four and a half minutes to upright, and we ran it for 2 minutes after upright. Thinking back on it, remember they weren't all really full up Wally, when we shut down. Actually, we let them run on for awhile. I suspect we probably should have filled it for 7 minutes plus 2 minutes.

SCHIRRA — Let me ask you this, because I came out slow. I was trying to find some gear; I couldn't find my sunglasses. I went over on your side, and then you were hurrying me up, and the choppers were coming. But I couldn't determine whether you had powered it down. Had you?

CUNNINGHAM — Oh, yes. We went B buses off. It wasn't like the simulator because there was a lot of light coming in.

SCHIRRA — Oh, that's right. It's the sunlight that gets bright. And the hatch was open. You're so used to getting light; in the simulator, it goes dark when…

CUNNINGHAM — That's right. When you turn the main buses off, it goes dark.

68-H-989

68-H-992

68-H-994

68-H-995

68-H-996

68-H-1054

SCHIRRA — That's the question I had.

CUNNINGHAM — Then we did go to the stable II position, stable II checklist, and the surprise I had. Remember at first it says if the battery bus is less than - I didn't really read this - but if the voltage is less than twenty-seven and one half volts, you're supposed to pull one of the batteries off the line. And I said, "Well, hell, the meter's reading zero," and then a couple of seconds later, I realized that I was reading main bus voltages instead of battery bus voltages.

SCHIRRA — By the way, let's say something at that point. That was the eeriest feeling I had. I didn't know where in the hell we were. I knew we were supposed to be with the computer I, and when that stabled II, I was very much alone. I wasn't alone in Gemini and Mercury. Thoughts like Scott Carpenter's incident went through my mind, and all of a sudden I didn't know what to do. I said, "Here we are stable II. We may be stuck there."

CUNNINGHAM — You know what added to it? You know, what added to it was the fact that the weather was so much worse, and we figured if we blew it, we must have blown it many, many miles. Because here we were sitting with weather that was not anywhere close to what we were expecting.

EISELE — Yes. I figured the computer had really bombed us into some place hundreds of miles away from where we should be.

SCHIRRA — We were sitting there, and Donn at this time said, "Does anybody feel sick?" And Walt and I wouldn't help him because he just went white and grabbed his barf bag, which was, by the way, a good technique, I wasn't as well prepared as Donn was for this, in this sense. Before we started down, we'd gone all over the things we were going to have in our suit pockets, (just so we wouldn't have any PTK's in our suit pockets), all the stuff we wanted to take off the spacecraft on us, and we also had a fecal bag. Donn was smart enough to break his bag down at the bag. I just had a package, and that's wrong. We should have had our bags out. I was just hurting myself, in that I was in a hurry, and I said, "Oh, I won't get seasick." Well, I lucked out and I didn't.

EISELE — Well, he didn't take a pill. His confidence kind of bothered me.

CUNNINGHAM — I've never been seasick in my life, but after being out in the Gulf, I was all in favor of taking a pill up there.

SCHIRRA — I don't think the other guys did this, not get seasick, unless they got sick and just got over it.

EISELE — That was my trouble. I had dry heaves; there was nothing in my stomach.

SCHIRRA — There was a lot of water on your stomach; you were pulling on that water gun the last 2 days. You were drinking water all the time.

EISELE — Yes, but water doesn't stay in your stomach very long. All I got up was some gastric juices and that damn Marzine pill that I had swallowed about an hour earlier.

CUNNINGHAM — We didn't do any of the next damn business because we had already planned on getting out of our suits. We didn't want to lug an extra 55 pounds around after landing.

SCHIRRA — I didn't manage to get all the way out of my suit by the time that the hatch was opened. I was down in the LEB wrestling with it, and it's awfully hard to get out of those suits. I can only say that the liner must be attached to the suit in order to get out of it easily. The neck ring and my arms both came out when I got the suit off. Everything else just peeled apart.

<u>5.3 Communications</u>   SCHIRRA — COMM was a problem; they just barely got us before touchdown. And then, they snapped out as we went under the water, and so did the VHF.

CUNNINGHAM — Then we got to the stable II checklist; we turned off the radio, and after uprighting again we turned it back on, and it worked fine. Incidentally, we had VHF COMM on the way down.

SCHIRRA — They heard us, and they heard me say "IFR clearance straight in, no delay expected." They got a big kick out of that one. They also got three way cuts on us on their electronic homing gear. They had lots of electronic gear. That's another one I want to bring in while I'm talking about COMM. This particular ship as an anti-submarine warfare ship has an airplane they call the E-1 electronics airborne CIC. They really had us cold. They picked the spacecraft up in the water on their radar. It has a 17-foot radar antenna. They picked us up, no strain. It's a damn good device to have out there on the recovery force. That backed up the cut we had; we had a three position cut. For some reason or other that beacon didn't work on descent.

CUNNINGHAM — I'm suspicious about the fact that we've got two separate antennas that come out, and I know that it's kind of a tricky antenna to stow before launch and to come out. I almost have the impression that it hung up, that the one that the beacons are on hung up and eventually broke loose.

SCHIRRA — Voice COMM was very good, I think. It might be worthwhile to bring this up. You keep forgetting that you don't have the big heavy transmitter that everybody else has, and you can't understand why you can't talk back when you hear everybody. That's just the problem; it never will be changed.

5.4 Spacecraft Status

5.5 Battery Power

Spacecraft's status are all GO, other than the batteries are probably low, and we all knew that.

5.6 Postlanding ECS System

CUNNINGHAM — By this time, after we'd cut the loads off - any of the main bus loads - we were sitting at about twenty-eight and a half volts on each battery bus, and it had been working its way up from the 25.2 we had on SEP, until we were actually up to about twenty-six during re-entry. We had been creeping back up, but for postlanding, we had about twenty-eight to twenty-eight and a half, something like that.

5.7 Ventilation

I goofed on the ventilation and internal temperatures; it all comes together as one thing. In the stable II position, you cannot get any ventilation. There's no suit band; you're just living on an open suit. There's another reason for not having the helmet on, not that I even thought of that beforehand. We would have had to have our helmets off. We would have had to take them off right away in any event.

SCHIRRA — Right after landing, as soon as everything settles down. We did know that we had to get the helmet off, but that was not one of my considerations prior to re-entry.

5.8 Internal Temperatures

SCHIRRA — We were really dying in there of the heat, I hit this thing and said, "Well, that must do something." Walt's got this sock hanging from his face, and whoosh, it's gone, and the whole cockpit occludes. It just fogged up.

CUNNINGHAM — I didn't even have a duct on the thing, and it was blowing down nicely on me. I think there is a point to make here, Wally, and that is that subsequent crews really - that little phase, when you run through the simulator on reentries, you generally don't really run through this stuff...

SCHIRRA — Well, what we didn't do, Walt, was play it all the way on water egress in the Gulf.

CUNNINGHAM — Yes, that's right, because we were so anxious to not...

SCHIRRA — We had one part we were trying to get done, which was to get that survival beacon radiating to the spacecraft. By the time we got into the Gulf (this version for egress), Walt went down into the LEB and we had the hatch open by that time. Walt came crawling out of there; he was getting sick; and from then on, it was all get out. I guess that's why we blew that particular phase of that training, or I would have played the switch, and we would have had the ducts out. We were in a hurry to get out of there. I guess that was our mistake; we shouldn't have done that. It wasn't fatal, but it's something the other crews can take advantage of. Oddly enough, in my estimation, the spacecraft was more comfortable to ride in as a boat in stable II. It's a lousy position to be in...

CUNNINGHAM — I agree with you.

SCHIRRA — ...but it damped better in the swells and waves...

CUNNINGHAM — Actually, there was far less motion...

SCHIRRA — I think we'll go ahead and make that a recommendation. You can't get fresh air, so that's a problem. There is no way to use that as a technique. There in stable II is where we saw - I think my description of the windows will hold now - 1, 3, and 5 getting water inside up to two panes away from us. It means they're vented, and that's why they got this condensation on them. There's no sense running detailed studies on the damn things; they've been washed off with salt water. They whirled up and down inside them just like you're trying to wash them. They're all scrubbed off very nicely. Now you can see water crystals in there. Numbers 2 and 4 were not vented, and it's quite obvious that water didn't come in. Another thing we noticed in stable II was a little bit of water down in the tunnel hatch area, which is our own water.

EISELE — We wiped off those glycol pipes for several hours before deorbit, so I'm sure that a good bit of water collected in there. It just ran the lowest point, which happened to be the tunnel hatch when we were upside down.

5.9 Spacecraft Attitude

EISELE — The spacecraft attitude was very poor. Donn's whole world came to an end. That's about it.

SCHIRRA — But when we got back to stable I, we were trying to get the postlanding ducts from Donn. He had them in his pocket, and he was down in the LEB bemoaning his fate, loudly bemoaning. We finally got all up, and Walt gave me one shortly. We couldn't feel any flow at all, and I went down below my girth ring. There's a postlanding vent valve control, and I said, "It's on NORMAL. Okay, Walt, pull the lever." And Walt dutifully pulled the lever up there which is the overlock. For some reason or other, I didn't turn the damn switch on.

CUNNINGHAM — It's supposed to go to HIGH.

SCHIRRA — It has a vent switch; I've looked at it for all these years and never used it.

CUNNINGHAM — We let it sit there for quite awhile, because I remember saying, "They're hanging there."

SCHIRRA — The real fun of this is I finally - sometime after...

5.10 Couch Position

SCHIRRA — On the couch position, as far as I could tell, I looked at the struts, and I'm sure that the people have done that since those couches didn't stroke from 1 mm.

CUNNINGHAM — It would take 22 g's to break it out, wouldn't it?

5.11 Internal Pressure

SCHIRRA — Internal. There was no problem with that. We did use the dump technique and locked up at the - what was it, 1,000 or whatever you...

CUNNINGHAM — We were locked up before the mains. Oh, no, between drogues and mains, we went to dump instead of just to boost on re-entry. We had time to do it, and this was just...

SCHIRRA — We were not rushed on the way down. We really weren't. In fact, I didn't make that point way back, but at .05 g in re-entry, I said, "Okay, tighten up, gang," so we tightened up on our straps. We tightened up again after drogues, tightened up again after mains. You're squeezing the couch to 1 g. That was my point. We really had ourselves tighten up. At zero g, you can't get your butt forward on the suit or the seat pan, and when you get the 1 g weight on there, you just really went in. The harness did move.

SCHIRRA — We used the locks on the harness positions in zero g for retention. I was worried about the straps; they became a little more supple, (if I could call it that) than they were originally.

EISELE — You did mention it was very hot in there.

SCHIRRA — Yes, indeed.

CUNNINGHAM — Just to make the point real clear on internal pressure, we did go to the dump position on the one cabin pressure relief valve, which allowed us to get rid of about one psi differential. And we did close both the cabin pressure relief valves at, I would estimate, 800 feet, something like that. Right, Wally? I didn't start reading to you until you called a thousand. Well, at someplace less than a thousand feet, we locked them up so that the pressure differential was not very much.

5.12 Recovery Operations

SCHIRRA — On recovery operations, we mentioned the fact that we didn't hit the SARAH. One of my biggest surprises was that I felt - I read the recovery stuff before we left.

5.13 Grappling Hook Deployment

SCHIRRA — I thought it was going to be a call from them to throw out the grappling hook if they wanted. It turns out that the only time they use a grappling hook is for the pyro medic type deployment. When you use choppers, you don't need the grappling hook. So that's the tip on that.

SCHIRRA — The ship wasn't even trained for it because they didn't have that requirement.

CUNNINGHAM — They hadn't even heard about it.

SCHIRRA — They were all surprised. The Air Boss, the carrier, and the skipper...

CUNNINGHAM — Where it did affect us though was when Wally said, "Do you want us to deploy the grappling hook?" because it requires a little lead time.

SCHIRRA — They couldn't understand me, said I was garbled.

CUNNINGHAM — We were talking to the chopper pilot, and he said he didn't hear it. He said if he'd heard it at all he probably would have said "Roger," meaning we would have been busy. Instead of getting out of the suits, we would have been busy going under the couches and trying to take the screws out and throw that silly thing out...

SCHIRRA — ...when he didn't really want it. At dinner that night, he said, "If I had said, 'Roger', he wouldn't have understood." That meant we would have gone all the way underneath the LEB under the couches to get that thing out. So that was kind of a bad one.

On the other item, I found out why they didn't want me to hoist aboard, which I might have considered; as it was, they were so far away from us. The reason they were not right there was because the skipper took the ship and moved it out of there. He wanted to get out from underneath us, and he took the choppers out from underneath us, too. That's the only risk, I think, in coming in in low ceiling areas. They don't have time to dodge you if you really are in the predicted landing place. So that was a pretty good hit, I'd say.

<u>5.14 Egress</u>

At any rate, that was one of the reasons why it took a little longer for recovery than it normally would have. We were about 4 or 5 miles from the carrier, away from the spot. If it had been the blue-bird day they had the day before, they would have been prepared and suspected that I would be hoisted aboard, but I agreed that I wasn't going to be. But it would have been perfectly all right to have been hoisted aboard on a clear, calm blue-bird day. Doc said the ship was an old ship built in '43 and he was a little worried about stressing the gear. This was just a feeling, not an engineering job. The egress out of there was no strain. They had two life rafts outside, had a JG scuba diver type and two other men there. They handled themselves very well; so there was no problem. We just got out one at a time, and then they picked up all three of us. There was drizzling rain when we were getting out. We just flat-out got good and wet anyway. That's one reason I don't like to get out. You just get sopping wet.

REP — Did they have COMM with you before you got out?

SCHIRRA — No, and this is interesting. In stable II the sea dye marker was leaking out. We could see it. So I said, "Oh, it must be in automatic deployment; I didn't know that." But it wasn't and it turns out that you have to deploy the sea dye marker to expose the phone Jack. They couldn't find the phone Jack. That's the reason they didn't get to that. But that's the key to it. They can't get to the phone Jack unless you deploy the sea dye marker. So it looks like SOP is - that you've got to deploy the sea dye marker no matter what. That was something we never even knew.

SCHIRRA — When we got the hatch open, as every time in the past, in the block I training, either in the tank or out in the Gulf, it was always the same: we wanted out fast. The other thing we wanted was to get the suits off. They are hot and terribly uncomfortable. We had to help each other get the zippers undone. I got out of the suit and into the raft. There was a scuba tank in the raft.

EISELE — We got sopping wet just from getting out of the spacecraft and getting in the raft. I was just about shot. If I had had to put on one of those air-tight suits that they're talking about for the lunar returns, I would probably have passed out. You could run a good risk of that happening to somebody, maybe losing a crew member because of that.

SCHIRRA — I recommend a little cargo net around the raft that they can go in and not drown so that they would be able to cool off. The internal medicine is something else you are going to have to work on, but externally, there is no reason to isolate it.

CUNNINGHAM — Stay away from any other suited operations. We definitely wanted to be out of the suit because of the load that it would put on us. Getting back into our inflight coveralls was difficult. We were all sticky and wet, but we insisted.

SCHIRRA — They did have clothes in the chopper for us to wear.

SCHIRRA — This comment should be logged under area 5.0 and had to do with postland hatch operation. All during the early part of the flight, we noted the pressure on the hatch decreasing, and there was no callout for it. I elected to put the lever that was in the PRESS position to the NEUTRAL position to isolate the bottle from the hatch cylinder in case the cylinder was leaking, and over a number of days, it's not unreasonable that it would leak out. This way, we could save what was left in the upper bottle, the initial bottle, for the hatch operation. In postlanding, when we got back to stable position I, Donn Eisele, who is normally our center couch hatch man, wasn't available. This is part of my point. Fortunately, I did work with it enough when I was involved with the design of the system and I knew how to work it, but I had never actually done it. In this case, I had to do it. Walt was busy helping Donn, and I was the only one available to work on the hatch at the time. I ran the press lever outboard, and nothing came up. That bottle was green, so I had to bring the second bottle on the line to get the hatch to open.

REP — How hard was it to operate?

SCHIRRA — No problem at all. I had never operated it before with gloves off.

REP — Barehanded?

SCHIRRA — I think that's the first thing we might as well face up to. If you were doing it, you are going to be barehanded. You don't need the counter balance in orbit; you better not in fact. There are two things from that: one is that all crewmen should be trained to run that hatch in that phase of flight, the end of the flight, not early in the flight because then you are in orderly progression of events like countdown. Because I was so involved in the design of the thing, I knew exactly how to do it. I've never trained for it, just fortunate in my case. We were in a hurry to get it open because Donn was in bad shape and needed some fresh air.

CUNNINGHAM — I didn't realize that fact. You went at it even though you hadn't worked it before; you didn't seem to have any problems.

SCHIRRA — No, I didn't because I was on the drawing board the day they designed that thing; that's the reason I knew about it. We were just talking about the fact that I had to use number 2 bottle to open that hatch.

CUNNINGHAM — Incidentally, it didn't really drive that hatch off with great dispatch. No great exuberance, no.

SCHIRRA — It was surprising though to open up and get rain in my face.

EISELE — Boy, did that feel good!

SCHIRRA — What a transition though from this great sound little vessel with after-odors to the outside world. That's a point I'm glad I thought of; it just crossed my mind. It had to do with valving; that's as far as I'm concerned.

5.16 Crew Pickup

SCHIRRA — I thought the pickup went off very well. It was lousy weather, and that chopper pilot really worked like a dog to get in there. He had a lot of wind, and the spacecraft was blowing along, and this was a real hard job.

SCHIRRA — He did great; he did very well. We got into the chopper,... was in there with some drinking water for us. Right away Donn recovered; almost immediately, and I think he said, "I'm now back in my element."

REP — In a chopper, flying?

EISELE — I was airborne, anyway. Back in my natural element.

SCHIRRA — It was kind of nice to see the doctor we had worked with there, and he was prepared to go over the side…

EISELE — Yes, he had a…

SCHIRRA — We took our trusty little combs and combed our hair and sat back and relaxed.

6.0 Systems OPERATION

6.1 Guidance and Navigation

6.1.1 ISS Modes

EISELE — Item 1. ISS modes. ISS CDU's appeared to work perfectly throughout the flight as far as we could tell. We always got sensible numbers on the DSKY, for instance, if we wanted to look at gimbal angles, and the coarse and fine alignment of the IMU and so forth. The interface between the computer and the IMU appeared to work nominally; in fact, it worked almost perfectly. We were really astounded with the performance of the whole system. IMU turn-on and turn-off was a very simple thing to do. It operated just as advertised. The caging (which we could do by manually calling the coarse align routine or in some of the normal alignments, cage the IMU or drive it to a certain attitude) seemed to work just fine; we had no trouble.

Actually, we never did use the cage switch. If we ever had occasion to cage the IMU - that is, put it to NULL, we did it by means of the computer with the VERB 41, coarse and fine aligning. The coarse alignments that took place in the alignment programs varied quite a bit in terms of the gyro torquing angle errors that we got in the subsequent fine alignments. I think the reason that we sometimes got rather large coarse align errors was because often the spacecraft was moving when the coarse aligning was going on, and rather than waste or use up TCS fuel to stop these rates, we simply let it drift on, and this generated considerable error, sometimes on the order of 5 degrees coarse align. This wasn't the problem either.

It was surprising the first time it happened, and I got to thinking about why it did happen, and it was obviously the spacecraft motion. Normally, a coarse align error, with the spacecraft reasonably stable, is on the order of a couple of degrees if you are going from one attitude on the ball to the other. Fine align routines worked beautifully. I was very pleased with the results of that. Usually, if you were doing a P51 followed by a P52, when you do the fine alignment the first time through, you would take out the coarse align error with the gyro torquing numbers; and the second time through when you do the fine align, these numbers would be down in the thousandths of degrees, typically, or hundredths of degrees at worst. I found that IMU drift over a period of several hours was very small. You do a P52 fine align, and you would find again that the gyro torquing errors were quite small. I am sure the quantitative data is available on the tapes and so on.

Display of attitude errors. Really we didn't make much use of attitude error displays that I can recall, just never found it necessary. The feature that we did use was the attitude set feature, where you use the attitude error needles to indicate a difference between what you have set on the attitude set knobs and what your actual attitude is, either in reference to the IMU or the GDC.

CUNNINGHAM — Did you mention under one of these categories on the alignments, that in all fairness in all alignments we did - and I don't have any idea how many, I must have made a dozen myself and you made a lot more than that - we never had a final difference greater than four balls 1.

EISELE — Four balls I was the biggest we got; in fact, I'd say two thirds of them were zeros.

6.1.2 Optical Subsystems

CUNNINGHAM — Very good optics performance, which is the next item here. Power, that must mean one power telescope which they are talking about. I have already discussed the optical qualities. Basically, optical qualities of that telescope were identical to what we see in the simulator. There is a great deal of light loss in going through the instrument, and there is some distortion and blurring at the outer edges. I guess that also covers the light transmittance. It's not too good; you have to get dark adapted before you can see stars very well.

Mechanical drive is excellent in both RESOLVE and DIRECT modes and at any of the three speed selections. The drives for the sextant telescope are just very smooth; and tracking anything, be it landmarks or horizon, or stars, whatever, is very easy to do. Even with the spacecraft rotating up to half a degree a second, you can track stars very easily in the sextant. And I guess the mechanical drive for both of them are comparable.

EISELE — This has to do with the dumping. I think I've covered that before, but we will mention it here. At certain times, notably near sunset and sunrise, if you happened to be dumping fluids through the overboard dump at the time you are looking through the optics, you will see snowflakes out there which look very much like stars. You see a whole field of them, and it just obscures the entire star field. You can't tell the stars from the flakes of frozen particles.

REP — Does that occur during dumping?

EISELE — Yes, it occurs during dumping, mainly just before sunset and just after sunrise, if it's broad daylight. Usually if you are looking at the earth or some bright view there, they don't show up; and in the darkness, there is no light from the sun to reflect on them. This will be a problem on lunar missions; and I guess on a lunar flight, you will have to plan ahead to do your alignments. You will have to plan your venting and dumps so that they occur at some time other than when you plan to do IMU alignments.

OSS moding, zero optics mode worked pretty much as advertised. There is a good deal of overshoot when you go to zero optics. We did not bother with the ground technique of driving the trunnion angle to near zero. We simply threw the switch.

6.1.3 Computer Subsystem

EISELE — Computer subsystems: I don't really have much to say regarding instructions of programs other than that they seemed to work substantially as advertised. The one anomaly which I have not yet gotten the full word on is the business of the improper exit from program 20 which apparently set or reset a mark flag such that the next time I attempted to do marks with it, it would not take the marks. I think this is an anomaly that should have been uncovered and put in the so-called program notes. It was apparently a constraint on using the computer that we did not know about before flight. In general, I think that the programs in SUNDISK have been critiqued and criticized long before flight, and they are time-consuming and tedious to the extent of extra button pushings over what would really be required. I'm sure that the Colossus program will rectify most of those shortcomings.

EISELE — The CSS timer: the only timer function that we were aware of on board was the occasions when we called up the CMC clock time. It was always right on the money with the CTE; we never had a problem with that. In order to keep that clock from running out of time running out of bits in the section of the computer - you have to power up the computer at least once every 24 hours. That was not a problem because we powered it up every 8 hours or so anyway just to keep the state vector integrated forward so that when you did need the computer, you wouldn't have to wait maybe 20 minutes for it to catch up to present time. The display and keyboard - I'll skip these other items because I don't know anything about that; those would have to do mostly with the internal workings of it and that would be derived from ground data.

The DSKY and keyboard worked quite well as far as I could tell. All the buttons worked; we didn't have a single failure of any little element in the registers; we had no failures or problems with any of the 0 buttons. The status lights and warning lights worked just as they should. We did have a few restarts during the mission. The only one that was of any concern was the one that took place when we were trying to do program 22 and mark on the horizon. This was a rather hastily conceived test, I think, and was not properly checked out on the ground before it was read up to us. When I performed this exercise, we got a program alarm, a restart light, a CMC light, and the computer hung up, froze such that we could not make any entries into it with the keyboard.

We deliberated several minutes before taking any action, and I finally decided to try the so-called GO JAM technique which is to simultaneously punch the MARK REJECT and the RESET buttons. I did that, and it freed the computer, took away the restart light and the CMC light, but the program alarm stayed on. I called up VERB 5 NOUN 9, and I got some alarm code which said, effectively, that the computer was trying to deal with square roots of negative numbers. That indicated that there was something badly wrong with trying to do landmarks when they're out on the earth's horizon. Anyway, we got out of that problem, and I wasn't sure at the time what we might have done to the erasable memory.

In the ensuing passes over the ground, they were able to verify that the erasable was still in good shape and that it hadn't really hurt anything. We got out of that one pretty clean. I did a flag bit check only once that I recall, really, and it was to set the prak flag for the deorbit alignment in which the ground loaded in REFSMMAT numbers. In order to align to that, you have to manually set that flag rather than do it through program 40. We did that, and it worked fine; we just called up the appropriate address, looked at the numbers, added one to the bit 4, and loaded it in. At one time or another, I did perform the CMC monitoring and the self-check and so forth. All those little tests behaved just as they were listed in the checklist, never found any real problem with the computer in the whole flight; it always checked out clean as a whistle. I never did a manual computer restart except for the GO JAM technique which I just described.

<u>6.1.3 Computer Subsystems</u>

SCHIRRA — This is a point of consideration if you go out 3 days, for example, and are trapped on the lunar mission. Is the computer going to be good? You can't get enough experience with it. We had a lot of SUNDISK time, a lot on the hybrid in Houston, SUNDISK, ME101, even the DCPS and the CMS here, so we had a pretty good feel for it. Right down to launch day, we were getting little sneaky, funny looking things as we called them, FLT's that came in from Houston and from Boston, little tricky ways of playing with SUNDISK. In real time, we found one where we exited program 20, a new way that we never heard of, and that was chasing the S-IVB for tracking. That was why we couldn't get it to MARK the next day. They found a way of doing it that was good. Then all of a sudden they conceived of an experiment which they did not cycle that through the computer, and that blew the computer for us.

EISELE — They didn't have time to run it on their hybrid, but they should have done it on the hybrid.

SCHIRRA — They had time after we bombed out. They had the data back in an hour and half. That's my point, and I would like to stress this very thoroughly. Nothing will ever be updated in that computer that hasn't been done someplace else before. That way, the reliability will stay up.

EISELE — It isn't that you hurt the computer per se. All you do is run a risk of perhaps messing up the erasable memory or resetting flags. If you have good ground contact where they can read out the erasable memory, they can fix all of that for you anyway. It is primarily a procedural difficulty that you run into in flight, which can mess things up.

SCHIRRA — But that is what got us out of the woods, and that was a sneaky way to restart a computer.

ALL — It's standard.

EISELE — We could get LOCK OUT like that.

SCHIRRA — I didn't even know Colossus has it.

EISELE — I imagine it does, or it may be the type that doesn't get into those locked conditions.

CUNNINGHAM — While we're discussing the procedures for G&N, I think we all have to face up to the fact of possibility of a new procedure coming up, and it ought to be checked out. The same thing holds for the other systems, too. It's like the servicing of the secondary water evaporator. We had a procedure passed up that everybody had insisted was physically impossible to accomplish for years.

SCHIRRA — Someone went and psyched it out. That was the forty stroke deal?

CUNNINGHAM — That was a four step procedure, but it involved turning the water on for 2 seconds and off for 3 seconds and doing this forty times.

SCHIRRA — Everybody has been going over this for 2 or 3 years to find a way to service the secondary water boiler, and they said there was no way. They all said that in real time there is.

EISELE — Did they check that out Walt? Or was that just somebody's good idea?

CUNNINGHAM — I just want to go into it briefly here. The reason the redundancy check was made each day is that they said you couldn't go more than about 24 or 30 hours before the water boiler dried out, and there would be no way of reservicing it. I'm hoping that in doing their work with the primary evaporator, somehow they checked that procedure out. They had passed that procedure up anyway, and it never should have been passed up if it was not done and verified several times in a vacuum chamber someplace with an evaporator.

SCHIRRA — On the computer, if everything is done in an orderly fashion, there are no surprises except for new programs that haven't been exercised or new parts of the total program that haven't been exercised, like this P20 exit. That was a real surprise to us. I guess the manual computer restart is our go-jam. That's what I interpret that to be. The other thing we were very worried about was gimbal lock every time we brought the IMU up. I think if the station is vacated so that you can control the spacecraft attitude, then to go on the SCS max deadband until you get back. I think it is going to drift. It seems to be boresighted for the gimbal lock area. It's a shock, particularly in earth orbit, when you get an alignment at night. You think you're just going to blow it.

REP — How about the flight objectives? Are you going to feel comfortable enough to get an update on board to do those.

EISELE — I never really checked many. I think the only one that I can remember looking at specifically was that prat flag for the deorbit alignment.

SCHIRRA — I think, particularly in a lunar mission, with people who look at that all the time, you shouldn't have to do all that.

EISELE — No, I don't think it should be part of normal procedures to go in and fool around with flag words because you can really mess up the works if you get in there and set some the wrong way.

SCHIRRA — I know one thing we never brought to anybody's attention. It may be in the checklist. I think we put it in and that is to brighten up the DSKY in the lower equipment bay when you're committed to the couches.

CUNNINGHAM — That's right. We got it in the checklist. We added it in the last couple weeks. It's lower equipment bay, DSKY bright.

SCHIRRA — That's just so you can see it, in case MDC fails.

CUNNINGHAM — There are certain failures where you can keep punching the numbers in from MDC on 2, but the lights don't come up so you can read it on one.

SCHIRRA — I think that's a real hot tip.

<u>6.1.4 Rendezvous Radar Modes and Programs</u>

EISELE — Man, I wish we'd had a rendezvous radar, but we didn't. We did have the rendezvous radar transponder, but we'll cover that…

SCHIRRA — We didn't have them, we had the transponder. We weren't too well prepared for that transponder, I must confess. We didn't have the procedure onboard.

CUNNINGHAM — That's right, we didn't have the procedure for checking it out beforehand. They passed it up.

SCHIRRA — The heater had to be on. We had to call for that. This is a little embarrassing from our truly professional attitude.

CUNNINGHAM — Well, I suspect I dropped the ball in not having that in the DTO.

SCHIRRA — That may be right.

CUNNINGHAM — The people that we've had to work with on several different occasions on that particular DTO have never seemed to be very familiar with what we have in the spacecraft. After the first couple of meetings, they had switched names and things that we didn't even have in the spacecraft. And I think there was a lot of money spent on this test, but there was not a lot of intercommunications where they understood how we had to run it and understood what was necessary to run it.

SCHIRRA — Your point is valid. You've got to give the crew the option of when they learn something to vary from it, and I could not get that point across in real time. When we found that perigee torquing problem, it was brutally expensive and yet the task they were asking us to perform required minimum deadband. Donn discussed it with this guy for months about the fact that we can find an answer. You don't have to have it in minimum deadband to get to this attitude and keep it in minimum deadband for 26 minutes. Just tell us what attitude you want us to start in, and we'll do that. That was the Roll Passive Thermal and the Pitch Passive Thermal. Just fly it to that and then you let it go. Just like you let go of a stick in an airplane. You don't have to have the autopilot to put you in a perfect attitude. Although I blew it in real time by acting up, I guess. The point is still valid and I don't want to lose that point. Accept the fact that we are going to learn something in the flight. That's why we're up there. And in all these years, I'll have to admit I was very content about IVA and as you saw enough movies you were perfectly happy with it. There is no problem in IVA. We had a lot of film on board just for that purpose. I wouldn't bother unless you just wanted some "gee whiz" pictures on IVA. We didn't carry film for that.

CUNNINGHAM — As a matter of fact we discussed several things. We had a list of possible subjects for IVA. We agreed it was so easy.

SCHIRRA — I said we had to have something.

CUNNINGHAM — That's right, you have to go back with evidence.

SCHIRRA — I do feel we can stop taking movies of IVA.

CUNNINGHAM — I fell, for IVA, there's no reason at all for anybody ever to get in a water tank. Not for the command module.

6.1.5 G&N Controls and Displays

SCHIRRA — We discussed EMS quite thoroughly. We talked about the fact that I could not get the GDC description on FDAI number 1. It was good thinking from the ground not to go ahead and fool with it. I agreed immediately because I knew I could bring it back. That's enough on that subject. Gimbal position, fuel pressure indicator, no problem there. I just called down in real time that when we pulsed in yaw, or in pitch, the appropriate GPI motion is discovered. We then tweaked with it. There's nothing wrong. It's just that it's there and you've got to be surprised to see it moving. It happened on the ground, too.

EISELE — The DELTA-V counter of the entry monitor system turned out to be quite accurate. We performed a bias check from time to time, and it was on the order of a tenth of a foot per second buildup in perhaps a minute or two of running. It was very small. We did have an anomaly which I think Wally's already mentioned, of the 90,000 coming up on the EMS DELTA-V counter when you were switching functions with the rotary knob. The only time that really bothered me was when it came up spontaneously when we were not switching; this just before the burn 6. We were doing an SCS burn, and we were going to let it cut off on the DELTA-V counter. I had loaded in the appropriate number, whatever feet per second it was, and we were sitting in DELTA-V and STAND BY. A few seconds later, Wally called my attention to the fact that we were reading 90,000 and some odd feet per second. Apparently, the thing had just spontaneously put that number in there. I recycled it, reset it, and it got through the burn fine, but we were really watching that one like a hawk. If you had that large number in there, the DELTA-V counter might not turn the engine off at the right time. This was an anomaly, but it never proved to be a serious problem.

The entry monitor system per se, the part that has to do with entry, failed miserably as we knew it would because our preflight test had shown that it consistently failed the little test that you do to verify it. In fact, during entry it proved to be completely useless in terms of flying a guided entry. The FDAI instruments were quite accurate; they were easy to read; and they were very useful instruments. Probably the best thing we had on there to fly by was that eight ball.

EISELE — I think I'll ask Wally to cover that. Apparently at one point, when he switched to put the GDC reference on number 1 ball, it caused the FDAI number 1 to do a 180-degree flip. We never troubleshot it because the ground advised not to do it for fear of fouling up the works somehow. I would like to mention that the one inherent problem you have with this three-gimbal platform is the gimbal lock problem. We went into gimbal lock one time, and we nearly did it on several other occasions. The problem seems to be that the three-gimbal platform in combination with this perigee torque thing was creating a buildup of high rates up to perhaps a half a degree a second or greater in the vicinity of perigee. This would torque the spacecraft around such that it would often approach gimbal lock very closely. If you weren't watching it very closely, it would drive it in. That's what happened to me that one time when I had the rates down very low. I had observed for about an hour that as the spacecraft went through some very mild cyclical motions, it would traverse out to perhaps 30 degrees yaw angle to one side or the other and then come back; so I was satisfied it would run and that it would take care of itself over a period of several minutes. I went on about something else, and just then, apparently, we went through perigee, and the thing torqued itself right into gimbal lock.

It was a little embarrassing and disconcerting, and from then on, we kept a very close watch on it. That could be a problem, incidentally, on a lunar mission. I don't know how much torquing you have to get on a translunar flight, but if you have the platform powered up and you intend to maintain some alignment continuously, you are going to have to post somebody on watch to keep an eye on the bloody thing or it's very apt to go into a gimbal lock and lock itself up. Gimbal position meters seemed to work as they should. The scaling and resolution on them is not as fine as you might like, but they seemed to be adequate to the task of monitoring the SPS gimbal position.

The attitude set control panel also functioned properly; we had no problem with it. We... at least I never went into an accurate check of any bias in the wheel settings themselves. If there were any biases, they were extremely small because we were able to make very close comparisons between IMU and GDC alignments through use of the attitude set wheel.

All I can say is that the rotational hand controllers worked just as advertised throughout the flight except for one time when we had an apparent sticking of a breakout switch in pitch on hand controller number 2. It was toward the end of a very active day, and we decided rather than troubleshoot it right then that we would power down the system and check it the next time we came up. The next time we came up, it wasn't there, so we never did find out what caused it or where it went. The number 2 controller hardly got used at all. We did run through a check of it through the use of the computer by calling up the appropriate channels and looking at the input channels to the computer. We could verify that the number 1 hand controller was putting out the right signals. I presume G&C switching interfacing refers to the manifold switches on the left-hand console. There are a great number of them, but they are arranged more or less logically, and they're not at all a problem, I don't think, to keep track of and manipulate. You do have to keep your mind on it because it's possible to select the wrong mode or perhaps be in one mode and intend to go to the other and forget it. We found, in general, that the switching worked nominally and there weren't any problems with it. Do you recall any problems with the switches on the left-hand panel?

SCHIRRA — No, not a one. I would like to know what the heck happened to that hand controller.

REP — Back up to B there, Wally, do you have a comment on the FDAI, the flip 180 degrees?

SCHIRRA — Yes, We could not transfer GDC to FDAI number 1. First time I did it, it worked I'd say about 5 or 6 minutes reading GDC. Then, all of a sudden, spontaneously, it just flipped almost 180 degrees, not exactly 180 degrees but within about 10 degrees of 180 in pitch. Roll and yaw were right where they were originally. Then I tried again later, I realigned the GDC, thought I'd lost it, then I found out that wasn't required, went back to ball number 2, looked at GDC, and it was fine. Then I tried to bring it back over to number 1 by selecting number 1. All proper switch procedures, that's my whole point because it wouldn't have gone there in the first place if it hadn't done it properly. Nothing to do with the ORDEAL box, and then it just went over and flipped right away. I could never get it to work. Then the ground said, "Don't do it anymore," and I agreed I wasn't going to, knowing I could bring that part of the spacecraft back and check it out. I'd rather not troubleshoot something like that. I didn't need it there, but that left me with no choice but to leave GDC on ball number 2 for reentry rather than put an ORDEAL display on there and subsequently stow the ORDEAL box. That's not a total failure in that sense, but it obviously shouldn't be doing that. It's a malfunction.

6.1.6 Procedural Data

EISELE — Okay. I guess we've covered the switching and interfacing procedural data. DSKY operations and VERB-NOUN formats: I think I've already mentioned previously that as far as I could tell, the DSKY operation was substantially nominal for the whole flight. The programs changed through their routines and displays as they should. All I can say is that the whole G&N system throughout the flight performed beautifully and as nearly perfect as you could ask for. If anyone has any specific question concerning program detail or procedure, I'd certainly be glad to answer them later, but I really don't have much to say other than it was a good show for the G&N system.

SCHIRRA — Attitude set, that's no problem. Hand controller, no problem. G & C switching interfacing, no problem. Procedural data, no problem.

6.2 Stabilization and Control

SCHIRRA — Okay, that's no problem. All attitude reference systems were great. The only thing I can stress was the surprise - and it shouldn't be - that if this feels like a big ball, just imagine how big it's going to feel when they pull off the S-IVB.

EISELE — And when you got the lunar module hanging on the front end to boot.

SCHIRRA — ACCEL command is a great mode and I like it. The only problem with ACCEL command is that you've got a "hot stick" and if anybody bumps it, you've blown it. Where in pulse, if you're "hot stick," all you get is one pulse if the guy bumps you. We had one case where it was a combination of problems: I left pitch in ACCEL command, and all three of us raced over to look out Walt's number 5 window to see the hurricane. Donn came up and kicked the stick, and I never before got back into my couch so fast. We had about 1 degree per second in pitch and I stopped it. That was the end of it. I goofed by leaving in ACCEL command and Donn goofed by hitting it.

EISELE — That's a good point. There's an awful lot of traffic in and out of that center couch and both hand controllers are right there. You do have to discipline yourself to remember to keep the doggoned stick locked up when you're not using it. You also have to discipline yourself when you're going through that passageway to be careful you don't bump into those things.

SCHIRRA — That reminds me, on the number 1 stick, which is the one between you and Walt, you made note of the fact that there was a cut in the rubber boot.

EISELE — No, I overlooked that. There was a small cut on the rubber bellows at the base of the hand controller.

SCHIRRA — On Walt's side?

EISELE — I think it was on Walt's side, on the inside.

SCHIRRA — It must have just come from Walt's egress or whatever. I looked over number 2 stick which is the one I used for attitude control and the rubber bellows was completely intact all the time. It wasn't after landing, and we want to make note of that cut on number 1 stick prior to landing, and none on number 2.

EISELE — That rubber is very delicate and it wears through quite easily. So you have to be careful.

6.2.1. Control

SCHIRRA — We ran a fairly careful calibration of how many pulses in pulse mode were required to produce a given rate in all three axes. The rate we used was .2 degrees per second. In roll, with two-quad authority rather than four, we had seven to eight pulses required for two tenths of a degree per second rate. For pitch and yaw, it was about ten to eleven pulses per two tenths of a degree per second rate, which really…

6.3 Service Propulsion

6.3.1 DELTA-V Thrust Switches

SCHIRRA — DELTA-V thrust switches, no problem. I guess everything was great. I'd rather not make a big discussion on something if there is no problem.

6.3.2 Engine Thrust Vector Alignment

SCHIRRA — The gimbal movement is detectable not by a physiological motion, but I think it is detectable from looking at the rate needles. If you are in 1 degree per second you can see the spacecraft tweak a little bit, particularly on a DAP check.

EISELE — I could feel them though, when they went.

SCHIRRA — I felt them on the ground; I didn't feel them in flight. I was looking for it. Maybe my eyes were conditioned on the rate needles, that's why I didn't feel them.

EISELE — When you're in tight deadband and you go to the G&N gimbal test where it throws them from plus 2 degrees to minus 2 degrees, it moves the spacecraft enough so that it actually triggers the jets.

6.3.3 DELTA-V Remaining Counter and Thumbwheel

SCHIRRA — Oh, it will. While it is in MTVC, just milk it. Don't fling it around or it'll damp you. The gimbal trim thumbwheels are pretty good. I wouldn't change them.

SCHIRRA — I guess the trouble might be in this. There isn't any thumbwheel. It's a rocker switch and that worked fine, other than the 90,000-foot anomaly that we mentioned earlier.

6.3.4 SPS Thrust Direct Arm Switch

SCHIRRA — I didn't even use it.

6.3.5 Direct Ullage Button

SCHIRRA — I didn't even use it.

6.3.6 Thrust On Button

SCHIRRA — Of course, we used it for all SCS.

6.3.7 SPS PC Indicator

SCHIRRA — I finally got to see that on the second burn. I didn't get to see it on the first.

CUNNINGHAM — I don't even think I looked at it.

SCHIRRA — Actually, I didn't see the big spikes that everybody said we'd see. But you may not, because it is a baseball bat hitting you. That spike is buried in all that. You don't see anything. …hanging on for that ride. From zero g to one, wow! It will show on the TM.

6.4 Reactor Control

SCHIRRA — All go, but for that one thing we discussed.

6.4.1 SM/RCS

SCHIRRA — I didn't see anything wrong, other than the fact that gauging apparently did not follow the ground at all. But we did notice we could look at the temperature and see the effect of gauging. If one was off a lot, the temperature was different from the others.

EISELE — The temperatures were all practically identical anyway.

SCHIRRA — One was supposed to be the highest - D. We lost right away. D gauging didn't work.

EISELE — Well, the quantity indicator didn't work.

SCHIRRA — By gauging, I meant quantity.

6.4.2 CM/RCS

SCHIRRA — The temperature on the CM/RCS thrusters never came down below 5 volts.

EISELE — I think we got a few 4.9's early in the flight.

SCHIRRA — We guttered that right from the beginning, because we never used it, and I didn't want to take out a checklist I'd call an emergency procedure. I think that's fine, because it was designed not to have to be used. They found a way they could be.

6.5 Electrical Power

SCHIRRA — What are we going to do about the battery charger? That's a NO-GO, I'd say, for a lunar mission.

CUNNINGHAM — Well, there's a couple of things you can do about the battery charger. First, they will get our battery charger back so they can take a look at it and find out if it was an anomalous battery charger, or if it is really a systems problem.

SCHIRRA — They were trying to make burns without using the battery, and I think that should be looked at.

CUNNINGHAM — Definitely.

SCHIRRA — We almost proposed that in flight.

CUNNINGHAM — When Wally saw that I was concerned about the state of the batteries that were just really dropping off fantastically, he started asking about turning it off for the burn, or even turning it on and taking the transient and determining...

SCHIRRA — Bring the gimbals up, that's a big load. You get them all up and then you turn it off. We have the gimbals on the line. We're about 4 minutes before the burn. We're already occupied. You start the count at 5:30. I wouldn't want to compress that.

CUNNINGHAM — At about four and one half minutes, the bus ties come on. From that time on, they are taking a certain part of the load. It is kind of interesting because of the low state of charge in our batteries - and they weren't carrying their share of the load, battery bus voltage - currents, remember, I said it should go up to about 8. And I don't think you ever saw it over 5.

SCHIRRA — What I'm getting at is this test can be done on the surface of the earth. It is not something that you have to go into orbit to check. You don't have to run an engine either. You just bring the gimbals up and run a careful electrical analysis of the whole system. That is why I didn't really make a big scene about it in flight later.

SCHIRRA — These are the kinds of things that are going through our minds because when I had that AC I AC bus 2 thing, and then the batteries had gone down, I was thinking damn, if I can come in direct/direct, I may be out in the Toulies, and how's my recovery posture? So all these things are going on, and so that's why I was on this subject.

REP — Well, they wanted to do some - that last charge you did was basically research charge, trying to get some better knowledge of the whole system; that was the only reason.

CUNNINGHAM — But that was research for the battery charger. It wasn't done because we wanted energy in the batteries.

SCHIRRA — We were sitting up there watching our battery profile just like we were watching fuel profile, and we called for it.

REP — They had that all computed out, and they figured the worst that could happen if they did that would be you would lose that battery; but if you did, they had all the margins plotted in on a RCS hybrid which still had 18 hours recovery time.

CUNNINGHAM — I'll tell you a ramification that I didn't go into yesterday, and that is that you are supposed to be able to sustain a battery failure and still continue. With that battery charger having minimal performance, I really question that capability because if you end up with two batteries, you're going to end up with a lower main bus A and B voltage than we had. We were cutting pretty close to where you would want to say, "Gee, I don't know what the hell is going on in that computer."

SCHIRRA — Well, that's the thing; that's what had us scared, too.

CUNNINGHAM — So, if you lose one battery...

SCHIRRA — We were gun shy all along on those buses.

CUNNINGHAM — That's right. If you had batteries that you recharged up to 40 amp hours every time you'd lose one, you'd throw two 40 amp hour batteries on. You wouldn't be in too bad a shape, because you'd still be close to 40 amp hours.

SCHIRRA — Walt, in defense, the other thing is that we discovered quite late that the batteries weren't holding up, and that was a real nightmare.

EISELE — That was a real crisis.

CUNNINGHAM — We know those batteries have never failed with less than five charges on them.

SCHIRRA — I'm sure that everybody was aware of the problem.

EISELE — Yes.

SCHIRRA — I guess we were hair-triggered in this sense: all of a sudden, people were getting confidence, but ours wasn't so high; we never really had supreme confidence in this bird. We've been really scared up there with those damn buses going off, and we weren't sure that couldn't happen again. I've never had a comfortable feeling about EMI in this spacecraft. There have been all sorts of ghosts. We've been scrupulously careful about running up telemetry in block all the time.

EISELE — I listed our instances of EMI already.

SCHIRRA — Oh, you did?

EISELE — Yes.

SCHIRRA — Good. The service module supply valve - Walt, and I have had a real go around on that. On re-entry, we turn the PLSS valve on and the service module supply up, and both must be done. They are really a bitch to get to, particularly in this case where we are really cinched in and strapped.

CUNNINGHAM — Tank pressure and quantity indicators worked as expected. There was one time when the surge tank pressure fell, and that was when we were deliberately filling the PLSS tanks; the occasion was replenishing after use of the oxygen masks. It worked as expected, replenished very quickly; the surge tanks pressure built up rapidly, and we isolated the PLSS tanks again. Tank heaters worked fine by all onboard indications. The oxygen pressure indicator switch, the one time shared ones, were fine, switching back and forth between the surge tank and tank 1. In all cases, the difference between the tank pressures and the surge tank pressure was compatible with the flow indication that we had available on the circulating fan switches. They worked as advertised. Apparently, the only problem was the glitch when the pressure switch would turn off the oxygen fans. After the problem was discovered, the remedial action was, as mentioned earlier, to operate the O2 tank 2 fans in the OFF position nominally and occasionally stir them up by going to the ON position for 3 to 5 minutes.

CUNNINGHAM — Continuing with electric power, main bus A and B fuel cell connect switches and indicators worked as expected. There were only two times during the flight that we actually open circuited fuel cell 2; one was about 163 hours, and the other one was just a couple of hours prior to deorbit. Switches worked as advertised, including the master alarm coming on when you hit the RESET switch; perfectly nominal operation. We used the pump switches before the fuel cell pumps, I assume. There was one actuation of the fuel cell pump 2 switch; I did that, and the first time I noticed fuel cell 2 having a high condenser exhaust temperature, I just reached up and flicked it off and on, more out of curiosity than anything else, I guess, to see if I noticed a glitch on it. I was just kind of temporarily wondering if the pump was really putting it out. At the time, I wasn't in contact with the ground, I don't believe, and I hadn't had a readout yet on whether the radiator outlet temperature and radiator inlet temperature for the electric power system was coming together or not; apparently, they were working just fine, so I didn't mess anymore with the pump service.

6.5.2 Battery Charger Switch

CUNNINGHAM — Battery charger switch worked as expected. Battery charger appeared to be working normal with the exception of the very, very quick tailing off of the charge current. We apparently have a very low battery charge rate; it started out initially on all three battery charges, which is the sum total of charges done on the flight. It would begin at about two and a half amps, and in less than an hour, I noticed on the last charge it was down to about .6 or .7 amps and moved right on into .5 amps. It seemed to hold there for some period of time, and the ground had a little bit of resolution on this switch and was showing a little lower numbers then I was. We secured when the ground was showing about .42 amps, which was kind of an agreed cutoff, but the significant point here is that it very quickly got down to .42 amps; and at that time, the battery had not been fully recharged at all. The ground apparently by integration of charge current over time kept track of how much energy was going back in the batteries, and I would like to say something about that - we will cover the batteries right here.

We had a continuing update of the battery capacity, or what it was loaded to at the present time; we had seven of these updates throughout the flight. In all cases, the batteries were down from where you might have liked to have had them for burns; and for deorbit, it was within the capability of the system at all times. However, I do not believe we were ever in good shape to sustain a battery loss and then continue for a possible hybrid deorbit, for example. The problem we faced up to preflight on when to charge the batteries dealt primarily with the problem of having a battery failure and still being able to maintain enough reserves on board at all times to sustain a hybrid deorbit. In order to accommodate this, the ground subsequent to our discussion and prior to flight, apparently decided to charge battery A after burn 2, but battery B after burn 3. We did the charge after burn 2; we ended up with 35 ampere hours in A and 30.4 ampere hours in B. After burn 3, we charged battery B back up, but at no time after that did battery B ever exceed battery A, even though it was charged later.

EISELE — I was pretty disappointed in the ampere hour readings we got on those things after charging them. I rather thought that we would get back to pretty close to full charge, and it didn't even approach that ever on either battery.

CUNNINGHAM — That's right.

REP — Did you think there was any inaccuracy in the charging meter?

EISELE — Well, no. The ampere hour readings we got from the ground - all we could do was read that. I'm just saying the numbers they gave us compared to the normal 40 ampere hours you could expect from a full battery.

CUNNINGHAM — Yes, the battery charger just doesn't put the juice back in that it is supposed to. It's going to be very interesting to see the results. They take those batteries postflight, Donn, and they'll discharge them on the bench and find out how much they get out of them. It's going to be kind of interesting because they are nominally rated 40 amp hours, but they are probably 50 amp hours; we were dealing with a 40 amp hour number. I would like to stress here, at this time, that several different people got together including the EECOMM prior to flight, and we agreed on some ground rules for when to charge the batteries and how to do it. This was presented to George Low, and I believe he bought it 2 days prior to flight; we did not conform to those ground rules; I won't go into them here. If we need to, I can haul them out; I believe I still have a copy of them. The batteries themselves being in a low state of charge left us with less than desirable main bus voltages for the burns. Although it was adequate, it was still lower than we had expected for the many months of training prior to that. The most significant aspect of this battery charging battery capacity problem is that when it came time to do the CM/SM SEP and at that point we don't have anything else left to do; we just got to SEP and re-enter we immediately got a main bus A and main bus B undervoltage.

At that time, I was monitoring the main buses; we hit the separation, and the main bus voltage went down to about 25.2 25.3 something like that on both main buses. I can't guarantee that a quick transient hadn't gone any lower than that, but we didn't - there was not a thing we could do about it at the time.

Donn expressed some concern about the G&N system which was key at this point, and since we had battery C tied in, there was not a thing we could do, and we watched the caution and warning lights glow yellow the rest of the way in. I might mention that this was a slightly traumatic experience at this point because we hadn't expected anything like it, really. I had hopes that we would still be above the min voltage. The loading for reentry could have been considered slightly different than nominal in that - I don't know if the preflight planning had considered having a secondary coolant loop on the line, although I had always intended it to be that way, so we had the secondary coolant pump flowing. However, we did not have any cabin fans on, and I am sure the nominal loading for re-entry included cabin fans, so we were probably pretty close to nominal, and we still had the undervoltage.

Along the subject of batteries, I guess we might mention the pyro batteries. The pyro batteries were checked several times throughout the flight; the first time, it was reading 37 volts on both batteries about halfway into the flight. Later on, it was checked several times just prior to deorbit, and I believe at that time it was sitting at about 36.8, and we brought them back on the line; for deorbit, when Donn put the circuit breakers in, we did have 36.8 volts.

<u>6.5.3 DC Monitor Group</u>

CUNNINGHAM — DC monitor group, that's the battery charger. Do you have anything to add to that, Donn?

EISELE — On the pyros? No, I checked the pyros two or three times on my watch, and they were always right up at 36.8 to 37 volts. They held up very well the whole flight.

CUNNINGHAM — I might add one thing to the re-entry loading. When we did activate the secondary coolant loop pump at 257 hours and 54 minutes, we got this main A main B undervoltage. Main A was 28 volts, and main B was 27 volts prior to the turn-on of the pump. Immediately afterwards, after we had had the alarm, we were showing twenty-six and a half volts apiece on it. We reset it, and it stayed up there. I might also mention that even though we had 25.2 volts right after CM/SM SEP, the main bus voltage did creep on back up, but I think we were probably pretty close to about 26 volts on both main buses as we were getting later on in the re-entry, down around drogues and in that area.

EISELE — I guess our main concern is that we might have been faced with an unguided entry at that point because the EMS had already proven itself no good; and I was worried that if we had lost the guidance system, then we would be faced with an open loop fixed bank angle type of thing, and there's no telling what kind of errors we would have had at our landing point. With the weather out there, we might have been out there for several hours before they found us, but, fortunately, that didn't happen. The G&N worked fine.

CUNNINGHAM — Wonder if we can go on record for the worst weather? Copters were sitting out there at 50 feet in IFR.

Okay, DC monitor group. DC voltmeter, to my knowledge, no significant errors in it, it worked fine; DC ammeter, likewise; DC selector switch, no problem.

<u>6.5.4 AC Monitor Group</u>

CUNNINGHAM — AC monitor group, AC voltmeter worked fine; we always had 114 - 116 volts AC.

6.5.5 AC Inverters

CUNNINGHAM — AC selector switch, no problem, worked fine. The AC inverters, we operated with inverter 1 to main A and AC bus 1 inverted to main B and AC to bus 2 throughout the flight with the exception of the inverter check prior to the 17-1 GO/NO-GO.

Incidentally, I didn't mention the inverter check earlier with that six revs systems check we were discussing. We might want to mention the inverter check. The inverter 3 was operated for the 17-1 GO/NO-GO on both main bus A, main bus B, AC bus 1, and AC bus 2; worked fine. The only other time inverter 3 was on the line was during the secondary coolant loop test power up; it was felt they were going to draw another 100 watts down by turning this on, and we did turn it on and run it for four and a half hours. We turned it off afterwards and never operated it again. Power control switches operated as expected. Inverter AC bus connector switches operated as expected. We had one significant glitch with the AC buses; however, it occurred more than once. AC bus 1 FAIL light - let me check the time here on when we had the AC bus 1.

EISELE — The first time that happened was on my first night watch.

REP — Yes. At 19 30.

EISELE — Yes.

CUNNINGHAM — Just reset it, didn't you?

EISELE — Yes, we found out later what happened.

CUNNINGHAM — We had several cases, and we didn't try to track down the trouble until we had both of them fail.

EISELE — Yes, those two fans would cycle on now and then and it turns out that when they would cycle off, you'd get a momentary surge and overvoltage condition on the AC bus. It would throw it off the line, and you would get the warning light, and you'd get the warning light coming back.

CUNNINGHAM — In some places, we had several AC bus 1 fails. They were apparently anomalous; we reset it, and it worked fine. At 61 hours and 14 minutes into the flight, both AC buses failed at the same time. Both buses reset; the ground did an exceptionally fine job in tracking down the trouble, and they finally correlated the O2 tank 1 and 2 fans going off on the pressure switch actuation as triggering the transient which gave a very, very short duration over voltage on AC buses, which automatically disconnected the inverters. From that time on, we operated with one fan on AUTO, the other fan OFF except for intermittently putting it ON for mixing of the CRYO's in tank 2. During the burns, I felt that in all cases, we operated with both of them off, but I can't swear on a couple whether we had them both off or not. The attempt was made to not have them on at critical times so in case it did glitch you wouldn't lose the bus. Inverter AC bus connector switches; main bus tie switches.

6.5.6 Main BUS Tie Switches

CUNNINGHAM — The main bus tie switches worked as expected throughout the flight. I guess I was a little bit surprised to see that in all cases the amperage on the battery buses was slightly lower than I expected when we tied the batteries onto the main buses.

This could probably be attributed to the fact that the batteries were always in a lower state of charge than we were used to seeing. Therefore, they weren't picking up as large a share of the load, and we left more of the fuel cells. The net result was that the main bus voltage was down a little bit, and we pulsed the fuel cell heating rate probably just a little bit. Going back to where we were discussing main A and main B voltages, we got main A and main B undervoltage when the secondary coolant loop pump was turned on prior to deorbit, at 258 hours and 15 minutes. We also had several others because battery voltage was running right about the trigger point, and it came on and off several times. We put fuel cell 2 back on the line and had no trouble with that until after separation.

There are a couple of isolated things I would like to mention about the DC system before leaving it. I made a note in the log at 216 hours and 40 minutes, which just happened to be one of these periods, that current on the fuel cells for the burns and this is just prior to the 530 when we start training to begin with - ran about 25 amps per fuel cell. When we were in drifting flight, depending on the state of the cyclic loads, it generally ran down around 16-17 amps per fuel cell. Sometimes cyclic loads would kick it up close to 20 amps per fuel cell. Another point to be covered here would be the electromagnetic interference or EMI. I have an entry in the log at 215 hours and 57 minutes to summarize a few of these things, to the effect that during one night pass or several night passes, we had tried turning exterior lights on. On this particular night pass, turning the exterior lights on and off gave an 1105 ALARM code on the computer which was downlinked too fast. Another item of EMI was the O2 fans were glitching the AC buses, but they were also sending transients out which at one time started the DET in the lower equipment bay. That was done when the O2 tank 2 fan was turned on. The DET spontaneously reset and spontaneously started counting till it stopped. That completes DC stuff, I think. I can complete one more item, and then we're through with EPS. Right?

6.5.7 NON ESS Bus Switch

CUNNINGHAM — Nonessential bus switch, worked as advertised, never moved out of the AC bus 1. The non essential bus was tied to main A throughout the flight.

6.5.9 G&N Power Switch

CUNNINGHAM — G&N power switch, whenever it came on, we put it to AC 1. When we powered down, the G&N power switch was turned off; we turned it on several times when we had not powered up the G&N in order to use the optics in the lower equipment bay. The last item under the electrical power is the cryogenic system, the tank pressure and quantity indicators.

6.5.11 Cryogenic System

CUNNINGHAM — The quantity indicators, I assume, were reading fairly accurately; there seemed to be a pretty good correlation between the ground and on board. The ground seemed to have better resolution and was able to read down...

EISELE — They had a better resolution, and I know the O_2 pressures in particular in fact, I think the hydrogen pressures were always low on board, lower than the true readings the ground had, but that didn't pose any problem. I noticed generally throughout the mission that the pressures in both the hydrogen and oxygen tended to hang at the low end of the green band on the meter.

CUNNINGHAM — Very definitely.

EISELE — And after awhile, we just assumed that was normal operation and didn't worry about it.

CUNNINGHAM — This was consistent with data we had preflight which indicated that that was the control range in these particular instruments, but I never remember ever seeing the pressure up at the high end of the green bands except at a time when we...

EISELE — We deliberately ran the stratification test up.

CUNNINGHAM — On hydrogen before the deorbit burn, I put the hydrogen heaters to ON instead of AUTO, and we purposely raised the hydrogen pressure up towards the top end. The tanks stayed balanced throughout with one exception. It took until about 167 hours into the flight to achieve an unbalance between hydrogen tank 1 and hydrogen tank 2 (which was reading at that time 3.4 per cent). Rather than wait to get to the 4 per cent unbalance level, I initiated the manual balancing. Manual balancing took about nine and a half hours, and when we completed the manual balancing, hydrogen tank 1 was reading 36.6 and hydrogen tank 2 36.4 percent. I may have neglected to mention that when we started, the hydrogen tank 1 was 43.2 and hydrogen tank 2 was 39.8. This data is actually included as part of one of the DTO's which was manual Cryo balancing if needed.

EISELE — I guess the point is that the manual technique does work very well if you do need to correct an imbalance.

CUNNINGHAM — Yes, we might stress here that it can take a considerable length of time for this balance to be achieved. The Cryo stratification test will be covered under the DTO's, however. Essentially, it looks like we have little or no problems with stratification. I make no special mention of a min DQ/DM region. As long as the pressures were never running towards the high end in the tanks, I really didn't even consider it at all. It seemed to be running pretty fine, and pressures always stayed down within the right ranges. We finished up onboard readings with 14 percent for the hydrogen and about...

EISELE — I wrote 29 percent oxygen. Wasn't it 24 per cent?

CUNNINGHAM — I don't remember exactly, but it was in the high 20's, I believe.

EISELE — The point is that there were plenty of volts at the end of the mission.

CUNNINGHAM — Somebody told me that we were 60 pounds ahead on oxygen by the end of the mission. Incidentally, we cover an area called consumables, don't we?

REP — Donn, you want to pick up where you stopped on the moding?

EISELE — We were talking about OSS moding - the zero optics mode. I was simply mentioning that we did not bother to run the trunnion angle down close to zero before switching to zero optics. We simply flipped it there and let it drive. It would overshoot several degrees and then come back to zero; we never had any problem with the optics the whole flight. I don't know how many times it went to zero, but it was, I would say, well over a hundred times. The manual modes I think I've already discussed; they worked beautifully. The thing tracks very smoothly, far better than we've seen in the simulator, which is a digital drive type of thing. The computer mode worked very well; the computer generally would drive the optics to a star very accurately. Usually, there'd be a little bit of bias or offset which could have been due to IMU slight misalignment, or some bias in the computer drive itself. It would usually drive out - say it was going to a star - it would drive out and overshoot...

(Break)

...means that for 1 degree per second it's about 1 pound of fuel, which is very, very expensive.

EISELE — If you pulsed it.

SCHIRRA — Pulsed it. I found that for any rate more than one tenth of a degree per second, it was much more practical to use acceleration command. I used RATE COMMAND only for attitude holding when we were translating if you either had ullage or were translating during the braking phases or rendezvous phases.

EISELE — For line of sight measurements during rendezvous also, that's about the only time.

SCHIRRA — For any other line-of-sight measurement such as the COAS alignment, pulse was the only way to go, other than when we switched from one star to another. I wanted to go RATE COMMAND there, but I had to have the cockpit completely dark, and as a result, I used the pulse in that case, but it was more expensive than I would have liked to have made it.

EISELE — I guess the point is that the pulse mode is your fundamental control mode for just about anything you want to do.

SCHIRRA — That's terribly luxurious.

EISELE — I think that the post-flight data will show that their design intention was way off what we really saw up there because that thing really cycled back and forth very rapidly.

SCHIRRA — That can be avoided, though; you don't need to redesign just to...

EISELE — Oh, no.

SCHIRRA — People have just got to understand that we know how to fly it.

EISELE — What you have to do is do your roll in pulse so that you control the roll deadband effectively by your manual inputs and not allow the automatic to do it. The other deadband modes seem to work pretty well. I don't know what the fuel usage rates actually were, but they were far less than the flight plan.

SCHIRRA — There's one we should make note of, and that was the early phase of the flight where we did the yaw deadband. I got some data on that in my zip flight plan here. When we were venting (while it was working the first part of the mission), it caused us to go off to the right, yaw right, and it cycled between 7.9 degrees yaw right and 7.1 degrees yaw right. So it actually flew on the edge of the deadband; it oscillated back and forth in that regime for a long period of time, never leaving it. I'm just trying to find out what the delta time was because it was rather surprising to stay over there like that.

SCHIRRA — I think it was a minute and 55 seconds, or a minute and 5 seconds. The conditions were SCS attitude 1, rate 2, limit cycle ON, attitude MAX, rate, attitude deadband MAX, rate 5. That roll, approximately 174 degrees, pitch 349 degrees, yaw varied between plus 007.10; that's 7 hours 17 minutes 3 seconds to plus 007.82 degrees which is a delta of .72 degrees. At 7 hours 18 minutes 56 seconds, which was 1 minute and 53 seconds, it cycled back and forth, roughly between these numbers, meaning it was yawed right and rode the right edge of the deadband.

The only variable that was causing this was the - this was not the perigee torque; this was early in the mission. This was caused by the steam vent water boiler combination, forward in the spacecraft. We tried all control modes, but for the very, very high rate modes, which weren't required, they did work during the rendezvous modes. I don't believe in spacecraft checkouts for control systems, like airplane drivers like to do it. It's very expensive. You use it; if it works right, it's fine, that's rather than this classical manual maneuver in G&C control mode .05 degrees per second,.5 degrees per second and 4 degrees per second. We never at any time flew at rates of 4 degrees per second. Even the pitch turnarounds were at two and a half to 3 degrees per second. As the degrees per second go up, the fuel consumption goes up, proportionately and violently.

EISELE — I think we hit every mode in there except those high rates

REP — The TVC's, DELTA-V's, RCS and SPS interface: any problem there?

SCHIRRA — No.

REP — Okay.

SCHIRRA — I believe we were right in our preflight decision of not checking out the command module RCS thrusters, both from a time-line basis and from a real-time observation that we had propellant right up to the thruster solenoids. There's no doubt in our minds that that even occurred.

SCHIRRA — Did you make remarks on the DSKY? I talked to Kenny on the phone. I felt that the DELTA-V counter display numbers, the DSKY numbers, and the mission event timer on the MDC all were subject to fadeout with bright sunlight on them, and they were not readable...

EISELE — Yes, that's right.

SCHIRRA — ...and that some type of cover, sun cover, should be provided. I would suggest that Frank Borman work that out himself without having a whole bunch of engineers get in the middle of the act, and I'll make that evident to Frank, what the problem is.

EISELE — Yes, you might

SCHIRRA — The first real realization we had of this problem was not being able to read the DELTA-V counter during number 5 burn. With that continually in drifting flight, we couldn't read the MET...

EISELE — The MET seemed to be the worst offender.

SCHIRRA — ...with the numeric switch full bright, I might add. On occasion, we couldn't read the DSKY when we looked down below; I didn't, anyway.

CUNNINGHAM — On the DELTA-V counter, we had G&N monitoring. That was a G&N burn when we took over, wasn't it? When we took over manually, was the DSKY still counting up that DELTA-V?

SCHIRRA — Oh, sure. That wouldn't shut if off.

CUNNINGHAM — I was just wondering if that one was visible at the same time, a little different sun angle.

SCHIRRA — It was. Well, I couldn't look at it first. Burn 5, you mean?

EISELE — Yes.

SCHIRRA — Yes, but the shutoff was depending on the DELTA-V counter. The DSKY is not sufficient for cutting a burn off manually.

EISELE — It only updates every 2 seconds, and 2 seconds is a lot of feet per second.

CUNNINGHAM — In 66 seconds, it was only 1600 or something?

SCHIRRA — It's roughly a 1 g burn, so we only burn another 60 feet per second on top of that.

SCHIRRA — The most glowing tribute I can give is that as far as I can tell, except for that hand controller anomaly - and I'm positive it was the hand controller - there was not one faulty thruster for the duration of the mission including CM and SM RCS and SPS. That's a big thruster!

EISELE — Yes.

SCHIRRA — Which is quite a tribute to anybody's propulsion system.

EISELE — Yes.

SCHIRRA — I think that's really a first.

EISELE — Just discuss the rotation hand controller.

SCHIRRA — We did try direct/direct, and the technique there is to take the stick all the way out to the soft stop and just blip from that, and you can get a short pulse of about one tenth of a degree per second which is sufficient to back up a pulse mode, or I think it is usable for a re-entry, but as you get g on, it's a very difficult task. This is merely coming up with the feeling that the soft stop is tough and then just go along a little bit and watch the result of this, rather than feel it or hear it. I guess we ought to describe the sounds of these thrusters. Donn, I think, felt that the best description is much like a man hitting a steel drum like the Bahamian bands, the steel band; and oddly enough, that analogy is quite good because pitch and yaw have different tones.

EISELE — Pitch had one note, and yaw had a note a little bit higher in frequency sort of like a bong, bong, bong, bong, and roll was a thud; it was a very dull...

SCHIRRA — Yes.

EISELE — Esthetically, roll wasn't as good. I was talking to George Page this morning, and they were all concerned about the audibles on the pad.

SCHIRRA — I told them we had those thrusters on. We heard them.

EISELE — I thought it was significant that they were much less noticeable there on the pad.

SCHIRRA — Than in flight.

EISELE — Than in flight.

SCHIRRA — Yes.

EISELE — And, in fact, you have to listen pretty close on the pad.

SCHIRRA — I think that's because they're insulated, and the sound was masked by atmosphere as well.

EISELE — They were wondering what degree to go to make sure the cameras were on thrusters, and I felt we would still have to verify them on TV.

REP — We were talking about control rotation translation, different modes here.

CUNNINGHAM — Well, our preferred mode was PULSE and an occasional ACCEL COMMAND input and, on very rare occasions, using RATE COMMAND.

SCHIRRA — I'd like to throw in a note of caution. I've talked to McDivitt and Borman about it for the record. The most colossal goof you can walk into - I had to learn that once - is to leave the BMAG in ATT I rate 2 and then switch back into them after you've maneuvered. So you want to go to the last place you were caged up at. That thing will really hum. Fortunately, you're only about 2 or 3 degrees away, but that spacecraft just went WHOOOOOM right into it.

It takes all the authority it's got in the system and just fires all thrusters and goes there. That's a very luxurious mistake. So that's the kind of goof you have to really watch for so that whenever you leave a precise attitude that you've been trying to hold with that thing with the BMAG's in BMAG rate I or rate 2, you get out of that attitude hold mode. It's a very dangerous thing.

Another problem we found was switching from PULSE to ACCEL COMMAND. Unless we switched rapidly through RATE COMMAND position, which is between the two, you get RATE COMMAND lock-up, meaning that you would stop the rates you had, either from ACCEL back to PULSE or PULSE to RATE COMMAND. This would waste your fuel, but you could set up a rate you wanted, and maybe you'd want to stop it with PULSE or ACCEL COMMAND, just reversing the modes. Going through RATE COMMAND, if you went slowly, you'd stop at RATE COMMAND; that got expensive. You might not want to stop it; you might want to increase it. Ideally - and that's for future design; I wouldn't change it in any of the command modules - RATE COMMAND should be on either end, not between the two modes. It's not a major crisis; it's just something that... technique hasn't been thought out too well. I can't fault the SCS other than those minor criticisms, and I call them that except for the hand controller malfunction. That bothered me to no end because that first appeared to ruin our hybrid deorbit. I could have used that anomaly pitched down and swapped hand controllers and used that as a pitch-down mode.

EISELE — Yes. that's what we talked about doing, in fact. We finally concluded we really hadn't lost the hybrid.

SCHIRRA — So we really hadn't lost the hybrid in that sense. Just had to turn the hand controller on to get a free pitch down in ACCEL COMMAND; just turn that hand controller off if we want to stop it. So we'd always maintain a hybrid deorbit even with that anomaly, assuming it came up again. The way we'd lose hybrid deorbit is to lose those two AC buses. That was all academic.

EISELE — Translator seemed to work fine; we didn't have any problem with it.

SCHIRRA — Never.

EISELE — In both G&N and SCS. I don't know what this means, automatic. We didn't do any automatic maneuvers in SCS; all it can do is attitude hold. It does that very satisfactorily. That minimum deadband is a very nice type deadband. It's very useful for things like line-of-sight measurements in rendezvous and also holding a precise attitude just before an SPS burn, but it's also a very expensive mode. One thing we noticed, - this is to a degree subjective because it was kind of hard to measure on board, but it seemed that the limit cycle switch didn't really help all that much, particularly in this tight deadband configuration. The limit cycle is supposed to cut down the number of firings, the frequency of them. It didn't seem to make much difference whether it was in or out because the thing in tight deadband would cycle rather rapidly and roll back and forth. You'd get a pulse every few seconds, and it would drive to the opposite side of the deadband, fire another one, and come back. You could get around this partly by trying to set up a single jet configuration. If you push and pull the right combination of circuit breakers...

SCHIRRA — Can't do that. You have to go into ACCEL COMMAND to do it.

EISELE — Yes.

SCHIRRA — The only way you can do that is to turn the roll attitude hold off and use PULSE in that mode, in that attitude, in ROLL. That's what I was complaining about in flight. It's very expensive to hold attitude in SCS minimum dead band, limit cycle OFF, minimum deadband, low rates. The roll would - well, attitude very technically would pulse back and forth at the rate of two tenths of a degree per second, holding this very tight deadband on a two-tenths of a degree roll attitude. That's terribly luxurious.

6.6 Environmental Control

6.6.1 Oxygen Subsystem

CUNNINGHAM — In general, we can state that the oxygen sub system and environmental control system provided excellent service throughout. The only possible anomalies that existed were associated with the O2 flow high. I say possible anomaly because in almost all cases where the O2 flow went high and we had a caution and warning light, we could track it down to something in the spacecraft. About 99 percent of the time, it was the waste management dump valve being left open after a urine dump.

SCHIRRA — Let's explain why that was, Donn, because it is a trap. Our technique was to vent the urine line with the same device we used to enrich the cabin. Yesterday, I talked to Kenny and recommended that it be put on the spacecraft for all subsequent flights as a vacuum cleaner. I couldn't think of a better way of vacuuming than that device itself. You could optimize a little, but I'd rather not go into a big design program; just leave it like it is.

CUNNINGHAM — They've got a 90-degree elbow in the thing that I would just as soon they didn't have. There is a 90-degree elbow when you start vacuuming.

SCHIRRA — It was just right for me to vacuum with frankly. I would go down that pipe and all that sort of stuff, and it worked fine. But I would rather not redesign something if it does do the job, just tell Kenny it's satisfactory. If you disagree, let's get that point out in the open.

CUNNINGHAM — It's not that significant. I felt like it was an off the shelf item.

SCHIRRA — That's what it's supposed to be.

CUNNINGHAM — They picked that one up in, - like a day. I suspected that they had one without a 90-degree elbow in it that they could pick up the same way. I would rather see a straight one than a bent one.

SCHIRRA — They needed more length; it didn't stick up in the cabin too far.

CUNNINGHAM — That's right, because they figured that most of its use would be sitting over there in the waste management panel, and most of its use is really sitting on the end of the urine dump line.

SCHIRRA — I guess that was a lousy place to stow that; you had to go to 1, 2, 3, 4 places to go through a urine dump procedure.

CUNNINGHAM — You're right. We should not have left that little valve there temporarily. It should have been over on the right hand where the tape was.

SCHIRRA — Yes, I don't know why we didn't move it over there. I thought of doing it once or twice; I just got in the habit of backing off. We should have stowed that thing temporarily...

REP — Where the tape was in the tape compartment.

EISELE — That little triangular box where the tape was stowed?

CUNNINGHAM — That's where we should have left that little vent thing.

EISELE — Oh, you mean when we weren't using it?

CUNNINGHAM — Yes, that would have been all right. Getting on to the anomalies: very early in the flight, we had the O2 flow pegged high for a significant period of time; I think it was about 3 to 6 hours in flight. The ground seemed to think it was a transducer problem. Onboard very shortly thereafter, we had discarded this possibility. The O2 flow-meter, as far as I am concerned, reflected accurately what was going on with the O2 system throughout the flight. The Delta-P between the surge tank and the oxygen tank pressures always correlated with the flow-meter when the flow-meter was less than pegged.

SCHIRRA — I would like to make a point here and get this down once and for all. The ground doesn't realize how much that flow-meter means to us. It's a very valuable piece of instrumentation. They don't understand that that is valuable. In checkout where they had hard line in the spacecraft, the ECS people here knew how valuable it is because they are on it all the time. They would warn us when they were going to get an alarm (which was very good head I thought because we were busy at these other times), so we weren't surprised. But Range doesn't understand how important that particular instrument is to us. That's your cue to all sorts of crises in oxygen.

SCHIRRA — Yes, it is.

CUNNINGHAM — Yes, I've been begging for that thing for a long time. Along this line, something I recommend in a memo to Deke about 2 months ago is that we should get a flow meter which goes higher than 1 pound per hour.

SCHIRRA — I remember making that when we hit up with the enrichment thing.

CUNNINGHAM — Yes.

SCHIRRA — There is one coming on the next spacecraft, I believe.

CUNNINGHAM — I don't think it's in. I recommend that they be made in line, and the reason for it is that there are certain components in the spacecraft which when they fail to open have fixed flow through them. For example, the cyclic accumulators; I'll leave that as one example. When you take and superimpose the cyclic accumulator failure on top of say the first 6 hours or 12 hours of flight where you are bleeding the cabin down, you got a flow rate of about 1.3 or 1.4 pounds per hour. We have a meter that's pegged and you can't do much with it. As far as reading it, you have to try to correlate between a Delta-P of a surge tank and the oxygen tank and its not very acceptable.

SCHIRRA — A specific case is the enrichment thing for through the urine dump. It happens to be somewhere between .6 and .8 pounds per hour. If you could read 2 pounds an hour, you'd cover most of these contingencies.

CUNNINGHAM — I don't think I would recommend changing the caution and warning limit. I think it is significant to keep it right where it is. The way it is now, caution/warning comes on when the meter pegs, and you don't know anything.

SCHIRRA — In contrast, I would discourage changing that limit.

CUNNINGHAM — That's right.

SCHIRRA — Because that's how we are reminded to go down and turn the dump off.

CUNNINGHAM — That's right.

SCHIRRA — Wonder how many times we forgot to do that.

CUNNINGHAM — We sit here and laugh about it, but everybody should understand that after 11 days of it...

SCHIRRA — We were still doing it.

CUNNINGHAM — We were still doing it, and this was after we swore - I know I took secret oaths to myself not to goof the urine dump system, and Wally and Donn would turn around and find a step out. It got so bad that I made a checklist. I wrote it down in my log; I wrote the checklist down, and when I got through, I looked through it and I had left a step out of it.

REP — This is the urine dump procedure?

CUNNINGHAM — That's right.

REP — Urination procedure.

SCHIRRA — Probably the only place we saw oxygen problems other than those early anomalies - I still don't know what the heck...

CUNNINGHAM — That's right. I said most of it was traced to this waste management system. I think we still have some possible anomalies existing.

SCHIRRA — The ground was saying that we had a failed sensor. I don't believe that on analysis. This goes back to my original thesis...

CUNNINGHAM — I talked to John Aaron on the phone about the ECS, and he said, "Hey, I goofed that one."

SCHIRRA — As it turned out, they did the same thing to me in Mercury. They goofed my suit temperature. When you have a gauge and the needle moves, the needle responds to delta's, the gauge, or the sensor hasn't failed. It may have shifted, but it hasn't failed. I think we all ought to learn that TM is not as good as a needle and analogue; TM is digital.

REP — In general, I think we were all quite happy with the oxygen system.

SCHIRRA — I guess that ought to remind me to remind FOD that all meters are analogued. They don't have anything analogued on the ground.

CUNNINGHAM — Wally, why don't you bring up the service module supply valve?

SCHIRRA — The service module and PLSS valves and where they are located: for future spacecraft, please don't have the poor command pilot running the ECS. That's a big mistake. I had to worry about dumping the cabin during boost in case the cabin relief valve didn't close. I was strapped in in a tight position toward reentry. I found I couldn't get to the service module supply valve which was called OFF after retro and I turned the wrong valve. I looked over there again and could just barely see it; it didn't have a bubble on it, or I probably wouldn't have seen it. I had the wrong one on; I called that out, went back and got the right one, and turned the other one back on.

REP — The PLSS valve, the service module supply valve? And you got some reservoirs right behind it. That's where the valve is. Three in a row there.

SCHIRRA — I never used it. Three valves in a row: PLSS, service module supply. Tell me what I'm thinking

CUNNINGHAM — Surge tank?

SCHIRRA — Surge tank valves. Yes. All three are difficult to turn, and they are almost impossible to see after CMS; no, actually after retro. It was called out for me to turn off the service module supply, and I reached over there almost blindly, turned off the surge tank which is wrong, and just out of the corner of my eye, I could see it again, so if I had had the helmet on, I probably wouldn't have seen it. That's not an excuse for having it off, but as a result, I could see it; I struggled like mad in this tight restraint, and I got it back on again. I was really grunting and groaning, and then I got it off again. I got the surge ON and the service module supply OFF; they are difficult to work. Something else that we didn't have happen to us and didn't have available to us - I might add as long as I'm over in that area - we talked many times about a swizzle stick to get to some of those circuit breakers. I did not have it, and I still don't know what I would have done if I had had to run some of those circuit breakers in a hard suit.

CUNNINGHAM — I had exactly the same problem on the right side. I think one swizzle stick would have done the job if we had had one.

SCHIRRA — Particularly for a one-man command module operation, this is a real big requirement. I think the swizzle stick should be required for the next mission, and if they do have to ride a hard suit, they're going to have to run some of this stuff.

CUNNINGHAM — Incidentally, while we're on the subject of the swizzle stick, I sweated throughout my training getting on the panel 275. After you get on the chutes, you've got three circuit breakers to push in and two circuit breakers to pull out. You do it completely blind. I had a pretty easy time of it because I didn't have my gloves on. I really breathed a sigh of relief. With the gloves on…

SCHIRRA — Let me ask you why we were doing this. We were doing this really to protect ourselves from an inadvertent chute separation.

CUNNINGHAM — No, no, not this one; those are two other circuit breakers. We're doing this to keep the batteries from being drained down by the main bus. You also have open circuits sitting still on the main bus that you just want to get cut off before you hit the water.

SCHIRRA — It's all "What if," though. You can get in a dangerous mode.

CUNNINGHAM — I think there are some things - it's not a lot of trouble maybe, but it's like your gimbal motor control circuit breakers. They're not deadface both sides where they run through the service module.

SCHIRRA — The system was designed so that you shouldn't have to do that. That is another backup deal that could put you into a dangerous mode in the first place if you did the wrong circuit breakers, could it not?

CUNNINGHAM — You could end up with less than all your power being on the right bus.

SCHIRRA — Post landing.

CUNNINGHAM — Yes.

SCHIRRA — Then it's no problem; you can look at it. After landing, you should look at it and reaffirm your positions.

EISELE — Yes. I did, incidentally.

SCHIRRA — I did, too. Before I got out, I went over and looked at it. Enough on that subject. Oh, one thing we did have happen, and I'm not sure where it's going to come up in here. We ran the PLSS down...

CUNNINGHAM — I was going to mention that right here, the PLSS valve under section B.

SCHIRRA — That's what I was trying to get at; that's why I'm here. When we tried out the emergency O2 masks, one mask triggered off on the test button, and that caused the O2 mask to flow. The only proper way to stop it is to put it on your face and breathe against it, which we tried out in the altitude chamber. I guess Donn was down below, and he triggered some kind of funny stuff. It lowered the PLSS tanks, and after that, I just refilled the PLSS.

CUNNINGHAM — The PLSS went down at that time to around 800 or maybe a little bit less.

SCHIRRA — Less than that.

CUNNINGHAM — We threw the surge tank on the line; we put the PLSS valve to FILL. The surge tank dropped immediately down to about 850, and in a very short time, it built right back up, and we isolated the PLSS tanks again.

SCHIRRA — Frankly, that was a DTO we hadn't anticipated flowing, and it worked fine. You could hear the PLSS recharge. That was interesting; I didn't expect to hear it. Did you expect to hear it?

CUNNINGHAM — No, I didn't.

SCHIRRA — It's a very audible noise, swir-r-r-rear.

CUNNINGHAM — That was the balancing of pressures; yes, I heard that. When you put the surge tank on, you immediately heard them going together.

SCHIRRA — The PLSS and the surge manifold together.

CUNNINGHAM — That's right, but we flew with the PLSS valve OFF throughout to keep the two systems isolated, the two onboard command module oxygen systems. Recognizing the fact that had we had to support a slow leak in the command module, we would have had to go to the FILL or ON position.

CUNNINGHAM — On all of these things, I can - surge shutoff valve. It was operated once inadvertently and opened back up again. Surge tank pressure relief valve was never utilized. No. We used the emergency O2 valve with the mask. The repress O2 valve was never actuated.

SCHIRRA — No.

CUNNINGHAM — We don't want to use that. The main regulator valves operated normally throughout. We checked them on each redundant component check; they were always running between 103 and 105 Psi for O2 manifold pressure. I'll cover the redundant component check separately probably under this section. There are some changes we made in flight on it. Water and glycol tanks pressure regulator, no comment. Water and glycol tanks pressure relief valve, no comment. Neither one of these valves were moved throughout the flight. Apparently, the emergency cabin pressure regulator worked fine on the redundant component check. The cabin pressure regulator the cabin pressure was regulating at the high end of the band of the control area; however, it was normal for our spacecraft. We knew before the flight that it would be operating between 5.2 and 5.4 psi. It did so very satisfactorily. On the numerous occasions when the waste management drain was left open, it would slowly bleed down the... and the demand reg kicked in and ran it right back to 5.4. I'd say it was a very tight cabin because we almost never had flow except after we had bled it down.

REP — They tell us it was less than one tenth pound per hour.

CUNNINGHAM — Is that right? I just had an intuitive feeling that it was a pretty tight cabin because it was always reading 5.4.

SCHIRRA — I'd like to add item 7 hygrometer readings. I'd like to get that knocked off on future flights. That's nowhere in the rest of the books. Walt's got the readings. We never called them down to anybody; they just stayed right in the books.

CUNNINGHAM — Right. Why don't I just summarize it?

SCHIRRA — I'd like to recommend that we not do that on subsequent flights. It's a waste of time. We did it all the way down except for the very last one because we wanted to stow it. And everybody bought stowing it.

CUNNINGHAM — We had a whole page that falls in the same category as the gas analyzer, a good one shot deal, just so you understand this.

SCHIRRA — So, I'd better get down and get that audiogram right now.

REP — What did you ask me about...

REP — We got those in the loop, I don't think we should hold them.

? — I don't want to just turn them loose and let a year or two...

? — the right guy is going to want those and it should be lab work and I think they should get the darn readings.

? — Yeah.

? — Okay.

SCHIRRA — I'd suggest you call Donn and see if he is going to come over tomorrow. I agree with it, his not being here now.

(Break)

6.6.2 Water Supply System

CUNNINGHAM — I'll continue with the water supply system. Waste tank inlet valve was not moved throughout the flight. Portable tank inlet valve was not moved throughout the flight. We did take off the cover on the waste tank servicing valve and attach the waste water dump fitting. The valve itself was actuated. The ground can check back on how many times we did dump waste water. I have a recommendation on the waste water dumping. They got quite concerned about dumping when it got to about 85 percent and wanted us to knock it off at someplace around 25 percent. It was fairly obvious to everyone on the ground that we were trying to push this off and not dump it until we got up to 90 to 95 percent. We ran it down to a little bit past 25, then down to the 10 to 15 percent meter reading on board. I'd recommend that we go ahead and continue to dump over a longer span so we don't have to do it any more often than necessary. The procedure itself - even though we had a flexible hose that was running across the cockpit - was really a piece of cake. It was one of those little tasks that was like a lot of the others; you had to watch it pretty close to cut it off.

EISELE — That is one where the little alarm clock would help. You could set it for 4 minutes or 8 minutes, whatever you determine dump time ought to be, to remind you to turn it off.

CUNNINGHAM — The time we got down to 10 percent there were two of us doing the task and two of us watching it, and we still had enough things going on where we got down to 10 percent before we shut it off. It's not catastrophic, however. The evaporators could always pull water from the potable water tank. The attachment that went on the waste tank servicing valve had a swage fitting, and we tightened it up as much as we felt we ought to with that great big wrench; yet it still continued to leak a little bit of water at the fitting, which we had to vacuum up each time when we got through.

EISELE — At the end of the dump, you'd have a spherical glob about the size of a 50-cent piece hanging onto the fitting.

CUNNINGHAM — It was just another source of water in the cockpit and another task to clean up, and we should probably try to get some kind of a better fitting there if we're going to use it. The fitting itself interfered with B8 where we had an awful lot of 16mm film stowed on this flight. We ended up taking all the film out and leaving it in temporary storage - which is like 8 or 10 film packs - and then only putting it back in at the end of the flight. There's a definite interference problem there, and that valve should be shorter - excuse me, the attachment should be shorter and probably come out at a different angle.

Pressure relief valve. That's probably the water tank pressure relief valve. To my knowledge, it did not operate. Chlorine injection port.

CUNNINGHAM — There was one onboard problem with the chlorination. It was the third chlorination of the water. And the LMP was conducting the chlorination. I placed the chlorine ampoule in the chlorinater, attached it into the bayonet fitting, and turned it. Apparently I did not turn it far enough, and it just barely caught in the bayonet fitting. When I made the first turn between that time and the time that I operated it, it slipped back out again. I just felt it. It wouldn't pull out, so I assumed it was in. I made one turn on the cap, and

I could see chlorine solution oozing out down around the bayonet fitting, using a flashlight I very quickly determined that I had not seated the thing all the way over. My recommendation is to make sure you visually see the bayonet attachment go all the way over. If I hadn't been watching, I could have cranked that in, and it could have put the whole business out. In zero g the chlorine solution doesn't come out and just fly away.

REP — It does not disperse, but tends to hang in space?

CUNNINGHAM — It stays right there, but we did have a chlorine problem to clean up. Several droplets did float free. We're still concerned about the chlorine being loose in there.

EISELE — I think it just highlights the hazard that you do have with the chlorine solution being in there in the first place. It can leak out and cause you problems.

CUNNINGHAM — The water started tasting bad when we were chlorinating every day. After the third day, we made an effort not to drink for an hour or so after we chlorinated the water. In order to chlorinate, we had to drink down about 8 ounces on our potable water tank. I still have some doubt as to whether this is enough to drain. I mentioned this to Wally when we first tried it. We had a potable water tank that was full we had to chlorinate, and we had to get some ullage volume in the tank to get this mixed. We should have been indicating 93 percent or less in order to be sure that the chlorine that we put in was getting down to the ullage volume. Then it would get mixed up, because it comes in and goes out on the same line. I would like to be shown that the recommended amount to be drained out, was sufficient. That could be the reason we got the bad taste in the water so soon. After the third straight chlorination of 3 days in a row, Donn took a drink from the water gun an hour at least after we chlorinated, and it almost made him sick. It was apparently too strong at that time.

EISELE — It was pretty bad.

CUNNINGHAM — On this particular day, the water still did not taste good 10 or 12 hours later. It was not refreshing. Going to every other day chlorination, the water tasted better. I hope we got a good analysis of the water postflight. I definitely recommend, and I think everybody concurs onboard, that we don't chlorinate any oftener than every other day. No problems with food preparation, as substantiated by some of the onboard movies. We used three different sources of water for food preparation and we disliked all three. The drinking water gun had more gas in it than either of the other two sources of water. You could get some very good water, and then all of a sudden one pulse would come through of gas...

EISELE — You'd get a mouthful of gas coming through.

CUNNINGHAM — That's right. Using the gun with a food bag, you'd have a full food bag that wasn't full of water. We found ways of getting the air out of the food bags. It's something that we all ought to talk procedurally to the subsequent crews, and save them a couple of days learning time. The cold water tap that was used in the cold water valve had next to the largest amount of gas in it. The hot water had the least amount of gas.

EISELE — It had hardly any.

CUNNINGHAM — I could hardly move the trigger on the water pistol by the tenth day. The cold water tap was getting somewhat the same way. It would stick back. It just didn't want to work as smooth. It wasn't near as bad as the water gun, but it was getting harder to operate.

EISELE — It would hang up a little.

CUNNINGHAM — The hot water tap worked fine throughout the mission. The hot water is absolutely the greatest thing we've had. There was plenty of hot water. We were never short and it was always very hot. When we had to let some of those meals sit for 15 minutes, they were still warm.

EISELE — We could run all three of our meals - the hot water dishes, and the temperature did not drop off at all, that I could tell. We also used it to clean up. You could take the clean towel and hold it up by the spout and squirt several shots of hot water on it.

CUNNINGHAM — Incidentally, you had to take a clean towel and hold it right around the spout because the spout's got the water coming out of the side.

EISELE — You have to be a little careful that you don't squirt water all over the SC.

REP — Was the taste of the cold water good, and was it cold enough?

CUNNINGHAM — Yes, except for one day,

EISELE — Toward the end of the mission - the chiller apparently ceased to function.

CUNNINGHAM — That's right, I felt it did.

EISELE — It was not near as cold and refreshing as it had been earlier.

CUNNINGHAM — The water when it was cool tasted good and very refreshing. About the ninth or tenth day there was about a 24 hour period when it became warmer. Then it seemed to get cooler again.

EISELE — Yes.

CUNNINGHAM — About the tenth day, the water gun started getting a kind of "garden hose" taste a couple of times.

EISELE — Yes, I noticed that.

CUNNINGHAM — We were all quite happy in general with the food preparation. The gas was a problem, and we ought to try to do something about - if there is a way. The drinking water shutoff valve was turned ON when we got in orbit, and turned OFF for de-orbit. Right.

EISELE — Yes.

CUNNINGHAM — The evaporator water control, the primary and secondary; I'll cover the secondary evaporator water control valve under the redundant component check, but they operated as advertised. The water gun I've already discussed, and the food preparation. Donn, do you have anything to add about the water gun?

EISELE — No.

CUNNINGHAM — One very small point, it would have been nice if we had logged the first reading on the water gun. It was not zero. It was some other strange number.

EISELE — My water bookkeeping was not kept up to date the last few days of the flight. I was drinking a lot of water.

CUNNINGHAM — It's a problem. I wasn't drinking enough water the last couple of days.

6.6.3 Water-Glycol System

CUNNINGHAM — The one very consistent anomaly existing in the primary glycol loop was the periodic drying out of the evaporator. It seemed to occur at random times; and when it finally did dry, it would occur rather rapidly. There is a good chance we can find this out post-flight since we do have the evaporator here. The secondary evaporator did not dry out; however, it never operated longer than seven and a half hours, and I don't believe we could draw any conclusions based on that. The glycol evaporator OUT temperature primary ran between 35 and 60 degrees F throughout the flight; the only time it got down below forty and down in the thirties was on an overshoot when the evaporator would come on the line. The radiator outlet temperature on the primary loop was always maintained roughly between 30 and 50 degrees. This led me to believe that we had essentially very good radiators, with only very slight degradation, if any, during boost. The radiator isolation test, which had been extremely high priority even before flight, I felt had taken on less significance after we took a look at the radiator performance. It seemed to really be performing very well.

EISELE — I don't know how the ground feels about it, or what kind of data they got. We ran practically the whole flight without that water boiler really doing much for us. We ran into high-powered conditions for hours at a time, and about the only time we noticed was that there was a slight cyclical behavior to...

CUNNINGHAM — There was a definitely more marked cycle, too.

EISELE — ...the temperatures. When you were on the sun side of earth, temperatures tended to go up; when you get around on the cold side, that was when they went down.

CUNNINGHAM — What happens is that that is the normal cycling that goes on, but it was more marked when we had the evaporator off.

EISELE — But there was a very slight difference, and it didn't make us uncomfortable, and it didn't hurt any of the equipment; we had typically nominal performance even without the water boiler going.

CUNNINGHAM — Those were the times when we got towards the high end of these ranges that I just mentioned. The radiator inlet temperature on the primary glycol loop was always between 60 and 70 degrees F, and the steam pressure worked as advertised; glycol discharge pressure was always nominal, both pumps. The accumulator quantity was a bit low; I think it probably was between about 39 and 45 percent.

EISELE — It was low when we took off.

CUNNINGHAM — It was at the low end of the range; it changed very little, so I never gave a thought towards refilling the accumulator at all. Primary and secondary maintained the same kind of values throughout the flight. The most significant item is the drying out of the evaporator. I consider that an unanswered anomaly. It is something we ought to try to find out about. However, in view of the way the radiators did work, I wouldn't have any reservations about operating the system. We felt very comfortable operating it that way for 10 to 11 days. I think the time it got the highest was when it was powered up for rendezvous.

An example of changing limits is after we started flying, they changed the limits. The ground rules have always been that if the primary glycol evaporator outlet temperature exceeded 60 degrees, activate the secondary loop. They came through for the rendezvous, and I believe that they stated to let it go as high as 80 degrees. I was just a little bit surprised at that because a short time after it dried out for the first time, they had given us a new temporary limitation of 70 degrees. I guess it shows they were willing to pulse the system in order to complete the rendezvous.

EISELE — Well, they were going to pulse us, too. If that glycol had gone to 80, that cabin would have gotten pretty darn warm.

CUNNINGHAM — I think that is another very significant point, Donn - they were willing to pulse the electronics a little higher, but you get very quickly into the range of where the electronics is not the key item. If the crew gets pretty doggoned warm and the glycol evaporator outlet temperatures get up above 50 to 55, it just is not taking the cooling out.

A lot of the subjective feelings of heat that we had on the sunny side, Donn, was whenever we were in the attitude HOLD mode because as you came up, you had the sun coming right in the window; when that happened you were hot. The suit loop temperature and the cabin temperature varied between 47 and 65 for a suit temperature, 60 to 75 for the cabin temperature nominally, and I couldn't really correlate that with comfort. Sometimes I felt uncomfortable when it was down at the low end of that range, sometimes at the high end of the range, and the closest correlation that I could ever make would be whether we had sun coming in the windows or not. As a matter of fact, I found the suit and cabin temperatures to be not very useful. They were long thermal constants, and they didn't really seem to mean a lot. If we saw the temperature up high and we were uncomfortable, we might throw a couple of clicks on the cyclic accumulator or something, but I never had the feeling that I was getting a lot of intelligence out of the two meters.

CUNNINGHAM — Cabin temperature control was never touched from lift-off to landing. It was set at max cold manually, and as far as I am concerned, the temperatures on board the spacecraft were quite tolerable and normally quite comfortable.

EISELE — Yes, it was a good environment.

CUNNINGHAM — We felt like the humidity did fluctuate back and forth; it was a function of location in the cabin. That might have been why Donn bugged out of the sack that he and I were sharing after about 6 days and slept over in Wally's sack. The primary glycol pump, no comment. The primary evaporator back pressure valves were probably working normally. I have to confess that I was a bit surprised that it took such a long time to close them sometimes. It took a long time to see a steam pressure react to closing of the back pressure valves. The instructions when you are turning down the primary evaporator are to hold the back pressure valve to INCREASE for a minute. I must confess that at times I held it for as long as 2 minutes, and there was quite often a long delay from the time I started operating it before I saw any increase in the steam pressure. When I say a long delay, I mean like a minute and 15 seconds or more sometimes. I can't be sure, but they may have been operating slower than we expected. The primary glycol evap temperature inlet valve in the ECS postinsertion checklist was placed to AUTO and never taken out of there except for the radiator isolation test.

The glycol reservoir outlet valve, inlet valve, and bypass valve were reconfigured in the postinsertion checklist prior to flowing the radiators, and the reservoir was never placed on the line afterward. The glycol-to-radiator primary valve …the radiators went to FLOW probably about 15 minutes after insertion when we got around to it on the checklist. We did not have to return to BYPASS. The radiator outlet temperature was lower than the inlet temperature after 3 or 4 minutes of flowing, and it was obvious right away that it was coming down. The only other time that that valve was actuated was for the secondary coolant test, and it went to BYPASS again prior to SEP. Primary glycol accumulator shutoff valve - no comment. ECS radiators, the flow control switch - we had several anomalies early in the flight, and I think it was about twice in the first 48 hours the radiator flow control switched to number 2. It was reset and put back in AUTO, and it operated normally after that.

I have to backtrack just a second to the primary glycol evaporator; I did mention that it dried out on several occasions, numerous occasions during the flight. The glycol evaporator after drying out, in all cases, was reserviced; sometimes immediately afterwards, sometimes after waiting for some 15 or 20 minutes; something like that. When it was placed back on the line, we followed a procedure as passed up from the ground, and it worked beautifully until all of a sudden it would just dry out. The explanation was given that under low cyclic heat loads, the water control valve was not doing the job it was supposed to.

It was not filling enough water to match the boiling rate of low cyclic loads. The last time that it dried out, and probably the reason it was the last time, was because of my servicing procedure. In reservicing it, we were supposed to put 2 minutes of water flow into it, and during that procedure, we ended up with two different distractions associated with updating the map. I would say that we had a good 3 and one-half to 4 minutes of water. I kind of doubt whether that would have incapacitated the evaporator, but at that time I had already decided I'd just as soon not put the primary evaporator back on the line for deorbit. The reason being at that time - but I was a bit concerned that with the excess water in the evaporator that when we did start boiling and open the back pressure valve we could have possible water carryover into the steam duct. Since the steam duct is the only one we have for both the primary and secondary evaporator, I just didn't want to take a chance on freezing the steam duct for reentry. I think the risk was probably low, but it was not out of the question for it to happen, and we did not need the primary evaporator. So that was a procedural goof on my part.

EISELE — The point is that thing is supposed to operate automatically, and it failed to do so. So it was in a failure mode to begin with. I don't consider it procedural goofs in the nature of leaving a valve on too long or not long enough.

CUNNINGHAM — There are so many things going on at the same time it is a real challenge to your concentration to get one task done.

EISELE — Well, I think in general we ended up with a great number of manual tasks that should have been automatic, either on account of inflight malfunctions or because of inadequate design. It wouldn't have been unreasonable when this servicing was going on to have the oxygen tank 2 fan, for example, to go to ON for 3 minutes, so you ended up with a couple of time sequences operating concurrently, and it became a problem. Or you might be looking for a certain target over the ground at a certain time. We would like to see the ground assisting us on these things.

CUNNINGHAM — Flow control switch seemed to work fine after the early part of the flight, and it was a repeat of the same kind of problem that we had on 2TV-1 run, and I believe possibly some of the chamber runs here. The manual selector switch was utilized once for the radiator isolation test and it worked fine. Suit heat exchanger secondary valve - the suit heat exchanger was on the secondary loop, and we actually got cooling whenever we flowed the secondary loop. And specifically, for reentry, we activated the secondary loop, did not do a cold soak, but did put the suit heat exchanger on the secondary loop and took it off of the primary loop.

Secondary glycol pump and accumulator - no comment.

Glycol radiator secondary valve was turned on for the first redundant component check and never after that.

Primary glycol evaporator control. I felt like the control was adequate with the possible exception of the comment I made on closing the back pressure valve. It seemed to take a little longer than I expected. Secondary glycol evaporator control worked fine, absolutely beautiful system for the length of time we ran it.

We might comment on the procedures that was passed up early in the flight, prior to doing the secondary coolant loop test. It was a way to reservice the secondary water evaporator in the event it should dry out as the primary did. This procedure involved putting the evaporator water control secondary valve to AUTO where it was already going to EVAP for 5 seconds, then to RESET for 10 seconds, and repeat that step for 40 cycles. In the event that we had had a secondary evaporator dry up, it's nice to have a procedure to reservice it. However, I do not know to what degree this procedure had been checked out prior to being passed up. I do know that the last 3 years prior to flight, I had been told consistently and regularly whenever I had queried North American systems people on the question that we could not reservice the secondary evaporator in flight. That was one of the big reasons we ran a redundant evaporator check every 24 hours to make sure it was serviced. I copied the procedure down, and naturally we would have used it had we had to. Because of someone being able to dream up the procedure in 3 or 4 days, whereas in 3 years it had not been worked out before, this brought up the comment about a "Mickey Mouse" procedure.

6.6.4 Suit Circuit

CUNNINGHAM — Direct O2 valve, apparently was not difficult to adjust to the flow that we needed; we had no trouble on the pad with it, did we?

SCHIRRA — No. It was like a signature type of valve. It is unique. John Young always had trouble with it. I just haven't touched on that particular valve, I guess. It infuriates John.

CUNNINGHAM — Okay, so the direct O2 valve worked as advertised. Suit flow valve - they were either in suit full flow, or after we took the suits off, they were in cabin flow throughout the flight. Cabin air return valve, the handle appeared to me to operate stiffly. I hadn't operated it too many times earlier. Did you feel like it was stiffer, or is it standard 101 suit return air valve? We might comment that it did accumulate an awful lot of lint, et cetera, on the screens, and we cleaned them off with tape from time to time.

EISELE — We did have to go around periodically and clean off that filter and also the ones on the suit hoses.

It seemed like about every 8 to 12 hours, they were due for a cleaning. They were clogged, and it made a very effective vacuum cleaning system.

CUNNINGHAM — I think we might stress trying to set up a procedure to do that regularly, more than once per 24 hours anyhow.

EISELE — I always did the suit plugs on my watch and occasionally tried to do the suit return valve if I could get to it without bothering Wally. They got cleaned at least twice a day, and they should be cleaned twice a day.

CUNNINGHAM — For planning purposes, you should plan ahead on cleaning the suit return air valve. One of the sleep stations is under there, and you have to open panel 382, and that interferes with the sleeping crewman. Oxygen demand regulator - apparently worked fine throughout. Suit compressors - no comment. CO2 canisters - I believe we will have to elaborate here. There were no problems in operating the CO2 canisters. At about 60 per cent through the flight, in changing one of the canisters, the LMP pulled the banana plug loose from the shorting plug.

EISELE — The shorting plug broke, and we did it manually just by hanging on to the structure. We had no discharge at all at any time.

CUNNINGHAM — From that time on, we made sure that we kept contact between the side of the container and the cartridge whenever we pulled it out. Changing the lithium hydroxide canister was very easy. We should make special note of the fact that stowage onboard spacecraft 101 was two lithium hydroxide canisters shy of what was required for a 10.8 day or 11 day flight.

EISELE — We were able to stretch what we had, fortunately, into the 11 days, which led us to the conclusion that probably you could make 30-hour cans out of those that you really wanted.

CUNNINGHAM — In all of our canister changes, the CO2 partial pressure was never above about .8 mm of mercury. At any rate, when we were faced with the problem of extending the life of the canisters, it was absolutely no problem. We extended one canister out to 5 mm of mercury down at the end, and I don't have that time here right now, but I believe that canister probably went at least 35 to 36 hours.

EISELE — Pretty close to it.

CUNNINGHAM — I would say we ought to enter into it if we want to try and save some good weight on the space craft. We ought to try to qualify these canisters for 30 hours. I felt like all of our canisters subjectively would go 30 hours with no strain at all.

Suit heat exchanger - no problem.

Water accumulators? They worked; I believe they worked as advertised throughout. If they ever missed a stroke I'm not sure that we would have detected it. I believe the ground asked one time about missing strokes. We happened to be at manual as a time stroke came up, and we were trying to operate with some manual cycling. If we felt like the humidity was getting a little bit high, or we saw water in the suit hoses, we did throw a couple manual strokes on the cyclic accumulators. Something which had never dawned on me in 3 or 4 years of operating this system was that cyclic accumulators stroke right at even 10 minutes. We always knew it was 10 minutes between strokes, and 10 seconds for a stroke, and if you want to watch to see that the cyclic accumulator is working, you can look at an even 10 minutes, on the GET. Like 50 minutes past the hour, on the hour, 10 minutes past the hour. I don't know if that's ever been called to anybody's attention before, but it made it a lot easier checking these things for operation.

Okay, I think what I would like to do here before I go to the gauging system is note the differences in the redundant component check in the ECS system from the checklist. We never did read it down to the ground, and I don't believe they are aware of the changes that we did make.

Okay, starting with the standard checklist ECS redundant component check, the procedure was modified in flight as follows. The first change went along with an agreement with the ground that we would only flow the secondary radiators the first time, check the temperature sensors. And the secondary radiators were isolated for the remainder of the flight. The urine dump heater, switching to redundant heater was never done. We felt that as long as we were on a good heater we were not going to change it. Evaporator water control secondary valve was not turned off after the redundant component check. It was in AUTO throughout the flight after we pulled the first ECS redundant component check. This was because the primary evaporator was acting up, and we wanted to be able to initiate secondary evaporators should we need it. You know, without climbing under the couch, and opening up panel 382.

I think the significant point here is we operated for 11 days with the valve in AUTO, and prior to the flight North American had some reservations about the AUTO position being susceptible to leaks in this loop. I personally would recommend leaving it in AUTO, and that saves you one trip into and out of panel 382 a day.

If somebody is sleeping down there it complicates things. In performing the secondary coolant loop activation for redundant component check, I neglected all of those steps associated with shutting down the primary coolant loop. I always felt the secondary coolant loop with a radiator bypass and the primary coolant loop was doing its normal job.

6.6.5 Gauging System

CUNNINGHAM — Temperature gauges - I read earlier what the range of the temperature gauges was in both the suit and the cabin temp. I felt that it did very little good to tell you really what the comfort level was in the cabin. Sometimes when we felt very hot the cabin temperature gauge was reading down in its low end of the operating range, and sometimes when we felt fine it was up toward the high end. Pressure meters, fine. Quantity meters on all consumables associated with the ECS system were GO. Flow rate, I can only stress again how important we thought the oxygen flow rate meter was. That's not listed as a mandatory piece of instrumentation for launch. Personally, I would like to think that that should be mandatory for flight, the O2 flow rate meter.

6.6.6 Waste Management System

CUNNINGHAM — The waste storage vent valve. I utilized the valve on about two occasions for opening up the waste storage compartment. However, I never had the feeling that this was necessary. I don't believe we ever got odors out of that waste storage box.

EISELE — No, we didn't.

CUNNINGHAM — Did you Wally?

SCHIRRA — No.

CUNNINGHAM — We opened it many times and saw little tiny bits of metal.

SCHIRRA — I told doc I didn't like all the pills wrapped in metal foil because they start floating around the cabin.

SCHIRRA — While we are talking about waste management, we had a lot more room in the command module to work on waste management; therefore, it wasn't a total nightmare, but it was a fantastic work load compared to other things. It took a long part of the day, and you had to plan way ahead for it.

EISELE — I thought it took about an hour - the whole deal - from preparation until you were completely through with it.

CUNNINGHAM — I wrote up a little thing about it that I would like to just put out as a memo to our guys in our office on it. I said to allow at least 45 minutes. I think everybody agrees, at least 45 minutes.

SCHIRRA — I think the significant thing is that whatever procedure we use, we are not prepared to handle what I would call a fluid bowel movement. That is where we were very... lucky. I was deathly afraid of that.

CUNNINGHAM — I think that is an emergency situation when you are faced with it, and I'll say that you probably are getting down to a two-man operation if you have that right now.

SCHIRRA — Let me make a point here. I asked Chuck Berry if we could possibly sit down with the appropriate engineers and doctors and say all the dirty words, and get it out of our system, and all the funny jokes, and then sit down and talk about this very seriously. I asked this of Stan White back at Langley, and no one has ever moved. I asked it of Dick Johnston, and I think it is kind of gross to go all the way back to the Gemini glove thing, which will suffice for the lunar mission.

CUNNINGHAM — I think I have an idea that I could add to a new kind of fecal cannister. All of these require flow rates, incidentally.

SCHIRRA — For AAP, there is no way that you can go along with a system like this.

CUNNINGHAM — If you want to make a note of it, I do have certain ideas that I think could possibly end up working with a modified type fecal cannister, as long as you have flow rate. I guess what I am saying is that you know how concerned I was before we flew, running around here begging everybody to take a bowel movement. I guess because the stools were relatively firm, it turned out that we didn't have any real bad problems.

SCHIRRA — It was just a mess.

CUNNINGHAM — That's right; it was a mess.

SCHIRRA — It really means you have to be off the loop completely; you have to take your communications away; you can't do anything. You are strictly off the line for about an hour.

EISELE — I did mine on the night watch while you guys were asleep so that I wouldn't disturb you, and I had the whole cabin to myself. What I would do was wait until I had a pass where I was going to be 45 minutes to an hour between stations - and usually during my watch there would be at least one pass like that. That's when I would do it because you have to take everything off, strip right down to do it.

SCHIRRA — Donn, it just occurred to me while you were talking that you are not going to have that on the lunar flight. You are in constant communications. There is always some message coming in. You just have to say, "The CMP is going to be off the line for 1 hour." The way we did it was idealized for the environment that we had, but I guess in this debriefing we've also got to project ourselves to the next one. I didn't dwell very much on the S-IB because it's history as far as I am concerned, other than for the AAP. I think we should go into the AAP debriefing as I discussed with Deke.

EISELE — The whole procedure is not all from an esthetic point of view, it is not as bad as I thought it would be, frankly. It is tedious and time consuming, but if you take your time, you can do it right.

CUNNINGHAM — I'd rather not go into all the details right here. I did spend a lot of time writing down stuff that I'd just as soon pass on to the guys that are going to be needing it and to Berry. In fact, Berry made a copy of what I wrote down about doing it. If we are talking systems-wise, we still have the operational problem of the interface between the man and the bag, et cetera. Systems-wise, things worked as they were expected to before we went in flight, on the waste management and fecal waste. On the urine system, I would have bet money before we flew that we would have freeze-ups. We were all absolutely amazed that the water dump system worked so perfectly.

SCHIRRA — We were very religious about prepping it.

CUNNINGHAM — That's right, and purging it afterwards.

SCHIRRA — We overpurged it most of the time.

CUNNINGHAM — I think we have already belabored the point of the dumps and the stars and the fire flies and the snowflakes. Have we really made it a point that this could be a critical problem in later moon flights? I don't know. This is one of Wally's little pet points, and I think he ought to elaborate on it a little bit.

SCHIRRA — My point is that in earth orbit the W/CDA of the particles is quite different in the spacecraft. As a result, it draws aft and separates from it. Eventually, you fly out of it.

CUNNINGHAM — You also go from a sunrise or a sunset situation, into a total darkness or a total light which changes it.

SCHIRRA — In sunrise or sunset, when I tried to do my coarse alignment, I could not find star 1 for 10 minutes after sunset. I was all set for it; I knew where they were. I had already seen the stars at dusk before. It wasn't a case of really trying to find them. I just couldn't see them. If the particles don't draw away from the spacecraft en route to the moon, we'd have a real nightmare. That is why I say that we should keep the platform up until we discern whether there is a problem or not. That is the only real frightening thing I saw in this mission. It really did scare me for a lunar mission, even more than seeing stars in daylight.

SLAYTON — That is the plan on C, to leave the platform on.

SCHIRRA — Then we will find out whether these do in fact draw away or not. They leave the spacecraft with enough velocity that they might go away just by that DELTA-V that is applied through the nozzle. There is a fantastic cloud of these things that go in all different directions. It is not just coming out that spray nozzle.

CUNNINGHAM — I brought up a point in flight that at first blush sounds just a little bit ridiculous maybe; I think he thought I was being facetious, but I did mean it half in seriousness. If you had a directable urine dump, you would have a means of controlling that spacecraft, except at perigee or something. Every time we dumped, we put torques on it, and if you could direct a nozzle out there, you could fly around for...

SCHIRRA — I didn't think it was facetious. I saw as much as two tenths of a degree per second.

CUNNINGHAM — I thought you might have been thinking I was making it all in jest, but I wasn't. I think if you had a directable urine nozzle or a waste water dump nozzle, you could fly around in earth orbit, take pictures - a poor man's control system.

SCHIRRA — It is not appropriate for Apollo, obviously.

CUNNINGHAM — If you could get all the vent stuff coming out of one hole maybe, then with a directable vane - turn around one way or another, you could do something with it.

SCHIRRA — Donn, do you remember what the peak thrust of a pulse is? It's not very far, not any hundred pounds.

EISELE — No, the effective ISP is about one-half or a third the normal - pretty low.

SCHIRRA — I know on Mercury I wanted less than a 1 pound thruster, for example. We didn't have pulses as such, but we used a small thruster. They were great. I'd say that in Mercury, we got about two tenths of a degree per second for a minimum fly-by-wire thrust in a 1-pound thruster, I bet you get more than that out of these overboard dumps. Although the acceleration is not there, you are getting the rate by letting it build up over a period of possibly a minute.

EISELE — If you dump water out of that waste tank, it really spins it up. You get a good healthy rate out of it.

SCHIRRA — While we are talking about dumping water. We actually saw the shadow of the spacecraft in these water particles.

CUNNINGHAM — Whenever the spacecraft was trailing the urine dump in orbit, it made a nice shadow back there. In fact, Wally and Donn saw the...

SCHIRRA — We saw the whole spacecraft; saw the engine, everything, the command module, the service module...

EISELE — And at one point, we were silhouetted against it.

CUNNINGHAM — It suffices to say that I wrote up the checklist we used for it, which is a significant number of steps, and I would just as soon leave the thing about waste management to a little memo. Another point to mention here that we didn't mention is the odor. The odor did hang during...

SCHIRRA — Yes, I don't know what we could do to solve that.

CUNNINGHAM — The only thing we could do, we did.

EISELE — We breathed out of the blue hose.

SCHIRRA — That was better than going to the mask. I guess that is an appropriate comment to make, especially towards the end of the mission when it began to definitely - we were clamping up our noses. We also noticed that our body odor was up. I understood from Frank Borman and Jim Lovell that they didn't feel that dirty. They didn't get the exercise we did, either. Even though we didn't break into a sweat or perspire while exercising, I suspect our wastes were coming out through our skin more so than...

CUNNINGHAM — One thing about this is that the waste management overboard drain valve got a lot of work. Some times I had the feeling that we were about to break all of the waste management valves. The waste management valves are not a nice operating valve. They go only one way. It looks like you can go either way because it's a 180 valve for VENT or CLOSE. After 5 or 6 days, you always turn it the right direction first. There should be an arrow on those valves showing the way that they move.

SCHIRRA — Walt, that is a good point that you are bringing up. Second, there are so many of these tool E valves - I hope the world doesn't follow that as a normal pattern for identification for what way a valve is pointed. It is a hex hole that tool E goes in. There's a tip of a guard, I guess, and you are not sure until you live in it for a few days which end is pointing in the right direction. It is a very bad standard to be used for subsequent vehicles is what I am trying to get across here - to identify where a valve is pointed. We learned, incidentally, each time we looked at them.

CUNNINGHAM — I have one more thing to add along the same lines; it is sharp in my mind now. The stowage box R13 has some handy-dandy handles on those ratchet things you fasten. If we could stick one of those on one lithium hydroxide fastener, (the canister cover) and one of them on panel 382 fastener, we'd have a whole bunch of tool E valves...

EISELE — You can't because those have to be flush.

SCHIRRA — You can't, Walt.

CUNNINGHAM — The lithium hydroxide canisters? What I am getting at is that we opened it, we hooked it back with tool E to fasten one or two of them, and every time we wanted to get down there to clean the screen or anything else, we had to go get a tool E and come down to do it. If we just had one of those...

SCHIRRA — Let me ask this. Didn't we find that that wasn't a very highly reliable thing?

CUNNINGHAM — Never had any failures with the ones on board.

SCHIRRA — Yes, I know, but each one of those is a potential failure.

CUNNINGHAM — There may be mitigating circumstances which won't handle it, but my feeling right now is that it sure would be handy.

SCHIRRA — I think it really is a nuisance to go around and undo those things with tool E all the time. What was that tool stowage thing for down there that we didn't have a tool for? Was that tool E, another version of it? On the water control panel, there is a hole that says tool stowage.

CUNNINGHAM — Oh, we used to have a tool stuck there.

EISELE — There used to be a tool that would stick in there.

CUNNINGHAM — That was its standard position.

EISELE — There is an extension in the tool kit that you can put on tool E, and it would probably fit in that hole.

SCHIRRA — It came back as a T-shaped tool that went up where my direct O2 knob is now, and that same T-shaped tool...

EISELE — It would be handy for exactly the best purposes.

CUNNINGHAM — I really think that if there is a way of throwing it on, it is a convenience type thing.

Dew-Point Hygrometer

SCHIRRA — The point is we took twelve different dew-point hygrometer readings, which is almost on a daily basis, and there is a lot of good data here. We found out where the moisture was. That's really what we were doing it for, in case there was any. The moisture collects on the coldest place on the spacecraft.

EISELE — Which is down under your seat where the cold pipes are.

SCHIRRA — From that, I see no reason to carry this device along. It's not an operational instrument any more than the cabin gas analyzer. We have all the data. This data has been sent in, here is a whole page of it right here. This should be sufficient to dispense with the hygrometer. We were using the suit return air valve, and we dropped that and went to inner condensate which collected on the pipes. In one case, we measured the pipe temperature, which was 52, and the wet bulb was 58. It had to condense; that's all there was to it. Whatever the spread was, the dew-point was higher than the pipe temperature, so the water had to go there. Oddly enough, back in Block I days, we saw this very often. Remember they had the air conditioning fouled up in that big vertical bay building in the plant? People came roaring in and started wiping pipes off because they weren't insulated. They reset the air conditioners somehow or another to lower the humidity. I've been told that 106, and possibly all on up, are insulated, and on a phone call to Kenny I suggested that he insulate what he can.

6.7 Telecommunications

6.7.1 Monitoring

SCHIRRA — I think the surgeons went about as far as they could to help us on the BIOMED switching (the three-position switch). It was a gross mistake on their part for not insisting on having the ground control it like anything else. It ended up as a crew task because they didn't win their fight. They did win it for later spacecraft. We were not unduly exercised on that...

EISELE — Once every 8 hours.

SCHIRRA — If you will recall, the original flight plan was absolutely unreal. We couldn't have abided by that; there was no way we could have. I gather they got the data they needed out of it, and unfortunately, we are in a problem. As far as I am concerned, the BIOMED harness is an open anomaly for this mission for two reasons. One, it failed; and I told Chuck Berry it's possible that Donn's failed as mine did as a result of exercising-against the seat belt. Mine failed because the lead was just too short; they put the bio-sensor in the wrong place. Changing configuration between where they placed the sensor between the last time I wore it and flight day, caused it to come apart. I taped it to make it stay together, and it broke down the next day.

EISELE — I guess we have already documented the hot signal conditioner elsewhere. That happened about 7 days into the flight.

SCHIRRA — I would like for you to get it on this thing. You told the doctors. How hot was it? Berry was telling me it runs about 98 to 100, which is not enough to detect.

EISELE — No, that's body temperature; you could hardly notice that. This was plenty warm, and it had been getting warmer over a period of a day or two. I could recollect that now and then I felt a little warm in my abdomen; and one day, it was quite warm, uncomfortably so, and that is when I started searching around to see what the problem was. It was one little single conditioner, so I was just going to take it out, and I thought, "That is the power supply for the whole thing, and I will just - "

SCHIRRA — The black one?

EISELE — No, it was the red one. I took it off and advised the ground, and they said, "Roger."

SCHIRRA — That shook me when I heard it.

EISELE — It wasn't hot enough to burn you, and it wasn't so hot that you couldn't hold it in your hand, but the fact is that there was a short in it, and it appeared to be getting worse over a period of a day or so.

SCHIRRA — To help you calibrate a temperature number, the water was about 150, and that was kind of hot.

EISELE — It is kind of hard to compare because of the heat transfer rates of different materials involved. I would say that it was probably 120 to 140 degrees by then, something like that. It was quite hot to the touch.

SCHIRRA — You're not supposed to get that kind of flow through there; something is wrong.

EISELE — Yes. It sure was.

SCHIRRA — Destroys my confidence in that report we had about triggers in the suit loop.

EISELE — I was concerned if I got a hot short in there that it might singe the cotton garment I was wearing and would have been...

SLAYTON — Theoretically, there is no possible way to get that much current in there, but it is an unknown thing that has to be explained.

EISELE — We took special care of the equipment. I don't know if they ever found it, but it was in the remaining fecal bag box, the box that the fecal bags were stored in.

6.7.1 Telecommunications Monitoring

CUNNINGHAM — I am assuming this means the status of Telecommunications System. We launched as nominally planned on all switch configurations, etc. Did you cover the COMM problem? Apparently, Duplex B wasn't working all the way through boost. I didn't notice a loss of COMM. I was monitoring meters instead of waiting for some of the calls. Apparently, there is an anomaly, a loss of COMM. Did you hear all the calls here at the Cape? Didn't you have a COMM loss here at the Cape?

SLAYTON — Redstone was down. We didn't hear them after the boost.

CUNNINGHAM — In monitoring the S-band antenna meter, we never lost S-band lock. It seems that we should have had S-band COMM. Wally said, that he did turn the S-band COMM up. I can't really account for not hearing one or the other. This is the first I had heard about it, and I am very surprised. Throughout the flight, the COMM operated just as you would have expected it to operate. Sometime in the first day, they lost the PCM, the real time PCM was down. The man on the console somehow or other (in looking through the malfunction procedures) skipped the first step, which is switch transponders, and went to the second step, which is switch the PMP to auxiliary.

The next morning when the day shift came on, they switched transponders, and everything was back to normal. We used the primary transponder, secondary power amplifier, on high throughout the flight from then on. I would like to comment that the S-band loss of lock problem in selecting the right antenna was definitely a pain and took a lot of time, but it was not as bad as we had expected before flight. The S-band power amplifier on high worked pretty good. We never Rogered transmission on antenna switching; we just went ahead and switched. We did not always wait for the ground to call for switching: at least I didn't. If I looked and the antenna meter was dropping down around where the down lock would have dropped out, I would switch to the opposite antenna. On rare occasions, they called for an antenna which was in-between the two that we had gone on. For all known fixed attitude maneuvers, I used the pre-programmed flight plan callout for an omni antenna. We're going to cover the DSE in separate categories. We did have a problem with the DSE.

6.7.2 Audio Center Controls

EISELE — Walt was complaining that his S-band thumbwheel was a little stiff, but he said later on that it loosened up. I didn't have any trouble with mine.

SCHIRRA — When I used Walt's, I didn't notice; I guess the S-band was a little stiff.

EISELE — One thing I noticed on mine was that after some length of time, it would go so that I could reach up there and manipulate it in the blind. I could do it by feel; I knew which switch and thumbwheel was which, and I knew which way to push on them. It wasn't as inconvenient as it was at first when I used to have to get out of the couch and go up and actually look at what I was doing. Also, on entry, strapped in without the helmet and gloves on, I found it was possible to reach up there and actually get a hold of that S-band volume knob.

REP — Oh, could you?

EISELE — Yes, sir. I don't know why I could do it on entry and not on launch. Maybe you don't get strapped in quite as tight; I don't know.

SCHIRRA — Let me ask you this, Donn, because some of the crews have a different way of wiring the launches. We discussed it and rejected it, I guess. It was for you to launch in backup so you would be over on my audio control.

EISELE — We talked about it, and I thought it was a pretty good idea, but it was kind of late in the game when it came up. We hadn't run any test or training on it, so I felt we should leave it the way it was. I recommend they try it out.

CUNNINGHAM — It sure sounds like a good bet to me.

SCHIRRA — It bugged me, and I was a little afraid to try it because by DB went down about 2 or 3 DB's when you came on my side.

EISELE — Little things like that could eat you up if you do it the first time on launch day or something.

CUNNINGHAM — Yes.

REP — But now do you feel you are missing anything? You obviously couldn't get S-band.

EISELE — No, but you two guys had it.

SCHIRRA — I might add that I finally ended up with my S-band at about position 2. I could hear the guy, but he was so weak I couldn't...

EISELE — That's another point. During the flight I found that by putting that S-band volume at around one and a half or 2, you could just barely hear the grass when it is not locked on. It is a very good key to the fact that you are coming up on a station when you hear that grass disappear because you know somebody is getting ready to talk to you, and it was very effective.

SCHIRRA — It was quite significant, that, and that sensitivity meter, I guess is the word for it, the S-band lockup...

CUNNINGHAM — It must have been a lock. There were times when I was somewhere and not looking at that meter, particularly on the night watch when I was up there by myself, or when I was down in the LEB. I heard that noise disappear, and I figured we were coming over a station.

CUNNINGHAM — A comment was made about my S-band thumbwheel being tight. It had always been tight pre-flight, and by about the eighth day, it was finally loose enough to where you could turn it without great strain.

6.7.3 VHF   CUNNINGHAM — I operated almost completely throughout the flight on VHF antenna left. A couple of times when I wondered why they weren't receiving us on VHF, I did switch to antenna right. I could find no difference in our COMM regardless of which VHF antenna I was on. I drew a kind of tentative conclusion that it was fairly insensitive to which VHF antenna I used, which was kind of a surprise. Squelches were left sitting at launch squelch values. I manipulated one of them once and set it right back to about five and a half. That was where we launched.

EISELE — Squelch control. We didn't use it at all to speak of. We launched apparently in the wrong mode. I'll say that because it didn't work very well. Check the recovery beacon. It worked fine once we got in stable 1, didn't it?

SCHIRRA — Yes. The ground has more data on the VHF AM COMM Mode from all the COMM checks. To my knowledge, they all worked out fine. The only possible problem with VHF was during boost, and I would have to have Wally elaborate on that. He apparently lost COMM with the ground, and they lost part of the time.

SCHIRRA — We went through that.

CUNNINGHAM — All the other COMM modes operated as prescribed. There was some anomalous problem in the VHF recovery beacon in that they did not receive the SARAH beacon until just prior to splashdown, although it had been turned on at someplace around 8500 or 9000 feet. A possible antenna deployment problem is the best I can make out of it after talking with the recovery people.

EISELE — I noticed that fairly early in the flight. I don't recall the exact time of the floodlights, but they are noted in the crew log. That is the only lighting failure we had, and those do not really pose a problem because we still had one element in each of the two floodlights in the LEB, and the optic switches you run pretty much by feel anyway because normally you have got your eye glued to the scope. At least, that is the way I ended up doing most of it.

SCHIRRA — What concerns me, Donn, is on the LEB flood lights. You recall on the strut between you and Walt, that light failed during CCDT, and it was replaced with a brand new one and very little light there?

EISELE — That's right.

SCHIRRA — And yet it failed again. So we are seeing what we had seen in Block I. The life of these things is not necessarily predictable.

EISELE — That's a good point. The floodlights just aren't all that reliable, but it's just that, fortunately, we have a large number of them in there, and each fixture has two elements in it. I do think that during spacecraft testing every…

SCHIRRA — Do you recall early in the mission when you were down in the LEB swearing and in complete shock about getting alignment? You were perfectly willing to do two or three alignments in one night pass at the end. I'll say this: don't take away the equivalent of two night passes for anybody to do his early alignment. To even bear you out on that, we needed it, for the rev check.

EISELE — How many days into the flight were you doing this? It was your first and only time to do a 53 and 54. The first time we had a urine dump, it took up 10 minutes. It was before…

CUNNINGHAM — Something there. You told us - and the water boiler suddenly decided to kick in.

EISELE — Wally did a P53; he did a P54; I was supposed to do some P52 alignments. I did three P52 alignments, and it was getting light. I think that's probably about as busy as we ever moved through a night.

SCHIRRA — You really get up-tightness on this thing because you want it to work right. The COAS alignment was a very difficult task, and I would like to remind Donn how difficult he thought that SCS alignment was, yet they turned out to be beautiful.

EISELE — But we thought we were busting ourselves apart to do them.

SCHIRRA — They're better than any Mercury or Gemini alignment ever was the whole time, less than a quarter of a degree.

EISELE — We came away with the thought that they had no qualms at all about using either one of those backup alignment techniques. You could get plenty good; you can get within a quarter of a degree with either one of them.

6.7.6 S-band

CUNNINGHAM — S-band TV operated normally. Tape position, no comment. Ranging, only one comment. On the down voice backup mode, I noticed that they left the ranging switch on during the test, and it apparently worked fine. I've always been under the impression that the two are mutually exclusive. If you turn the down voice backup on, you ought to turn ranging off in order to get a better signal-to-noise ratio. It may turn out that it is insignificant in earth orbit and that for lunar distances, we would be better off turning ranging off.

Oscillator, no comment.

Power amplifier, no comment.

Transponder: we covered earlier, the secondary transponder failing. It is my understanding that had it been necessary, we could still have used the secondary transponder at least for ranging. Emergency voice and keying all worked out just fine. I find the key to be a little awkward, but usable. S-band up-data apparently okay. Throughout the flight we never had to take a VERB 71 update. We took it twice for the landmark tracking exercises in case we had inadvertently changed our state vector. We had one to load in onboard. Other than that, all up-data link seemed to work fine. Operationally, the S-band antenna selector switch is a sorry system. You have two switches, and it should be a single rotary switch for omni A,B,C, and D. I operated probably 95 per cent of the time in omni A and C. I didn't really have to move the second switch; it was selected in omni, and I moved back and forth between omni A and omni C. The antenna switching from callouts from the ground have been covered. I think we ought to leave it exactly that way. Have them make a blind call, no answer, then switch to the opposite antenna. Comparison of the USB and VHF up-voice quality. What do you think, Donn? I didn't really notice a big difference, but the ground said that the S-band was much better than VHF.

EISELE — I could tell very little difference.

CUNNINGHAM — Me, too. I would say they were about the same.

EISELE — S-band might have been a little clearer, but there wasn't that much difference.

6.7.8 Power Switches

CUNNINGHAM — We did use PMP auxiliary for awhile, and apparently it worked fine.

6.7.9 Telemetry
Switches

CUNNINGHAM — Telemetry switches, no problem.

6.7.10 Flight Quality
Recorder

CUNNINGHAM — Flight quality recorder, apparently it worked fine.

6.7.11 Voice Record
Indicator

CUNNINGHAM — Voice record indicator, apparently worked fine.

6.7.12 PTT Switches

CUNNINGHAM — PTT switches, had no complaints. Have any complaints, Donn?

EISELE — No.

CUNNINGHAM — It is a fairly large switch, but it's the smallest size you can make. After we utilized all of the different straps on the inflight coverall and the constant wear garment, I felt like it was a pretty usable system, hanging where I could get at it. It isn't a big problem. The complaint is that you have very few small wires going through there, and yet you have a great big umbilical.

6.7.13 VOX Circuitry

CUNNINGHAM — We never did operate on VOX throughout the flight. We should have done that just to fill the square.

6.7.14 The USB
Emergency Keying

CUNNINGHAM — The USB emergency keying, no comment; it worked fine.

6.7.15 DSE Storage

CUNNINGHAM — DSE storage is the only subject in this particular heading that I would like to expand a little bit. The data storage equipment serves two purposes, the data and the voice. I will not concern myself with the data; that's a ground problem. There are times when we are out of ground contact and high bits are required. That's where we interface with the data storage.

What I am concerned about is the voice storage, the tape dump, and the fact that the tape recorder had to be rewound before it could be dumped and had to be rewound again in order to be used. Time and time again throughout the flight, we had things that we wanted to record, and the first thing that had to be asked was "do we have the tape recorder?" We got down to a procedure where if the tape motion flag was gray (meaning it was running) and we were out of touch with a station, we assumed that we could record.

If we were in touch with a station-supposedly over a ground contact and it was gray, we couldn't count on recording on it because it could just as easily have been in the rewind mode, and that's why we had tape motion. On numerous occasions - I wouldn't care to estimate how many - we left the ground site without having the tape recorder turned back to record and over to us. This is because the ground did not get the last command in to run forward in the RECORD mode, or because they took longer to dump than they had expected. Longer dump times were caused by a shorter pass than they had expected, or because we had possibly placed some high bit rate data on it. I think we ought to mention that we very seldom, ran it on high bit rate.

EISELE — I remember on one occasion that I asked you to go high bit rate for some reason or another, and it tore them all up. They were really terrible, belligerent. When we got over the next station, they called up loud and clear that they sure didn't like to have that high bit rate on there in the middle of the tape. Apparently, there is some problem of switching from low to high and back again.

CUNNINGHAM — That's not really the problem.

SLAYTON — That is the replay; they have to do it real time as I understand it.

EISELE — I understood their problem. Their high bit rate is one for one on the dump. It was only on for a minute, and I didn't understand.

CUNNINGHAM — We record at 15 inches per second, and it dumps at 120 inches per second. If you have high bit rate, they want to dump it back at 15 inches per second. At the time, you said let's go high bit rate. I went to high bit rate so we could put the displays on, and now they have a problem. They now have that dumped back at 120 inches per second, and you've got aliasing on the tape.

EISELE — It was during the landmarks that we did this, and on that particular pass all the DELTA-R's and DELTA-V's were zero anyway. If there is ever a question on it, we can square it away.

CUNNINGHAM — The real problem that we face here is that the ground has to have a full time man tabulating the run time that is on the tapes and how long it takes to get it rewound. In the interim of coming up with a better system, we could do what we finally did towards the tail end of the flight. Occasionally, the ground asked us to go ahead and command reset after we left the station.

EISELE — One time, I did that on my own. I wanted the tape to run; I wanted to record something. I heard about that later, too. That somehow glitched them. The message I got from those two incidents to not touch those tape switches unless you coordinate and brief with the ground ahead of time.

CUNNINGHAM — You didn't mention that last incident to me. Wally kept asking about tapes and I was always reluctant. I didn't want to take the tape over if we left with it running unless they have given us COMMAND RESET. Here's what can happen. They rewound it; they play half of it back; they break lock or something and can't get the command up; or they're losing the station and they stop. If you start going then, you lose all the data that's already been...

EISELE — I know they are losing data, but it seems to me that the tape up there with the voice recordings on it is just as valuable as the data. Now they have been getting systems data for hours and hours on end.

CUNNINGHAM — Nobody is arguing that point. I don't think we should even address our discussion at anything but the voice. If you had voice on there an hour before, it might have been important voice; when you get to the station, they rewind and start dumping it. You get half-way through your important transmission. All I am concerned about is the voice channel. In losing the stations, they stop it. They want to catch another station 10 minutes later. Now we start recording it; if we have taken COMMAND RESET now, we lose whatever we've recorded before.

EISELE — I finally settled down to just a very simple rule. As long as it was gray and not over a station, I would assume that I could record; and if it wasn't gray, I wouldn't mess with it; I just went ahead and wrote down what I wanted to say. That seemed to be the only way, which was kind of a surprise. I had a notion that the tape was more or less at our disposal when we wanted to use it. That was not always the case.

CUNNINGHAM — That's certainly true.

EISELE — Other crews ought to take this into account when they are planning their details of how to record on board.

CUNNINGHAM — I think that we have got to have a separate voice recorder in the spacecraft as soon as we can. We commutate it onto the regular PCM and dump it. That's the only real long-time solution. In the meantime, all we can work on is trying to get a little more cooperation between the ground and flight. Ideally, you'd like to let the ground run it completely, but there may be cases where the ground would be ahead by asking you to rewind the tape before the next site. That saves them 8 minutes.

EISELE — The message that I got was that in general you should not ever do anything with that COMMAND RESET switch unless you have gone over it ahead of time with the ground. Otherwise when you come over the next station, they are assuming that the switches are still their last selected position. When they find that they are not, it takes them awhile to unscramble what you've done and set it right again.

CUNNINGHAM — It isn't just for the DSE. The problem with it is that when you hit the COMMAND RESET, you gang bar all of the commanded switches to what you had, and they may have been reconfiguring those. The COMMAND RESET function did seem to work normally. The times when they asked me to throw it and I did throw it, we apparently were in the right mode.

EISELE — Before we go into miscellaneous systems, landmark tracking was not in the DTO's listing, and I would like to record a few comments on that.

SLAYTON — Let's go back to those -

CUNNINGHAM — We're going to use that as a checklist later.

6.8 Miscellaneous Systems and GFE

EISELE — The lighting on the DELTA-V counter, the DSKY, and the mission event timer all on the main display console can be washed out by sunlight.

6.8.1 Cabin Lighting System and Controls

SCHIRRA — The first time it really became a critical event was during that burn 5, and I couldn't read the darn numbers. The point I am getting at is to make Frank Borman aware of the problem and let him go fix it with a bunch of engineers involved.

EISELE — It looks like you might be able to put some small low shades around the edge of the...

SCHIRRA — You could almost tape a piece of card over it.

EISELE — Yes, that would work pretty good; it would keep the direct sunlight from hitting it. It seemed to be just because of the very bright sunlight impinging directly on the surface. It is not the total background light that causes the problem.

SCHIRRA — You noticed in the films how bright it was on occasion, and at other times, it was quite dark.

EISELE — We didn't use the sunshades at all either, and I guess the main reason I didn't want to use them was because I like to see out and see the ground when we could because part of our flight was to get pictures of the ground. On a lunar mission, maybe you would not want to do that; maybe you could put the shades up and avoid the problem to some degree with perhaps shading the two side windows or something.

SCHIRRA — If you are not burning, I agree the sunshade might be good for IFR. If you had a burn and went whistling off, you might want to look out for attitude reference as your last warning if you're tumbling.

EISELE — I would never cover up the rendezvous windows. It's something for Frank to think about. I think the other crews should be aware of that lighting system problem.

SCHIRRA — I guess I would state that I would just as soon dispose of the window shades, unless the crew envisions sleeping in the couches; then you had better have them.

EISELE — Yes, for our type of mission, yes. We never did use them.

SCHIRRA — Frank tells me they expect to sleep one time in the couches.

EISELE — You might want to keep some of the window shades.

SCHIRRA — You might want to keep the window shades. I guess you better not delete those yet, Deke. Just tell the other crews to tell us how the hell they are going to work.

EISELE — We had three lighting failures, and they all took place in the lower equipment bay.

SCHIRRA — I thought lighting controls were great. No problem with the controls, but, Donn, you should bring up the failures…

EISELE — The floodlights behaved just like they do in the simulator. They do not really dim smoothly from minimal brightness all the way up to full bright. They are kind of spotty; and, occasionally, we got one that would flicker a little bit, but, in general, they were fine. The EL was great. The three failures we had were in the lower equipment bay, and we had one element of each of the two LEB floodlights go out at different times. We also had one patch of the EL go out on the G&N control panel, that little square that contains the optic switches.

SCHIRRA — The optic switches. I couldn't read them. But you need all the aid you can get, and that's where those sunshades are appropriate for the COAS thing, and where those covers are appropriate.

CUNNINGHAM — Floodlight shading.

SCHIRRA — You really have to black out to acquire, and on occasions when Donn was in a hurry, we just had a blackout so he could acquire the stars if they were in a difficult area of the sky. We tried to help; I don't know whether it helped any at all to call stars from other windows.

EISELE — Yes, I was going to mention that. I noticed particularly during the P53 and 54 that Walt was in the LEB looking through the optics; I was over in the right seat staring at the stars; and you were in the left seat staring at them. Between the three of us, we managed to map out the celestial sphere pretty well and know which ones we had available. It wasn't a matter of not being able to recognize or see any; it's just a matter of picking ones that were close so that you didn't have to fly all over the sky looking for them.

EISELE — We got along just fine on that.

6.8.2 CLOCKS

EISELE — The clocks are the next thing.

CUNNINGHAM — Did you say anything at all about the clocks?

EISELE — No, we haven't gotten into it. I think we did mention the lighting problem on the clocks? If you get direct sunlight on the MET and the DELTA-V counter, it will wash out even when the numerics are turned up full bright. The means ought to be taken to reduce time on those floods so that you do save them for flight.

SCHIRRA — That's a very appropriate comment. Why don't you develop those because we always came in there and found integral lights on and flood lights on?

EISELE — Yes, it's part of the general tendency of test crews or the people who write the test procedures to not specify that floodlights and the EL lights be turned off when they are not needed. I think there is some work to be done to reduce the time on the floods and the EL before flight. The EL seems to be very reliable, and I don't think we have a problem there, but those floods do burn out. DSKY's have the same problem, although that's not as bad. You can always look down the LEB, and in fact, for the MET, I ended up using the one down in the LEB a good bit. I could just lean over and read it from the center couch when the MDC was blanked out with sunlight. We did have a problem with the MET on the main panel. It tended to lose time, and we had to correct it twice during the flight. Towards the end of the flight, it didn't lose any time at all. It seemed to work better the last half of the flight than it did the first half.

6.8.3 Event Timers and Controls

EISELE — The event timer in the LEB was used only for rendezvous. Other than that, we didn't make any use of it at all. It seemed to be very unreliable at that time, and I never did get around to checking it out again to see if it was a one time type of malfunction or whether it was repeatable. The thing would drop numbers or jump two digits in the tens row for minutes. It was not a very reliable timer, and I ended up using my wristwatch for rendezvous rather than the event timer.

The one on the main panel acted up on one occasion late in the flight. At that point, I was very happy that I had two wristwatches on because we still weren't sure about the MET on the main panel. With the event timer acting up, we could have been insufficient timepieces. I think that carrying the fourth watch on board is a good idea, just to back up those onboard digital clocks in case they don't work. The controls on the event timer and on the MET worked just as advertised. We had no trouble thinking the event timer was the computer clock or any other reference. One thing we would've liked to have had was some sort of an alarm system, just a little kitchen timer that you could set for however many minutes you want to time some function. Did we already cover that?

CUNNINGHAM — Did you mention the delta timer?

SCHIRRA — Oh, the delta timer. We mentioned a DET failure on nine.

EISELE — Yes, that was a one time thing, and it never failed after that.

SCHIRRA — We cycled it a number of times after that, and it worked. It went up in units of 10.

CUNNINGHAM — One other thing on the DET: When Wally had to turn the oxygen fans to ON, the DET spontaneously started in the LEB.

SCHIRRA — A tip for the crews: where we had trouble keeping track of time on the MET was when I had to run my DET to keep track of the elapsed time, the mission time, which you normally don't do.

CUNNINGHAM — When it had sun on it.

SCHIRRA — I couldn't read it over there for some periods, especially during those daylight passes when we were trying to get ready for a landmark track and things like that.

EISELE — From the other seats, you can look at the one in the LEB, but from your seat, you can't. You have to get out of it to see the LEB clock.

6.8.4 Accelerometer Indicator

EISELE — The accelerometer seemed to work just the way it should all the way through. We could monitor accelerations during boost, during entry, and during SPS burns. It seemed to read fairly accurately as nearly as we could tell. It is easy to read. During the orbit part of the mission, we had some little discs that we placed over those instruments so that they would not shine so brightly during darkened periods. There is a bright white light on the accelerometer and also on the altimeter, which is objectionable when you are trying to maintain a darkened cabin. Those little discs worked out real well, didn't they Wally?

SCHIRRA — Yes, I think they should be provided for subsequent flights.

EISELE — They sure helped.

SCHIRRA — I would like to pursue that point. The hardest task I had in the mission as far as pulling everything together was that COAS alignment. I was really nervous, and I know you guys knew it. I was up and down Walt's back rather violently for having a urine dump right when I was looking for my stars. It was real quiet, and I was the only guy doing anything at that point. What I had to do is yell MARK, and all you had to do is punch a button because the computer was set up, All of a sudden, all I could see was 90 million sparkles out there when I was looking for a full moon, and I went out of my gourd. I had wasted the whole rev getting set up for that thing, it was loose deadband.

CUNNINGHAM — I think it was because we were kind of uptight about a particular objective. It's only fair to say that after they did settle out we did do a 53 or 54 and three P52's all in one night pass.

SCHIRRA — So it was amazing how highly confident we were at that point, but we didn't know it.

6.8.5 Electrical Cables and Adapters

SCHIRRA — I was very concerned about cables, wires, hoses, and things like that. I guess in a shirt-sleeve environment it's not so bad, because you have the hoses stowed, and all you have to do is lug the cobra cable along with you. That did bug me a lot with my short one, I'll have to admit, because then I had to keep straightening it out.

EISELE — Yes, after a while you learn which way to turn so you won't get wrapped up in it. You learn how to rig it up when you first put it on, for example, after you've been sleeping, so that you don't get tied around the other guys' COMM cables. These were very minor problems, and I think that after the first day or two, we didn't have any trouble with our COMM cable interfering.

SCHIRRA — That's a good thought, too. When we changed seats, we did change cables. That was much easier for the burns.

CUNNINGHAM — For the burns, that worked out.

SCHIRRA — This would be appropriate for subsequent crews when they put different people in different seats for the events we were talking about.

CUNNINGHAM — I think we finally got all the connectors working right on the adapters on that spacecraft. It was a long hard fight to get it done, before lift-off. We had a nightmare with the little short ones like the power cable to the movie camera going on at the right places. We never could get the one to work down in the LEB, and it finally did and we never used it. We made note of that; never used it for lighting or anything.

EISELE — That electric power cable was typical of the ones we've seen in the past. It had a failure mode in that the light that is supposed to tell you that the machine is running stayed ON when you turned it OFF; however, it turned the camera OFF almost every time.

CUNNINGHAM — That's our cable, a little light in there that has a fuse block and all that good stuff.

EISELE — I can't figure out why the light is there, it doesn't work right.

SCHIRRA — When you turn the camera OFF, the light stays ON.

EISELE — When you turn the power OFF to the cable, the light will go out, and next time you start over fresh. You recock it…

CUNNINGHAM — I don't really see what that light was supposed to tell me because the camera would run and you could hear it.

EISELE — I don't think it does anything, but it gives you something to think about when you're using it. It out-psyched me every time. I would try to guess when it would be ON, and it never was.

CUNNINGHAM — I don't remember any failures or anomalies with any of the cables, though. They seemed to work fine: we never had to drag out a spare.

EISELE — I think what I would like to make plain though is that I still would never delete those spares. It was a campaign to get them on, and I think you ought to have the spares.

SCHIRRA — If you recall, we had a spare camera body that we were worried about, a movie camera body, because we didn't know about IVA. We though that was the biggest thing we had to do on this mission other than DTO's. It turned out that it wasn't a problem, but we were prepared for a camera failure. I don't think you need two movie cameras for IVA, but I do think that in lieu of what we have seen we need two Hasselblads.

EISELE — It depends on what you want to get done, Deke; if it's an unknown, and you really want to get it, then you should have two in there.

CUNNINGHAM — What you might go to is just the body.

REP — The lens? The lens are interchangeable.

SCHIRRA — Did you guys feel that we were in a spaghetti bowl?

CUNNINGHAM — Never did.

SCHIRRA — We thought we would be with the water gun out and all the other stuff; it really did scare me.

CUNNINGHAM — There was a lot of stuff out, but it didn't seem to get in the way. There was a lot of stuff hanging loose, and it didn't always look so neat, but it wasn't in the way at all.

SCHIRRA — I think our collective discipline was very good. We didn't leave things out; we put them away all the time. The only thing we were sloppy on - and it wasn't in the way - was the urine dump thing because you were using it all the time.

CUNNINGHAM — The other thing is that the people cleaning up the spacecraft on the carrier couldn't believe it. They said, "Boy, this is a clean spacecraft!"

EISELE — We left some things lying out that we hadn't planned on, like suits were lying there.

SCHIRRA — We did very good housekeeping, and that's a requirement. We very rarely took out more than we needed. Like meals, we took out only three meals at a time. At the end, when we wanted to empty a box, we had the most.

EISELE — Yes, there were two meals per man out.

CUNNINGHAM — Back when we brought up the spaghetti bowl, the only real problems we had with cables interfering was actually us guys; our cables interfered with each other, crossing the cables. That's the only interference problem we had.

SCHIRRA — Once in awhile, the water gun would get messed up through there, but it wasn't bad. Not enough to make a crisis. I thought it would be.

6.8.6 Crew Compartment Configuration

SCHIRRA — Crew compartment configuration.

EISELE — Just mentioned that, about stuff being out.

SCHIRRA — I think the other thing I would like to make note of is that we were luxurious as far as volumes for stowage; gosh, it was great. If you took clothes off, you could go to the stowage locker and put them in there temporarily, and there's lots of room in there for stowage. There was in our configuration.

EISELE — The Velcro patches on the wall are very useful for holding just anything, cameras, meals, pencils, anything at all that you had out. You could glue it to the wall, and it would stay there.

CUNNINGHAM — We plan on trying to update the proposed Velcro usage from what we used and what we didn't use. I will say that some Velcro was terrible.

CUNNINGHAM — I used it. I wouldn't make a case for deleting it. All I am saying is I certainly couldn't make a case for using it and I noticed that I went for the first 3 days without my booties on, which had the Velcro. Donn went for the last 3 or 4 days without his booties on which meant that you couldn't use the Velcro at the duty station. I thought it might be nice to have it for waste management. I stripped all the way down and all I had was my skivvies around my legs I didn't have my booties on.

SCHIRRA — I used it for urine dump, is what I am getting at. Donn, it seemed just floated around the LEB during urination.

CUNNINGHAM — Yes, I always braced myself between the walls.

SCHIRRA — Everybody has their own little habits. Now when I used it for fecal jobs, I used that strap routine to keep me in.

CUNNINGHAM — Did you?

SCHIRRA — Yes.

CUNNINGHAM — You are the only guy I know that ever used it for anything.

SCHIRRA — Yes. I couldn't get a good grip on my toes on the struts and the strings that held the L-shaped back down.

CUNNINGHAM — Okay, what I am saying is - I would, if it were me, try to talk people out of trying to add a lot of Velcro down there for footholds.

SCHIRRA — There we all concur.

CUNNINGHAM — And I would never go to anything fancier.

SCHIRRA — No. If you saw the films he had his feet on it. You don't need it. I did sightings from the side. So the Velcro for the G&N station is not required. As long as it is in, leave it there. It does help a little bit. Maybe one guy will like it and another may not. They don't need to have any more.

CUNNINGHAM — I think it might pay to relocate some Velcro patches in the LEB. The ones to the left and the right of the guidance and control panel down there are in the way of the left and right crewmember's feet because their feet are down there moving around. If you hang something on the wall, it is apt to get kicked loose. On the other hand, there is no Velcro, in the center below the EL lighted checklist. I would suggest that on other spacecraft you take some of that Velcro off the left and right panels where the food lockers are and move it over to the location below the EL checklist on the gimmick panel.

SCHIRRA — Don't you think it is incumbent upon us to help the guys on this subject? Physically, like help Borman with his shades for those lighted things and Velcro.

REP — Yes, I think they would be happy to get any recommendations you have in that area. Those are pretty well locked in on 103 anyway right now.

SCHIRRA — Like anything else Deke, you try to come back having learned something. We should be able to respond to some of this stuff. If it will make it easier for them, let's do it.

REP — If there is anything they don't have that you think they ought to have, that is the thing to discuss. I don't think we want to go in and start tearing anything out of there.

SCHIRRA — No, I agree. It's true.

CUNNINGHAM — Along with it, the next flight is operated more like ours than any others will be. Bill Anders and Fred Haise were in the other day and they said after we get through with debriefing for all the crews, they would like to sit down and talk to me about watching systems, for example. I think we ought to do a lot of that in the long run.

SCHIRRA — Well, Walt has some comments about deleting some mirrors.

CUNNINGHAM — Stowage was kind of random. We just put things on the wall where you happened to be or where you thought you were going to need them and we made extensive use of the temporary stowage bags and of the little compartments - F1 and F2. Very handy for any assorted items you wanted to put in.

SCHIRRA — An interesting observation; when we broke the suits down, we used those right away. Donn stored the gloves in them.

CUNNINGHAM — Temporary, until we got the suits and put the gloves back on the suits and stowed the whole thing. We were talking about Velcro. Velcro patches without many scratches around them haven't been used very much, as far as looking at our spacecraft was concerned.

SCHIRRA — You see a lot of traffic around some Velcro patches and some just fresh as a daisy. I wrote in the spacecraft, "not used."

<u>6.8.7 Mirrors</u>

SCHIRRA — Mirrors, you want to talk about…

CUNNINGHAM — Yes, it's in here someplace. We ran several different items that I think all of us recommend strongly, although you will probably run into some opposition individually from follow-on crews. That lower equipment bay rotation hand controller back is deadweight.

SCHIRRA — We are backing Dave Scott directly on that. That deal of taking both sticks down there, and we're saying IVA is so easy you don't have to do that.

CUNNINGHAM — Donn flies the thing by leaning back here and flicking the hand controller if necessary.

SCHIRRA — Well, Donn, do you really feel if you were alone in there and you had to do a midcourse from there you could do it? Or would you have to have a translation down there? Or would you go up to the seat?

EISELE — Oh, I think I would go up to the seat and do it. It's no big deal to get from the LEB to either left or right seat and it takes about 3 seconds to glide from that location.

SCHIRRA — I would suggest that the other crews consider what we did before, because we were so worried about our hand controllers and the cables. Leave the things where they are unless you have a failure. The risk of breaking one of those cables is still very high. We got kind of scared one time when they started getting caught. As a matter of fact that's the way we want to handle them though.

REP — It's a valid comment, but before anything changes, I think we ought to come in with a flight crew ops RECP with everybody having a chance to put an input in anyway.

SCHIRRA — I don't want to stuff it down their throats.

REP — No.

SCHIRRA — The point is that no one is really as aware of that fact as we are. We are IVA experts. Donn particularly can evaluate that problem because he was on it 8 hours a day.

REP — Any time we can get out stuff that we don't need, we ought to get it out.

SCHIRRA — All we had to do was watch out for each other because there is a little traffic in contact with Donn. The reason the requirement is there, is the one-man rendezvous.

EISELE — I had an occasion now and then during my watch to use the hand controller, particularly when I was trying to setup for an alignment - say preparation for a burn and you might have to know rates or something. It was no problem at all just to go from the LEB back up to the left couch if I wanted to look at the displays or grab either hand controller no matter which one and take it out. I found no need at all to mount one down in the LEB.

SCHIRRA — Oh, another thing we decided. Donn was a little worried about how to see the FDAI. We used the mirror on my side, just preset it. You could get down in the LEB and look in the mirror and see the FDAI reflection.

EISELE — That is a good tip for a one-man effort. Use one of those mirrors to monitor the 8-ball from the LEB.

CUNNINGHAM — At any rate we mentioned the hand controller bracket. The other thing is, there are two mirrors still left on the right hand side that were there to monitor down the X-axis of the spacecraft. They are absolutely useless for anything except looking at yourself in the morning, admiring your beard, and combing your hair.

SCHIRRA — You have side mirrors for that anyway.

CUNNINGHAM — I would suggest we keep the articulated mirrors, the ones with the joints you can pull out because you are going to need them if you have to get pressurized and strapped in. The other two mirrors are absolutely dead weight.

SCHIRRA — I would delete them and get them out of the way. They are almost in the way. Leave the bonded structure there, and naturally the bracket, but take all the unscrewable and unboltable stuff off and junk it.

CUNNINGHAM — If there is any way to get rid of the scar weight left from the fecal canister do that.

SCHIRRA — That can be done. I looked at that.

REP — Stuff like that can all be done in line someplace.

SCHIRRA — You just take a screwdriver to it Deke, and take it out. It is just a case of getting inside and doing it. We almost started taking it off ourselves but it wasn't worth it.

6.8.8 COAS

SCHIRRA — On the COAS, very late in the game, maybe about 6 weeks to 2 months before flight, I asked and was granted a third COAS bulb to be in the COAS in its boost position. That is the only bulb we used. It didn't get hurt at all during boost. I think it is a good idea. You don't even have to go down below and get one. The reason I asked for this was, if I had an abort I could immediately take the COAS off that side panel and bring it up to the window and I had a good visual reference system for direct X-axis appraisal.

REP — The 103 guys asked for the same thing and I don't understand why we don't have a bulb in boost.

SCHIRRA — They said the bulb would destroy itself during boost.

EISELE — It's the only one I used. I never even used the two spares.

SCHIRRA — Okay, on the clothing I think each of us should make our remarks - Walt and I of course…

EISELE — Can I go back to COAS one time. I would like to…

SCHIRRA — Well let's get that COAS boresight down officially.

EISELE — Yes. As it turned out, we ended up doing two COAS boresight checks in the flight. I did the first one on the first night watch and found that it was about a degree off in both axes from what it should be for the X-axis. I have them here.

SCHIRRA — Oh, you have them here?

EISELE — Yes, there was - to begin with, the first one. We had a shaft angle of 359 degrees and a trunnion of

56.4 degrees, which worked out to be 1 degree off in pitch and yaw from what the true spacecraft X-axis should be. That is related to the IMU, of course, the NAV base. Later in the flight, and this was after the COAS had been removed and stowed and reinstalled, we did another one. This was just before or during the time you were doing P53's Wally.

SCHIRRA — Yes.

EISELE — The shaft angle at that time was exactly the same within a couple of thousandths. Then the trunnion angle shifted by a tenth of a degree. The point is that it is very repeatable. Once you have done a decent calibration you can remove it from the mounting and put it back on and have reasonable confidence that you still have good numbers.

SCHIRRA — Good point. I forgot that. The guys were asking me how repeatable was it.

EISELE — It was a tenth of a degree.

SCHIRRA — It is very repeatable.

EISELE — We felt pretty good about that, finding out that the COAS mounting was that solid and that you didn't have to worry too much about bumping it and knocking it out of line.

SCHIRRA — I think it is worthwhile noting, even though we were a degree off, in both axes, X-Y in that sense, this was not boresighted as other spacecraft will be. We did not have a docking ring up there to boresight to.

EISELE — We didn't really require boresighting. All we required was to know what the alignment was. Of course, we got that from the sextant alignment check.

SCHIRRA — Did you redo these numbers in your mind, is it in the northeast quarter where the urine is? Is that right? Maybe you ought to work on it for a while.

EISELE — Yes, I could work it out again. I psyched out the same quadrant. I don't remember what the numbers were, but I psyched out the same thing.

SCHIRRA — What I mean by the northeast quadrant is that the target on the boresight, that is the COAS Plus, is to the left, and down from the target.

EISELE — From the target. That's right.

SCHIRRA — One degree in each direction. There is another thing on the COAS, I remarked on in real time I think. It is almost impossible to have that darned reticle show up against a cloud background over the earth.

EISELE — Yes, it's not much good in the daytime.

SCHIRRA — It is great for the dimout thing. I have some more coming out of my mind now. I have this big song and dance from everybody that because the stars were not at infinity in the simulator and the way everything was boresighted in the simulator, the light loss in the simulator was not representative of the real world. I was going out of my mind up there using my left eye to see the star and my right eye to look through COAS. It was a great light loss through the COAS. They said it was because the simulator was like that and people ran studies and they ran that little star check back in Houston. Dean Grimm did it and you can see 6 and 7 magnitude stars and all sorts of stuff. If that is the case all I can say is, you see more through the window in the real world than I thought we would. And that is possibly true. I went out of my mind with stars like Fomalhaut and Alpharatz that are around first magnitude. Carrying them into the center of the COAS for that COAS alignment. So there is a great light loss.

CUNNINGHAM — Well, we have to face it - the stars out the windows are fantastic.

SCHIRRA — Yes, I think Walt's first observation, - all of us then, of course, saw it, the Magellanic clouds, proved a point.

CUNNINGHAM — Yes, they were distinct. I mean it was about like the normal. You know I looked at it for several nights in a row, kind of hesitant to say anything about what I was seeing.

SCHIRRA — Did we log that airglow, that high airglow?

EISELE — You've got it in the flight plan. You had to verify your sanity.

SCHIRRA — Yes, I really needed help on that one. It was one of our mutual night watches. I saw the red arcs that I described in Mercury, and never saw again in Gemini nor did anybody else. And that is way above the airglow, about 5 degrees above it. I would say about 15 or 20 degrees above the horizon.

EISELE — I think it is a little more than that. I looked out. I could see it over something like that on my side window. But it was a definite distinct layer. The separation between the two was - I didn't think it was quite that much. I thought it was about the same as the thickness of the lower airglow and then the upper airglow was fairly wide. Wider than the lower one probably.

SCHIRRA — We spent a lot of time, by the way, with the COAS, while we are talking about airglow and the optics, trying to measure the thickness of it. It varies fantastically. Depending upon what time of day or night (space day or night) the night airglow was, I am pretty well convinced, somewhere around between 2.5 and 2.8 degrees.

CUNNINGHAM — I got one excellent measurement I would like to have somebody do the arithmetic on. I watched a star or planet 90 degrees to our line of flight, so from the top of the airglow down to occulting, and there should be no error in it essentially from our motion. I would certainly like to have somebody check that out.

SCHIRRA — Walt and I were talking about the time I took the planet Mercury and took it through, in Mercury, and they got all the information out of it. That occulting, you've got to remember, counts refraction. You can see below the earth.

CUNNINGHAM — Yes, but refraction can be fairly decently calculated.

SCHIRRA — I agree. I just mean I want people to make note of that.

CUNNINGHAM — Oh yes.

SCHIRRA — About a month after they said I couldn't possibly see Mercury someone realized it was refraction.

REP — Well, I have the data and I will get it to the right people. I would like to have it.

CUNNINGHAM — Okay, where are we on this thing?

6.8.9 Clothing

CUNNINGHAM — Clothing, PGA. It is so nice to get out of it and it is so bad to put it back on.

EISELE — It's amazing. Soon as you get it back on, you go back to your elephantine psychosis. Once you take it off, you ought to never have to put that thing back on.

SCHIRRA — It's amazing. We lost all of our mobility. We'd go flitting about below the couches as you saw on that film. When we had the suits on it was a nightmare to go below the couches.

CUNNINGHAM — It sure was.

SCHIRRA — This was in the docked position. I could just barely get in the couch.

REP — Let's go with the underwear here.

SCHIRRA — The underwear is part of our biomed harness problem. They don't stabilize that harness well enough. It can move down 2 or 3 inches so the length of wires becomes kind of critical. At the same time I was just amazed to see that garbage all over Walt's chest. He had some leads that were 8 inches too long, others were too short.

CUNNINGHAM — I had a rat's nest in there.

SCHIRRA — My point is: onboard you have four sensors and we changed the sensor on Walt and that invalidated the biomed harness, so all this discussion was very academic I thought. We didn't have much time to argue about it or discuss it. The biomed harness is really a whole bunch of wires together. It is not one integral system as most people thought, and to change a piece of wire was not a big crisis. They could have made a wire the right length without disrupting the whole program or changing the characteristics of it.

CUNNINGHAM — I think the underwear stabilized it quite well though. I would rather have it on the underwear than strapped to my skin. I thought at first I would like to have a third set to change into, but actually we changed about 7 days into the flight.

SCHIRRA — That was a real treat, changing into that second set.

EISELE — That really was.

SCHIRRA — Well, I have got a point on this thing that I mentioned to the doctor and I think we ought to do it here. When you exercise with the seat belt on - in retrospect, I think we should have taken our biomed harness off.

EISELE — Well, now that is a thought. I might take it off to exercise.

CUNNINGHAM — The problem is that it is spread over a long period of time. When you and I were up, we would exercise as we could get it in. We might have it on and try to exercise over maybe a couple of hours.

SCHIRRA — Do you think maybe the doctors will go along with not having that on and having us exercise? As long as we put it back on again?

SCHIRRA — They shouldn't need biomed data while a guy is exercising. That research should be done.

CUNNINGHAM — Incidentally, I had probably most of the marks of the three of us on those sensors after we took them off. But in all honesty, I didn't know that they were there during the flight at all. Now, I do have a comment on the underwear, though. The trap door; there are two ways of having a bowel movement in there, either through the trap door, or dropping your drawers and getting comfortable.

SCHIRRA — There's only one way in that sense.

CUNNINGHAM — That's exactly right. I tried it the first way; I fought it out and did it the first way with that trap door back there. The trap door is too small for that, and it's so much easier the other way that we might as well not have a trap door. There is not a thing that that trap door in the back does, and I'd suggest that we don't have it.

SCHIRRA — The flight coveralls, I would say off hand were fine. There is only one thing we discovered fairly late in the mission. The hole up here is different from Walt's because he's got a different setup on where his switches go. It brought this big blob of wire up here, and what I ended up doing, very late, was bringing the cobra cable connector through the middle of the jacket and mating it up there, and that took all the junk off my shoulder. You still have that thing sitting out here like that.

REP — I know but if you did away with that loop, you see, it would be down here.

CUNNINGHAM — If you made your cable the right length, it wouldn't bother you. If the cable was right on the light-weight headset. The cable is too long, and they just simply doubled it over and it makes a big lump out of the side of your head. We had a make-work-fix on ours, and I think we should get away from that make-work-fix. It was irritating, and I caught myself twice during the flight with this thing sticking up, turning the wrong direction and talking to the wrong thing.

SCHIRRA — Yes.

CUNNINGHAM — You have this big thing set up like a microphone.

SCHIRRA — The other thing I'd like to suggest is on the flight coveralls; that's what you are going to wear most of the mission. The pockets did not close up right; this Velcro game was not very good. Little bits and things you want to get rid of, you couldn't keep in there, so you had to go somewhere else. Those blue suits that we came home in were the kind we used to fly airplanes. They have zipper pockets all over the place and you can keep trash in this one, and snot rags in this one. We just had two pockets on there, and a strap-on, theoretically, which still had a big hole in it. We didn't use the strap-ons at all, never used them.

CUNNINGHAM — The strap-ons are bad pockets.

SCHIRRA — We took our scissors out of the strap-ons, and we never used that pocket again, we snapped them to the spacecraft.

EISELE — Well, the main reason that the strap-ons are not very good is that the flap doesn't come down far enough. You have this big gap; I think you need to relocate the Velcro or else put a zipper on that one.

CUNNINGHAM — It was a problem, if you strapped it onto your leg with your flight coveralls on. It was just something else you had to unfasten to take the coveralls off, and nobody would mess with it.

SCHIRRA — I forgot who promoted the idea of picking up debris with tape; I guess you did Walt, to get the garbage off the filters.

REP — I did mention that to you preflight. That was to get Beta fibers off your skin.

SCHIRRA — It sure was a saving device.

EISELE — George Low said, "I've been doing it for years on my blue serge suits."

SCHIRRA — My Navy blues, that's the only thing that can clean the darn things. We kept some tape up on the instrument panel. If we got a washer or a nut or bolt floating by, it was the only way we could trap it. Believe me, we were going out of our minds trying to hold this stuff. You put it in your pocket, it would come back out again. We'd put it on this tape up there, and later we would put it away. A piece of tape on the instrument panel is a great thing for a repository for a while. Then you can roll it up and stow it. That tape was pretty valuable stuff all throughout the mission.

CUNNINGHAM — Incidentally, we would have used almost no tape throughout the mission except for the fact that we used it to fix our head sets. That is where we used most of the tape.

SCHIRRA — That's where the tape went.

CUNNINGHAM — We thought we took that tape along to wrap the food bags. I did one food bag, where I put a piece of tape on it. With all the other food bags we wrapped up the food, stuck it inside the bag that it came in, very tightly incidentally, took the piece of tape that was on the outside of it, and just taped that bag closed. It was labeled, they knew it was your meal, what day, everything else.

SCHIRRA — The tape goes on the outside of the bag, just to make the point clear, we were so used to it.

CUNNINGHAM — It was a label for the meal. You can peel that off, and use it to wrap up afterwards.

SCHIRRA — We just used a long piece of tape, not the little short one.

EISELE — I think you ought to have that tape along, because it's kind of like having a pair of pliers, you know, all purpose type thing.

SCHIRRA — Yes. That is something else we are going right into the COMM helmet. The microphone on the light-weight headset started breaking off, right at the root. The tube started to break. I jury-rigged it right away in the beginning when I first saw it. I spent about an hour on it with the tape after that, and it held up throughout the whole flight, I had to rebuild it. We wouldn't have been able to use it.

CUNNINGHAM — That was the light-weight headset. I had one other problem with the light-weight headset. The tube that ran up to the fitted earpiece came off. Apparently it's supposed to be glued. I'm not sure that it ever had any glue on it, but it came off from the earpiece some time on the third day.

SCHIRRA — From the molded ear plug.

CUNNINGHAM — Yes, from the molded ear plug, and at numerous times throughout the flight from then on I would discover myself without COMM, because the tube would come right off when I moved my head.

SCHIRRA — Interesting enough, we all three had different kinds of chin straps. One of the nicest things that happened, it turned out. At the last minute Marshall Horton gave me another kind of chin strap that was stuffed in my pocket. I'm glad he did because on reentry, our beards were so irritating, our skin was so tender, that the chin cup did bother me. I used this alternate underneath my chin. My beard didn't bother me at all. At the beginning of the flight, that football player's chin cup worked perfectly to keep it stable, I gather Donn and Walt went along this line, too, But I think those three types of chin straps are in the inventory. Let the guys take their choice. Watch it on the plastic chin cup for return. Any of them are bad, and I think you really want to have something you can put underneath your chin when you have a beard.

REP — Where was yours, Donn, for reentry? Where was your chin strap?

EISELE — My chin strap? I wore it across my chin.

REP — On reentry?

SCHIRRA — But it did bother you? Remember I asked you that.

EISELE — Yes, it's irritating, and it's bothersome.

CUNNINGHAM — I never had any problems, it never bothered me when I had it under my chin.

SCHIRRA — Yes, yes.

SCHIRRA — To start out I had this cold and I was super sensitive to drafts. That was why I kept them on. They felt good there because they really are a barrier. They're not at all porous is what I'm trying to say. So whenever the hoses were blowing, I didn't feel that draft coming through. I guess that helped me considerably. And I slept in them, but I was hot and sweaty and all that kind of stuff. As I improved in physical condition, I would say about the sixth or seventh night, I took them off every night. But I didn't do that earlier in the mission. We stowed them. We slept in the sleeping bag every time we went to sleep.

EISELE — When we said free floating, they must have thought we were both on the couches - just floating around in the cabin. What they meant was we weren't hanging on to anything; we were just inside the bag.

CUNNINGHAM — To us it was very plain. There was a significant difference between sleeping free floating - We learned a whole new vocabulary.

SCHIRRA — In 11 days you do; so we have to be very careful the way we talk, I guess. To get it back to our own guys even in lay terms. It's amazing, but that's what can happen in that length of time.

EISELE — I thought the flight coveralls are very comfortable at times. I know on my watch when the spacecraft was powered down and everything was quiet particularly on the dark passes, on the dark side, at night it got pretty chilly. And I welcomed having those things on including the boots.

SCHIRRA — You saw the powered down mode, so your opinion is really important.

EISELE — I would recommend that you continue to take them along because you may find you get chilly without them.

CUNNINGHAM — Well, I definitely recommend you keep the things too. I found them very comfortable to wear.

EISELE — Well, you need the pockets too. You got two pockets and wings, and you need the places to stick your pencils.

CUNNINGHAM — You use the pockets quite a bit. I wore mine during the day. I never wore them at night except one night when I forgot to take my pants off.

SCHIRRA — Oh, really. We did discuss the pockets. They have to be improved for holding small objects. It may be that others will have colds, and that's why I transferred my Kleenex at first. Then we used the ORDEAL box for Kleenex stowage. It's perfect for it. That we labeled the snot locker. There's only two we should talk about I guess. They're the launch day UCD and the normal urine disposal. On the launch day, UCD we still stowed in the suit bags with the suits. We did not find a real good use for the UCD clamps. Think we can delete those UCD clamps? I never used it. In fact, I would propose we do if you have this condition, even if you wear the suit for 3 days, for example, to the moon. You take the UCD off, you take that roll on off, and you throw it away into the waste can.

CUNNINGHAM — Yes.

SCHIRRA — And you put a fresh one on when you go to use that thing again because you've got them in the medical kit then, three or four of them in there. That's the way to handle that guy with a launch day roll; just dispose it, don't use that clamp and make your mess with the Kleenex and everything else and just dump the whole load and delete those clamps.

EISELE — I didn't use the clamp at all. I hated doing just that. I got it out again with a roll-on that was all gummy, so I just threw it away and got a new one.

SCHIRRA — Now the other thing, I'm anti-bead roll-on.

CUNNINGHAM — I'm a very pro-bead roll-on.

SCHIRRA — The easiest way to solve that is to get the right size roll-on and have beads on them because they can always cut the bead off.

CUNNINGHAM — Yes. Incidentally, to cut the bead off, it would have been very useful. I found that one criticism I had of the roll-ons; they did not retain themselves on the UCD. And I think if I'd of had a bead on that I wanted to cut off, I could have stretched it around there again and it would have stayed. Several of us had those pull off when we really didn't want to.

SCHIRRA — I might add that I had one roll-on that was larger than the rest, and that's why I had trouble with it that time. By the way, that's an interesting observation. Remember when they were trying at the last minute when they were going to give us some smaller ones because they said we'd shrink. That's not true.

CUNNINGHAM — No, I agree.

EISELE — Well, I thought the UCD was convenient and easy to use. It worked fine. I didn't have any trouble with mine at all. I think I changed roll-ons about four times because after a while they developed little pin hole leaks, and you have to throw them away. But that isn't a problem either. You just slip a new one on and go.

CUNNINGHAM — Yes, I had one roll-on that developed a leak. You apparently saw it when it started spraying

SCHIRRA — You had a pin hole leak, and it was coming right at me, that's why I saw it.

CUNNINGHAM — But I found that it was not inconvenient to use. Everybody developed his own technique. I don't think that you necessarily clean yours the way I did. But it was quite a ways into it before I - you recall rinsing them out. It was the first water. We just kind of stuck them out thereby drying them out, and putting them back in. Wally had a very good point, they stayed wet inside, down there. I was always sitting there rerolling it, and cussing because it was all wet with urine. And Wally, I noticed he kept sticking his away, and I said what's the story. He said well, I roll it when I need it. Then I don't mind it so much.

EISELE — Started using the water gun to clean them out, and if you're careful, you don't get the water gun on the roll-on.

SCHIRRA — In other words, if you use the water gun to clean the valve so it wouldn't get gummy, not the roll-on.

CUNNINGHAM — You try not to touch the roll-on.

SCHIRRA — But that did work out.

CUNNINGHAM — I think that's a very important thing.

EISELE — I think we had misgivings about trying that at first, but it's not a bit hard to break the water stream, and cleaned it out very well.

CUNNINGHAM — Something that I did that I thought was very useful, it helped in that it was dry the next time that I started rolling. After a couple of days, it got so that I would take the Kleenex and I'd twist it up and stick it down in there. Which kind of dried it, and then you'd squeeze the roll-on out. In other words, it'd be dry the next time you rolled it down.

SCHIRRA — Stowage areas, I think what we said covered that earlier.

EISELE — Yes, I guess the message here is that there's plenty of places to stow things, and you've got lots of options. And probably no two crews will do everything exactly the same, and that's fine too, because you set it up to suit yourself.

CUNNINGHAM — There's one stowage problem we did have. You guys never saw it, but I did every morning. The place where we had the dosimeter and the camera bracket. The camera bracket was not retained tight enough in there. You'd open the lid up and the camera bracket would float out. We also had the O2 partial pressure thing, and it just set there.

SCHIRRA — I did have that problem because I was slapping it in there trying to get something else in there.

EISELE — Yes, and it just set there. So we did have a piece of equipment that was not restrained. You know late in the game, we decided to stow it down there. That particular compartment wasn't restrained.

SCHIRRA — Now that you've brought up the subject, we had another problem. That was the lithium hydroxide canister, that Block I version. We had to practically stress my couch to close the lid on that.

EISELE — Oh yes. It was just the one container.

SCHIRRA — Beneath my feet.

EISELE — One beneath Wally's couch that we could not get the lid down very easily.

CUNNINGHAM — It took me 10 minutes, and we finally finished the last hydroxide canister.

EISELE — But the rest of them all worked fine. That was the only stowage container that we had any trouble with.

6.8.10 PGA Connecting Equipment

CUNNINGHAM — No, I didn't have any problem with hoses.

SCHIRRA — We had the Beta covered cobra cables and the cover right up at the connector and was really badly frayed at the end. No, that's not going to be a continuing problem because they are all black fluorel. I think our spare was black fluorel, in fact. We would have had those, but they failed through PIA at the last minute, and they didn't have any replacements. So we had one spare and that's all. As I understand it, the next mission will have black fluorel. If they're not, this should be pushed for. We had lint stuff all over the place at the end of this mission. That's because this stuff was starting to fail. The hoses connected up with no strain when we got back.

CUNNINGHAM — But we didn't have any trouble with plugs that didn't mate up or hose connectors.

SCHIRRA — The only thing I would like to say about the PGA connecting equipment is that blasted cable that comes up underneath your chin, it drove me batty all the time I had it on. They tried to do something about it, but we're using a battleship cable routing for little tiny wires. And when you get to the BIOMED sensor, you got a little feathery wire and you get to where it connects to something else, it's a battleship cable. The thing sticks right in your neck and is very annoying.

CUNNINGHAM — I've got another stowage problem, gang. Spare roll-ons and in R11 are not retained well enough. They are always floating free in the compartment.

SCHIRRA — Yes, there's a well. It's obvious that if anybody looks at it. But somebody's got to fix it.

EISELE — Yes, the problem that I had there too, was that when I need one, I had to reach in and pull out the little packs and usually I had to pull out all three before I got to mine.

CUNNINGHAM — They floated around back there and I kept pushing them back.

EISELE — It would have been better if they had been secured so you could reach and grab the one that you knew was yours.

6.8.11 Crew Couches

SCHIRRA — Easily defects and odd defects, I found it very irritating. On the crew couches, it's sort of academic to discuss them. They work quite well. I was particularly pleased with the translation controller. It was fixed just right. Solid beam bar was much better than that rinky-dink on that side. The one thing that we should register is on the foot pans. Donn had a real nightmare. And we came in with an open item really and he was in trouble.

EISELE — My foot pan was not locked for entry.

SCHIRRA — This was getting too late then to mess around with it. My foot pan was locked up on more than one side, and Donn was down there...

CUNNINGHAM — Donn also had much trouble getting his left foot out of the restraint.

SCHIRRA — Concerning this part, the other couches are going to be like that. Let's see, my outboard side of the foot pan wouldn't lock up. Is that right?

EISELE — I can't remember which one.

SCHIRRA — We started donning the couches at T minus burn minus 45 minutes.

EISELE — Yes.

SCHIRRA — And he got his foot so locked up in there, he couldn't get it out again. And Walt had to unstrap him, go down and get it back in again.

EISELE — Then after Walt did that, that's when we found that my foot pan again was not locked in and by then it was T minus 25 minutes, and...

SCHIRRA — We didn't have time.

EISELE — We said to hell with it. We're going home. Well, the reason that I wasn't worried about it was that I had plenty of knee clearance in the center seat. I wasn't worried about jamming my knees.

SCHIRRA — We discussed it, if we were really worried we were going to go around one more rev.

EISELE — It was inconceivable to me that the couch would ever stroke far enough to run my feet into the LEB. You would have to go 2 or 3 feet there before you hit anything.

SCHIRRA — Donn has this big open area above his knees, so we weren't worried about it. Walt and I didn't have that kind of area. If it had been Walt or myself on the same foot re-straightening, we would have scrubbed that retro and taken another rev. That's how bad it was. I'm sure if Mission Control had known the recovery weather was that bad we would have gone ahead.

6.8.12 Restraints

SCHIRRA — Hand straps - that's absolutely a waste of the material.

EISELE — That's a good item for deletion as far as I'm concerned.

SCHIRRA — Take the labels, handles off as well. The EVA boys think you've got to have handholds all over the place, and the IVA boys, we three only, say we never use it. We used wickets. Walt had one classic experiment with a circuit breaker, and moved all over the place and didn't even actuate it. We're trying to make it quite clear we did not actuate one switch, pull, or depress the circuit breaker that was supposed to be out, ever, for the whole mission. Not one.

CUNNINGHAM — Frankly, we had our backs against the MDC time and time again.

SCHIRRA — We were doing flips. We never knocked a thing.

EISELE — Oh, we floated into the switches now and then but we were moving so slow, and the wickets protect them so well.

SCHIRRA — The only important thing we had was that hand controller.

EISELE — When we talk about handholds - we're talking about the ones on the struts down here. The one that's under my knees, incidentally, I used every time I tried to sit and get into the couch. Not zero g, one g.

SCHIRRA — You get trapped in the one g world. That's the point.

EISELE — They're great for the one g, but you don't need them in orbit that much.

CUNNINGHAM — You've got three up there though around your...

EISELE — The center one is the only one that ever got grabbed at all, and I'm not sure of that.

SCHIRRA — Well, we tried to delete the ones on the struts and the other guys, EVA people, said you've got to have them.

EISELE — They're redundant - they're probably more redundant than the dumb Brooklyn Bridge structure for the hand controller. I don't know what the G&N station restrain is. Does anybody know what that's supposed to be?

SCHIRRA — That's the foot.

EISELE — Oh, is that Velcro on the floor? That didn't work out too well because there is enough torque or set or something into the COMM cable which tends to lift you upward away from the floor when you've got it on. It just pulls your feet right off that stuff, and you don't need it anyway. The film shows the normal position that you assume when you work the G&N controls down there and you've got your buttocks against the edge of the center couch and you got your two hands on those handles and that's all the restraint you need.

SCHIRRA — The other thing I would like to make note of because we talked about earlier - that strap thing. If it were on the spacecraft, I wouldn't go out looking for it. If it just happened to be there -

EISELE — What strap?

SCHIRRA — The series of snap straps that

EISELE — Oh yes.

SCHIRRA — I'm sure I could learn to do without it. I just got into the habit of using it. And that isn't required. That was also part of the G&N restraint. It was secure around your waist and hook on to things.

CUNNINGHAM — Another thing to keep in mind, people getting ready to go into this IVA environment is the body really likes the fetal position. You don't get quite into it, but if you're standing relaxed doing anything like G&N station, Donn was in the fetal position.

SCHIRRA — Your whole body relaxes for you with your knee coming up and you go into the fetal position.

EISELE — Yes, the no-load configuration of your body is just that.

SCHIRRA — Sleeping restraints, there were some straps in the sleeping bag, but I didn't understand that at all. There was only one around the waist.

CUNNINGHAM — Those were for sleeping on top of the sleeping bag. I'll tell you the benefit of the sleeping bag.

SCHIRRA — What was the strap up at the head there that hooked on to something?

CUNNINGHAM — I don't know what that was. Early in the game I was one of those advocates who would say we don't even need the sleeping bag. Go strap yourself to the bottom of the couch. One benefit to the sleeping bag - it allows an inanimate object that's asleep down there to stay located in one spot so the other guy that's awake doesn't keep pushing him around to get him out of the way.

EISELE — Keep him from floating away.

CUNNINGHAM — And I'll tell you along those lines, there's something I didn't like about the sleeping bag if you're going to have it at all. The straps that retained the feet joined the sleeping bag up about...

SCHIRRA — About 3 feet up the back from where your feet were.

EISELE — That's right.

SCHIRRA — Towards your waist.

EISELE — I would have preferred that the bag had the straps out each end.

SCHIRRA — You want the sleeping bag to be a cocoon. To move around inside the sleeping bag but don't move the sleeping bag around.

CUNNINGHAM — That's exactly right. And that was irritating to me at that...

EISELE — I never did understand why they built it that way.

CUNNINGHAM — Do you see what we're getting to on the straps?

6.8.13 Flight Data Files

EISELE — I thought they worked out very well. A tin box by Walt's elbow, and the...

SCHIRRA — We just had the one compartment. We deleted the one on my side; we didn't need it. The only cards I carried were those flip cards in the - on the sixth rev thing.

CUNNINGHAM — I think we had adequate inflight data stowage. The only thing about R12 on the right hand side, it was an individual tuning pound, so to speak, for spacecraft 101, but it had two metal hooks to retain the bottom of it and a strap on the top and one hook was always coming out. It was kind of catty wampus loose. It's the kind of thing that should have been mated a little better. On the flight data, we ought to mention that. We carried a half a dozen clips which was not enough for one for each hook. It worked out okay for us; every time that Donn was awake, we could collect from him and start all over. Very handy, you could use them to hook - hook it to...

SCHIRRA — The flight plan on top of the master caution panel. The flight plan was out all the time. Everybody had access to this because we lived with this thing as you can see.

EISELE — Yes, the flight plan was out constantly.

SCHIRRA — You've got to have a reminder. Just like you fly, this is your knee board.

CUNNINGHAM — Yes, it really is, you just refer to it all the time.

SCHIRRA — I think it's interesting to look at our flight plan with the stuff that's in it, and the CAP COMM's a lot of stuff in that too.

EISELE — This is part of the data file right there. Those clips were really handy for holding checklists onto the wall and keeping your place in the book at the same time.

SCHIRRA — That's the only solution we know of for a book with many pages. Now for the little six rev one, I think that's a good technique that would be the kind of thing you might take with TLI, for example. I'd hook that, because we hadn't learned the clip technique yet. I'd hook that to one of my wickets on my left side; the clip technique made it a lot easier for me. Okay. We made all our burns in the docked or rendezvous positions.

EISELE — Except the deorbit.

SCHIRRA — I'm sorry. Except the deorbit, and, of course, boost. We didn't have our foot pans up. We had the leg pans down to the - break of the knee. On two burns, I was in the right seat. I'm not sure if that was true of all the other burns - at least the headrest was down and I just slid down the couch a little ways and braced my head there.

CUNNINGHAM — I used one shoulder harness.

SCHIRRA — The first time up we did the first burn, we had shoulder harnesses on, we had seat belts on, we weren't sure we weren't going to do this the rest of the mission either. We didn't get exactly super casual about those burns.

CUNNINGHAM — No. When it got time for the burns, I'd try to force myself against it so I didn't get snapped.

SCHIRRA — Yes. It's like a catapult shot. I think that's the same when you know that you got to have your head back or you're going to get snapped.

6.8.14 Inflight Tool Set and Work shelf

EISELE — Well, there wasn't any work shelf. We threw that off a long time ago. I thought the tool set, for what little we used it, was fine. The only thing we used out of it was the wrench, because we had a spare E tool anyway.

SCHIRRA — Didn't we use a long adapter for one deal?

EISELE — Yes, we might have one time. Yes. When you were taking that panel off to get back to the water.

SCHIRRA — Yes.

EISELE — Where the water was on the pipes. It was fine. It held the tools in place properly, so you could get at them whenever you needed it.

6.8.15 Food

SCHIRRA — I think the food has been discussed appropriately with the doctors, but I do feel we've got to play the food much more carefully. This is wrong to save weight in food by bringing up the caloric intake of the food with sweet things.

EISELE — I've summarized it by saying, "Don't load up on bite-sized too much; don't load up on beef bites."

SCHIRRA — Boy, he was so anti-beef bite, it was unbelievable.

CUNNINGHAM — Don't load up on calories - 2000 is plenty and I feel that very strongly and I was converted. I've got another note here which is slightly facetious, "Try to take two breakfasts and one other meal." That's because the good stuff seems to be at breakfast -

SCHIRRA — Well, the real point - and the crews may not get this from the doctor's report: First, you're suffering from a bland diet - there's no salt in it. And, I think that's one reason why we craved the bacon cubes so much, we wanted salt.

EISELE — Yes.

SCHIRRA — And I'm convinced your system cries for stuff it wants. We also craved chewy stuff like, but not this crumbly stuff, meat type of stuff like beef pot roast or reconstituted meat stuff, that was so palatable. The warmed food is a whole new world. I'd also like to add that the coffee should be changed to a better kind of coffee...

EISELE — A better brand.

SCHIRRA — It was a high for me whenever I had it.

EISELE — I wish I'd had one every meal like you did.

SCHIRRA — Yes.

EISELE — I had one for breakfast. But that ought to be a crew option and if a guy wants coffee every meal, he ought to be able to have it, too.

SCHIRRA — Yes. It's not a big deal - just a very thin little teeny line.

EISELE — You know I was - we mentioned this before flight and decided not to bother, but I'm just wondering if vitamin pills might not be of some use on a long mission like this because...

SCHIRRA — As a supplement?

EISELE — Yes, I think we tend to get run down. For instance, our colds might not have been quite as severe if we had had a good supply of vitamins. Another point about them...

CUNNINGHAM — And particularly if you get up there and don't eat all your food.

EISELE — That's exactly what I was going to bring up. The doctor says, "No, you've got a balanced diet."

CUNNINGHAM — If you eat it all, maybe you do.

EISELE — It comes to the point where you're not eating all that balanced diet.

SCHIRRA — You know what they could do - and let's make a note of that. I didn't make it to the doctors. We didn't put the bacteria pill in the juices, because we felt that wasn't required. We put it in all of the reconstituted food that could develop bacteria and explode. Maybe you could put a vitamin pill in there in lieu of one of those yellow pills.

CUNNINGHAM — Oh, I see.

EISELE — Just make sure you don't get mixed up and eat the wrong kind.

CUNNINGHAM — You know I kept a meal for 2 weeks in my desk drawer to see if it would swell up and it didn't.

SCHIRRA — It didn't?

CUNNINGHAM — No.

SCHIRRA — That's a nasty routine to put that pill in there.

CUNNINGHAM — The other thing about those pills is they're just like rocks.

SCHIRRA — Yes, but you don't have to break them, they do melt with just a little bit of moisture that's in that little plastic bag.

CUNNINGHAM — Yes, but we eat the meal before they melt.

SCHIRRA — You're right.

CUNNINGHAM — A softer pill, it's got a little coating on it. Put it in and squeeze it.

SCHIRRA — I guess what you're saying is, we shouldn't mess with the pills at all in any of the food. With the work loads, it's a nuisance. Because you have to cut the bag - get the pill out and hold the pill, open up the mouth spout again, stick it down in there and squeeze it inside.

CUNNINGHAM — Some of the foods sustained a failure of the type like the bite-sized or some of the cinnamon bread cubes. One of them would get crushed, and I think this happened in packing, you know they're generally pretty strong stuff, but in packing you might have one little meal that's got broken and then you didn't dare take the meal apart. We did a couple of times and all the crumbs would start coming out. Another thing is we had several food bag failures – re-constitutable food bags - between three and five.

EISELE — You were the one with the bad luck. I don't think I had a one fail.

CUNNINGHAM — Yes. Well, one failure was very interesting and at the place where you're supposed to be able to get the spout to eat out of, it had no opening into the bag. It was completely sealed.

SCHIRRA — That was the fold up spout?

CUNNINGHAM — Yes. I had two other bags that failed in a way that - the material would squirt out not through the spout but through the next layer, and you ended up with a mess. Generally, the food bags lasted. I was surprised we had so few failures really.

SCHIRRA — Well, one of the keys that we found was powdered food in the food bag drifted around the bags, it meant the bag lost its seal. It's a good quality control check. Not for us in flight - it's too late then. Preflight if you see food, powdered, moving around in the bag, it means it's a bad bag and it should be sent back for evaluation. We didn't see any like that. Remember earlier when we had those sample deals?

EISELE — Yes.

SCHIRRA — Some of them were like that. The other thing that was done towards the end of the mission - I'd use the water pistol trigger to fill a used bag and drink out of that.

EISELE — Yes. I'd save the fruit juice bags.

SCHIRRA — Yes. I never seemed to remember to do it. Eventually, I just said "Aw, to heck with it." Wrestling with a gun is a lot of work.

EISELE — It makes your thumb sore.

6.8.16 Personal
Hygiene Equipment

SCHIRRA — How about personal hygiene equipment? I'd like to add right away, Donn saved me, both Donn and I have hair that's long enough to comb and that comb was really a high point for me. It sort of massaged your scalp a little bit and it made you feel a little bit better each day if you could just see yourself looking…

EISELE — Yes, we each had an aluminum pocket comb on there.

CUNNINGHAM — I knew they were combing their hair because I kept cleaning the lint off the hoses.

SCHIRRA — You were shedding more skin than we were hair.

CUNNINGHAM — You know, I shed skin when I got back.

SCHIRRA — I know. I saw your arms.

CUNNINGHAM — My arms, my back.

EISELE — I liked the dental equipment on there. I sure liked the toothbrush and the toothpaste.

SCHIRRA — I wouldn't delete the dental floss though none of us used it.

CUNNINGHAM — I noticed nobody used it either. In fact, it started catching on some of the Velcro.

SCHIRRA — Yes. But I think there are people who have the habit of using it, and I'd rather not change that factor.

EISELE — Yes.

SCHIRRA — It didn't get in the way other than your point there, Walt.

CUNNINGHAM — No, I thought the dental equipment was very satisfactory.

SCHIRRA — I might add, though, if you did use dental floss, I don't think you would do it again after you were through with it.

CUNNINGHAM — String was a problem - whenever we had pieces of string it was a pain to get all together in one gob and stuck in.

EISELE — Oh, that's an interesting point, regarding stowage.

SCHIRRA — Yes.

EISELE — We used the stowage box for the ORDEAL unit as a flight location for the Kleenexes after they were used.

SCHIRRA — And for little teeny things, like the pill things we used the slit in the waste can.

CUNNINGHAM — Yes. One thing about it - we might make note of the fact that we had seven towel bags and I found that was enough. I had one extra clean one when I came down.

EISELE — Towels were great.

CUNNINGHAM — The other thing is that we had two boxes of paper towels on prior to flight and we ended up with one left but we'd have been one shy for our particular mission had we not added the two.

SCHIRRA — In addition, someone else may go who has a lot more bowel movements than we did. We had a low number. Particularly my two in there that averaged it down.

EISELE — Was it five, four and two?

SCHIRRA — Yes. You use at least 4 to 5 Kleenex per bowel movement. More likely five. That could have eaten into that box if we didn't have that last one. I think we just had enough is what I'm getting at. Course it was the colds that ate them all up. I also - I personally needed to use that little stimulus on the end of the toothbrush.

EISELE — I used it, too.

CUNNINGHAM — Yes.

EISELE — I used it whenever I thought about it.

6.8.16 Personal Hygiene Equipment

SCHIRRA — There are differences of opinion about the little wet-washes with the food. Walt used them to clean up after waste management programs, I guess. I decided all of a sudden I was collecting too many of them. They sort of supplement the towels, if you keep a moist towel. Again, we're talking about something that is very optional. They're not objectionable. They're packaged and I don't think there's any sense in pulling it out at this point.

CUNNINGHAM — If you use them though, it's almost impossible to keep up with them. There's one every meal, there's one in every fecal bag and it's not too hard to find out all of a sudden you've got six sitting around.

SCHIRRA — You rat-hole them, you know for a big event or something like that. Next thing you know they're all popping out.

CUNNINGHAM — I do have a criticism on those. Some of them I used were moist and nice. The others were just like they had been on the shelf for months and months and were almost dry.

SCHIRRA — The problem there is you can't get a little bit of moisture out of the gun, you have to take a whole shot. You couldn't rewet those.

EISELE — Whenever you wanted to wet something you'd take a big towel and catch it out of the good station. That hot water. The only thing that is wrong, I guess, and I don't know how you could handle it - we started collecting a lot of hair in that cockpit. Body hair, whisker hair, or hair hair.

CUNNINGHAM — This might be an appropriate place to digress and talk about combing the hair. We did make note of the fact that when Wally and I got up in the morning, it took about 45 minutes from the time we got out of the sack until the time we were laying in the couch ready to go, with all our COMM on and everything else. That 45 minutes was used up for such things as rolling up the sleeping bag. I'd take a radiation dosimeter reading, we'd both get a chance at the urine disposal, take a towel and wipe our face off, get dressed, get our COMM all hooked up, comb our hair, and in general get to the point where we're really with it.

SCHIRRA — In the spacecraft, you're expected to perform right now and answer up with sharp answers and face up to the day. I guess what we're trying to say is when a man comes off the off-watch, the way the menu was set up, you were supposed to eat and go to sleep right away which is not the way we do it on the ground. We did shift off that program to a reasonable breakfast, lunch, and dinner with a block of 16 hours in there.

CUNNINGHAM — Incidentally, that 45 minutes getting ready to go didn't include any breakfast and I'd say 45 minutes comfortably. I think that's non plannable for the flight plan. I really do. Just like the meals cannot be blocked out like that. You should allow the time, but specifying that this 30 minutes is used for eating is almost a laugh. You just never eat in that 30 minutes.

SCHIRRA — Well, each bag for example Deke, takes you 5 minutes to get the water in the bag. The bag will take say 15 to 30 minutes for reconstitution. Right there, you've had to drop something to do that.

CUNNINGHAM — Every once in a while it was quiet enough so we could finish eating in 45 minutes, an hour or so. Each meal took a couple of hours. You kept doing other things too. We had the food out and we would go about the normal tasks and keep eating as we did them.

SCHIRRA — One of the things that kept us ahead of the time line, which was not in there, Donn started the day a rev early, and that's how we always held our heads up. He would go out and get a P51, at least a P51, and get the spacecraft constrained in some kind of attitude. That last day, our time line was about 3 to 4 hours from the published flight plan. We put that much more in it. That particular series was tight right down the line. It was tight all the way down. I'd say in show biz words we were overbooked all the way home. We really were.

EISELE — I think the way we had it planned out though was close but it never pushed us over. Do you want to go into the inflight exercising. I think we probably can handle that one between the two of us.

SCHIRRA — Yes, I think Walt and I were real fans of it. Walt almost went into shock when he saw me use it so much. It just made us feel good and that's the whole point. You need a device to work on, there really isn't a good place to work against the spacecraft, you just can't get stress going in there.

CUNNINGHAM — I think we were thinking that - and this is differing from isometric, now you are long enough to reach clear across the spacecraft and push on the two walls, but isometrics doesn't give you the satisfied feeling that isotonics do. I think at the time we felt like we were going to have all this work to do moving around in the spacecraft and it just isn't any work.

SCHIRRA — There's no work. That's what's so disappointing. That's why you hear us say, let's go from 2900 calories down to 2000 calories. Now I had 24 and I gave a lot of it away.

EISELE — I thought you said you had 2000.

SCHIRRA — Yes, 22 - 23 somewhere in there.

CUNNINGHAM — I had 2500 calories and that was a mistake.

SCHIRRA — At any rate we used the exerciser, unfortunately the film didn't show too well. We hooked fixed straps on the hand holds, either the left or right seat above the left or right hand as appropriate... and pedaled down in the LEB from the left couch on one side or the right couch,... to the point where it got hot, You couldn't touch the capstan.

CUNNINGHAM — Another variation of that is if I held the hand holds in my hand, I found I got a certain amount of isometric and probably isotonic, too from pulling on that thing. To a much lesser degree, Wally and I both utilized the hand holds on our feet and pulling on the ropes. I think I did that mostly just to even up a little bit. We both must have had in our mind to keep the legs moving for the biceps.

EISELE — At any rate we can't endorse too heartily having an exerciser on board and we've all covered, in our debriefing with the doctors, the fact that if they really have our best interests at heart, the object is to keep the protocol out and allow this a free running business.

7.3 Visual Sightings in Orbit

SCHIRRA — One thing, Walt saw a - well go ahead, Walt.

CUNNINGHAM — Well, I saw a satellite and at the time I saw it, we logged it on the tape. Neither Donn nor I was aware that those were not supposed to be mentioned live over the air. Wally brought it to our attention. I logged it on tape. It was a satellite passing through the Southern Cross.

SCHIRRA — Let's make it clear that this is a far, far away thing, much as you see from the surface of the earth.

CUNNINGHAM — Right.

SCHIRRA — We did not see, at least I don't recall and I don't think Donn ever mentioned seeing, anything that had recognizable detail other than those things that we took with us.

CUNNINGHAM — Never.

SCHIRRA — Geographical landmarks, I'd say were covered completely by film. The only thing that surprised us was one of the Apollo landmarks, and Walt was doing that one.

CUNNINGHAM — There was a bridge across the inlet and it wasn't on the landmark map. We had what was considered a fairly recent map but there was a point of land coming out that had been bridged, very definitely.

SCHIRRA — I'd like to make a point, Deke, so that our directorate gets straight on these landmarks and they put a date on when it is most current. The last time it has been checked out. This was one of these not too far away places, another country, but we almost blew the landmark. It was wide open weather and I was sitting up there in the window looking at it. Donn was looking through another window and Walt was down below and all three of us finally decided that was it. We took a picture of it and if it comes out we'll document that landmark. Cloud coverage, we had a lot.

CUNNINGHAM — Wally and I did quite a bit of work looking at air glows day and night and trying to log them. I think, many times, that we got descriptions on tape and during that sunrise, I went live with trying to get the colors of the sky.

SCHIRRA — I'd like to get that red arc thing and document where it was, That's going to be a job.

CUNNINGHAM — This is an appropriate place to bring this up. Wally did see the high air glow again and I saw it, too. (Laughter)... other celestial sightings. I didn't realize they hadn't been seen before, but I had some very good sightings on the Magellanic clouds.

SCHIRRA — These had never been sighted before.

CUNNINGHAM — After I realized I'd been looking at them for several different nights, I called Wally's and Donn's attention to them and I think everybody saw them.

8.0 EXPERIMENTS

CUNNINGHAM — Okay. We're down to 4. Cytogenetic blood studies.

SCHIRRA — All right. Now I finally agree; we had a pretty long knock down drag out on that particular experiment. An invasion, I call it, it is radioisotope. For the other crews' benefit, we bought it. One of the reasons I finally bought it was that this imposition would not be made on a "spec" lunar mission, if I can call it that. The experimenter, Dr. Johnson, is with me on this and is perfectly willing to negotiate this. I suspect if the next mission goes as we are thinking, that they may need this just to close the loop and that might not be a bad way to do it and get it over with. I don't think that crew is going to undergo any higher risk than we are except they're just farther away. I would almost say that might be a good place to knock off all that stuff.

8.2 Synoptic Weather Photography

SCHIRRA — I guess we should, in this area at least, mention the cyclonic effect which we saw in the clouds. After Gladys, the tops of thunder storms in South America looked just like the eye of a hurricane. You could see the very tight vortex effect. We did get a couple of good fixes on it. Whether they turn out or not is another thing. It's a phenomena I have never heard reported before. Maybe people know about it. I was quite surprised to see it. This just brings up this area so someone can get into it.

SCHIRRA — By thruster fires at night, you could see the pitch and yaw and roll. Particularly those that fired forward.

CUNNINGHAM — I might mention that I couldn't tell which thruster was firing by the glow on my side.

SCHIRRA — It did affect sighting but you just stopped firing.

CUNNINGHAM — We also had sparklers coming off the thrusters when you fired.

SCHIRRA — Walt did make an attempt to catch an SPS burn with the movie camera in place.

CUNNINGHAM — Apparently didn't get a thing.

SCHIRRA — I think, on that thing, we're going to find out what magazine we used. We'll go back and see their master print and we'll look for something on it. It's very dim light, we know that, we'll see what we can find out. We just ran wide open, it was a fiftieth at two, to see if we could catch it. You know we always worried about that kind of stuff.

EISELE — One thing about it, we made a lot of burns at what would be considered local night, and I don't ever remember any disruption of out-the-window views.

SCHIRRA — Well, my point is we always worried about trying to hold attitude with stars or horizon. I don't think we could. Those views were awfully bright.

EISELE — The thing about it, you know, is we were always IFR.

SCHIRRA — I know, that is what I am trying to say. I found that I would have had trouble looking out if I had to do an SM RCS deorbit thruster firing toward the command module, not the service module. CM RCS thrusters really were bright. Even during re-entry we got bright.

CUNNINGHAM — It was a real bright pink cloud.

SCHIRRA — Oh, pastel sky, I never saw that before.

CUNNINGHAM — You know I mentioned that to some of the Gemini guys though and Tom mentioned that he had seen it. Very faint pink, well before .05 g.

SCHIRRA — Yes. Just like everything went pink. Just like light pink paste.

CUNNINGHAM — He mentioned where it was, too; I am sure that they saw it.

SCHIRRA — I just never looked out that way, I guess. There are so many windows. You can see all five windows with pink cloud.

8.5 Lower Body Negative Pressure

SCHIRRA — I feel this should be cancelled out altogether. It's a half an hour wasted every time you do it and you do it too often. I worked very hard to make it repeatable, not moving around and fouling them up. There are three things that this experiment is going to come up with: one, that you change because you go into space. I'll concede the fact that you do, because you also go into pure oxygen environment. Two, that you need to exercise, and we concede that fact because we are exercising. Three, that you might want to wear some device around your legs to stimulate your lower body by having a negative pressure across it. That is objectionable and not a practicable solution, so the experiment only validates something we know. I see no reason to continue proving something we know. We know that pure oxygen environment is against us. It has to be because it's not the way we live.

CUNNINGHAM — Another aspect of it is just the lying down, not zero g, just inactivity.

SCHIRRA — I think it's a lot of fun to collect data on this but it's a great imposition to lie in that thing, on the ship, on the bench. The post-flight physical just takes too much time. Most of it's experiments. We went right along with them and cooperated all the way so we could try to get some of this stuff out of the way, but that's the one thing we ask. I could tell the crews are looking at us. If we bought them, they say they're going to have to buy them. I hope that isn't the way it turns out. I think we can probably knock off M011 and M023 without any great crisis.

9.0 PREMISSION PLANNING

SCHIRRA — Okay. Premission planning and mission planning, I think, was pretty well firmed up right from the beginning. We didn't have any great perturbations in that. The only problem was that the trajectory kept changing. I cannot forget, even now, how all of a sudden SECO changed at the last minute and everyone was aware of it. We were flexible enough, almost flexible enough I'd say, to respond. In the flight itself when I didn't hear the Mode 4 call out, I was wondering whether that late change caused it or the transmission wasn't good. It turned out transmission wasn't good. But all the simulations we have done, we've done with the 9 plus 53 SECO and that would really eat us up in later missions. This is a pretty casual one because we know how to earth orbit pretty well.

SLAYTON — We got the loop closed on that.

SCHIRRA — In the flight plan, all I can say is that we had a pretty well defined flight plan and we kept bringing it down to the point where everybody in the country had a copy of the flight plan that we flew. I went home and saw one; I saw one in the hotel; they were all over the place well before the flight. Fantastic distribution.

CUNNINGHAM — I've got several comments on the flight plan, though.

SCHIRRA — The premission planning or real time?

CUNNINGHAM — No, the actual flight plan we flew.

SCHIRRA — Listen, that's in the next area.

CUNNINGHAM — Okay.

SCHIRRA — This is premission. The changes to the spacecraft did bite us at the end. The battery problem bit us in real time, and that just happened to be a late discovery. I agree with that. We were very concerned about the foot pan changes at the last minute, and that bit us at retro. I think we froze up pretty well. There weren't many open items. The EMS, at the last minute, failed. I agree that we shouldn't change it. I think we can get around that because it's not necessarily space important to check that out. You can check it out with the centrifuge.

SCHIRRA — For example, we went out of our minds trying to find that banana plug that worked on the canisters. We couldn't find it, and frankly we cheated. We just held the can and the structure, which was just as good a ground as any wire.

CUNNINGHAM — We changed the first canister without it.

SCHIRRA — Two thirds of the way through the mission, the thing broke anyway. So we ended up going back with what we had done in the first place. This is the kind of stuff that can happen. That was pretty fast response for a period of 10 to 12 days. I know when the event occurred; it was in the 103 chamber. Towards the end, you just can't afford these changes, which is what I am trying to get at. Casual changes take a long time.

9.4 Mission Rules

SCHIRRA — I think we've had a real good exercise on that; particularly because of Walt's many, many Saturday working sessions with Glynn Lunney's assistant's controllers. I think Walt spent as much time with John Arion as he spent with Donn and I going over Mission rules and systems. So we were in very good shape. I think this is probably the reason we were as reluctant in flight to bow out on systems discussions. The knowledge that Houston had in the Mission Control Center was no less than ours. All of the malfunctions were done by the flight crews. In other words, they were hammered through by Jack Schweigert, with Walt working on them.

CUNNINGHAM — I think it is significant to mention that point here, because I made a big effort to have a joint operation of this system. I say joint, in that, routine FOD, ourselves and John Arion were in favor of it. We had working sessions where I knew what John Arion thought about it and we agreed. As a matter of fact, we never had any big discrepancies in our thinking.

For example, this accounts for the procedure for servicing a secondary evaporator. I knew that was a big surprise to John, too. I didn't have to call out and say, "Hey, John. What do you think?" Because he had been working along with me for a couple of years to try and obtain a way to do that. So I heartily recommend - and I don't know if anyone will be inclined to - but I think the people on the EECOM system are the best help you can have on the Apollo Missions. You just can't operate it by yourself. They saved me time and time again, by asking, "Hey, you guys still purging?", when we got all hung up on something else.

SCHIRRA — We discussed that particular subject. The real problem that is going to come from this is now that the malfunctions are done, they could be modified. There is going to be a difference; but on the first flight you can afford to work extra hard to guarantee that the systems will be good. However, the next crews that come along don't know how John Arion thought about that subject that day because they weren't in that meeting. So this kind of process will soften a little bit, where the next guy in the right seat is not going to be able to talk to John Arion. This is what I am trying to get across. Walt could always see John Arion sitting at the console and remember the meeting where they were talking about that subject. So apply to John Arion what you remembered of the subject and perhaps John might remember something that Walt forgot. I could see this very plainly all of the time.

CUNNINGHAM — I've talked to John Arion twice since I have been back and several times he commented on a couple of things he had passed up because he knew he had to, but he knew I was already working on it. I think it is a great working relationship; I really do.

SCHIRRA — That's part of the reason why we felt a lot freer to talk to these guys; because we had worked with them. We also spent a lot of time with the flight controllers. So much, that we lost sight of the fact that we were talking to each other. But we didn't realize we were talking to the world about our inside work.

CUNNINGHAM — Another big plus as far as the mission rules went: we have a lot of things to review, and it helped greatly for Glynn Lunney to have these working sessions with his people and everyone else concerned, even if we weren't there. He would send out a note of interest that described what went on at that meeting. Also, he put out some summaries; the Summary Flight Plan was absolutely a dream. It was the greatest thing. The Summary Flight Plan and Summary Mission Rules aided us tremendously.

SCHIRRA — As a result, when we had our mission rules review in Houston on Monday, we were done in about two and one half to 3 hours. For first flight, that's unbelievable. We used to go for days on this stuff. We've worked our way along quite far since then, and Jerry Griffin has condensed those mission rules. He had a whole new format for mission rules. I don't know whether you noticed it or not, but you could read the bold version and then you could go back through it in depth and get the numbers in two sections. That was a pretty, little, short version.

CUNNINGHAM — There were two things that I carried around with me all of the time; the Mission Rules Summary and the Summary Flight Plan. Premission planning: some of these items do have to do with preplanning. For example, the food and the eat periods as compared to the sleep periods. We've probably mentioned the fact that they were pushing our daily cycles all over the place. Wally and I got to bed about 4 or 5 a.m.

SCHIRRA — We brought this up yesterday.

CUNNINGHAM — Now, the food: they've got to change from the scheduling and put the eat periods immediately prior to sleep periods.

SCHIRRA — I brought that up, too, and you're right; that's a very big problem.

CUNNINGHAM — In regard to ACQ and LOS times, we mentioned the orbit change, but we got to the point where our ACQ times were 4 minutes off and we were really running pretty much according to preflight trajectories. Yet our ACQ and LOS times didn't seem to be reflected here.

SCHIRRA — This is what bit us. Remember I said the trajectory had been changed all along and that burn number 3 changed our ACQ and LOS times. Even our 50 foot per second changed it a little bit. The point is, we take our flight plan up and that's our knee board, and if it's off, we keep correcting it. By the way, I should add, it was good technique. Our guys used it in giving us the time of the next ACQ because then we would update our flight plan. We covered that in the SIMs, and that was one of the things that we got out of our SIMs. I don't think you want a total update on that. Do you see your mercury at 5.6? That's all they did; and, if you were really interested in it, you filed it.

REP — They were also pretty good about calling up and saying, "We've got you and we're standing by."

SCHIRRA — It's funny how we got in the position of wanting to acknowledge, but they gave up, at least on Tananarive. Did you understand that we could hear you every time in Tananarive? We couldn't seem to get back to you.

REP — Yes, we were listening.

SCHIRRA — That's amazing! We went right over the place. We were able to see the station.

CUNNINGHAM — Still on flight planning and premission planning. A note I made, after Wally and I had our little no COMM, Wally mentioned yesterday the no COMM.

SCHIRRA — Walt, that's here in mission control and I've already worked that one out.

CUNNINGHAM — We had an agreement before flight concerning the no COMM landing sites in the flight plan; but we didn't find it square in making that complete. We had block data on board for six revs, but our no COMM landing sites were like twelve revs up.

SCHIRRA — Walt is trying to say that we really had a whole 24 hour update, GO/NO-GO, rev by rev, but no data on board. No rev on that last clearance. Walt was cleared, we'll say, to the eighth day.

CUNNINGHAM — Here is it cleared to 35.4 after 24 hours, for example, and we had block data on board for through REV 24.

SCHIRRA — Something might have happened in that period, and we got past the six rev block, which is what we did one night. I said, "Walt, by the rules, we should go home right now", and we'd be dead if we were going to do it. Donn was asleep and we would start killing time by discussing it. That's why I wanted him to log it; that is, you are "out on a limb" and you expect that. This is too much of a problem, on the lunar mission. You've got one rev.

CUNNINGHAM — What I am saying is: the no COMM voice procedures what we had agreed upon before flight must be elaborated by having some data on board for the rev that you are cleared to. It can be done very easily.

SCHIRRA — If you make a burn, you're going to update right after it.

CUNNINGHAM — Yes.

SCHIRRA — I think this is something we can sit down and talk to Glen about. This has been annoying me and I do want to talk to him about that particular area. We pushed this towards the end where we bought 6-4 from lift-off on the no COMM case, instead of blowing the mission at the end of 1 year. In all the history of this business, I've never had a good clear feeling on how far I can go without COMM. At least we had that feeling from the first day, and that was a comfort. The checklists are on us, Deke. I think we were pretty well aware of what was done with that. It would take us 2 days to discuss checklists, if we do that at all.

CUNNINGHAM — I think it is only significant to add that we made some small modifications on the procedures that I thought were ironed out completely. I would like to pass those modifications on individually to the following crews.

SCHIRRA — That's why we fly them.

EISELE — This is where we really pass it on to the next crew.

SLAYTON — I'm sure that everybody is pretty well agreed (as far as I know) that we want these things broken up by mission phases.

CUNNINGHAM — This is the thing that is a departure from what we did.

10.0 MISSION CONTROL

SCHIRRA — I'd like to go on record saying MCC was exquisite. Really, they get down to the real big issues, and that's my whole point. The real big issue is that the mission was flawless from both sides.

CUNNINGHAM — Yes.

SCHIRRA — I'll never forget the first time I started working with them. We had some blue streaks, and they were pretty bad, but we smoothed them off. Part of what we are trying to get at is that we knew what we were doing in that spacecraft, and I think they knew we knew. But there was some old inflexibility we had from the old days. If it's in writing, that's the way it's got to be, and that's not right. We were up there flying for 10 days and not for 3 revs or 15 minutes. We had time to learn something, think about it, and assess it; and we had time to think ahead of the flight plan.

Donn, we mentioned just a minute ago that you actually stayed a rev or two ahead of the flight plan by aligning before we got up so that we were always up. That's why we could take umbrage with some of these things and why we legitimately thought we were going to have an audience on it. We couldn't wait to debrief after the event; we wanted to get it done before the event. The real big things where we really could get hurt were the burns, insertion, rendezvous, and reentry. These were really critical and were handled exquisitely. The way they set us up for that rendezvous, I just can't believe that it could have been done any better. In fact, if they had done worse, we probably would have blown it. There is no way that you can find fault with the way that thing was controlled. That means that we got little insignificant stuff like taking away 5 pounds of fuel when it should have been 1 pound of fuel. This is academic when we probably left 150 pounds of fuel in that thing, the way I see it, we probably left about 400 pounds.

REP — That's right.

EISELE — I expect we did at least that. Okay.

10.1 GO/NO-GO's

SCHIRRA — GO/NO-GO's are all appropriately delivered; we did discuss that a little bit earlier. Overlapping on GO/NO-GO's: there were cases where we weren't covered on the next area, the planned recovery points or the alternate ones and the updates. For example, if we had a GO/NO-GO for another day with six revs block update but it was between that point and a real GO/NO-GO, we didn't really know what to do.

CUNNINGHAM — I'd suggest that in the future there always be a place called in the flight plan like GO/NO-GO for 77-1. Right there, you can just list a block.

10.2 PTP and ATP Updates

CUNNINGHAM — So you GO/NO-GO for 1711, updates follow, and you get the same thing that we had for our block update.

SCHIRRA — That's your final clearance with the ground.

CUNNINGHAM — They may be reluctant to project that far ahead. There was no reluctance for letting us go that far with no COMM. I think this was just a little place we forgot to fill; rather we forgot to cover the gap.

EISELE — Wally and I spent some time one night talking about how we could deorbit without any block data. We had it figured out how we were going to come in anyway.

CUNNINGHAM — We had a DR, one where we would deorbit on the update map.

SCHIRRA — It kept us busy for about 4 hours when there was nothing else to do, so this way we had thought about it.

10.3 Consumables

AS for consumables, what we have always said and always felt very strongly is that we wanted the ground to do the trend flights; we didn't want to do them on board. We did want to know our fuel trend plot. When we finally got straightened up, they called up the number that we wanted for our onboard chart. I think this worked out well. For example, they called the electrical power up, and we always kept wondering. Walt, do you remember whether we had a 50-amp-hour or a 40-amp-hour battery? I'm convinced now that we had a 40-amp-hour battery.

CUNNINGHAM — No, we won't know until we drain those. North America had batteries that were as good as any of the others. What we didn't do was put the energy back in them. As far as the consumables go, the ground did everything that they should have done on the oxygen electric power. They kept track of the RCS fuel because our onboard gauging wasn't worth a hoot.

EISELE — I'd like to see them take those batteries of ours and bring them up to full charge, put a load on them such as we had, and see if they can deliver.

SCHIRRA — They will discharge them and charge them, and discharge them and charge them.

CUNNINGHAM — I just wonder whether they really delivered the spec bus voltage if they were fully charged. I don't know. The most significant thing to do with those batteries after they get back is to see if they have the energy left in them which we calculated. This will verify all the planning that was done on them, all the bookkeeping that was done on them. What they do at North American is take and put a fix discharge rate on it and measure all the energy that's going out. They say, "Yes, we did have 51 amp hours - maybe - total left in."

REP — Yes, but would you have 26 volts?

CUNNINGHAM — We did have when the batteries were up.

SCHIRRA — I think we have a point here that we're trying to straighten out in real time. If there was a 50-amp-hour battery instead of a 40-amp-hour battery, the data they were working with was starting on the base line of 40. The batteries we've had under the gun for a long time were considered by some as a 50-amp-hour battery. Now let me make my point, I want to get across finally that whatever the amp hour was on the batteries, they were under voltage when we had CM SEP. That's what I'm concerned about; I don't want that to go unseen. That scared me; I felt I lost a computer. You start off calling it fifty and then you book-keep it at forty which was the way battery C was booked. I was shocked to see that command module undervoltage when we had separation; that's my point. That load is predictable; it's known that you can run a command module there. The batteries are under the gun. That's the whole subject. Whether the technique is book-keeping or anything else, unloading the batteries must be done.

EISELE — It's probably the most serious thing that happened in the flight, when you get right down to it.

SCHIRRA — That really shook me. Now let's go to RCS fuel. I assume we're talking first about SM RCS fuel. I said somewhere along the line that when I buy the SPS, it means we use a hybrid to get home on if it doesn't work. I don't know whether it will happen in real time or not, but I was trying to conserve fuel if we had something to do with it. I don't want to just blow it away for the fun of blowing fuel. But Deke left me with the feeling that the ground was going to try to preserve an SM RCS deorbit right down to the end of the mission, or at least a DAP SM RCS... at the end of the mission. That's where we ended up. That wasn't my intention, I did realize that that was the way it was going; that's why I was sort of ginchy about blowing 40 pounds of fuel in a day on a silly experiment that we knew better than to perform. We should get 3 or 4 pounds of fuel to arc around ourselves on our own time when we're a couple of a hundred pounds above the hybrid. Do you see what I'm trying to get at? It was poor; somehow we lost our communications in real time.

When we first talked about hybrid, I wanted something that would back up the SPS. I didn't know what it was. It was a pig in the poke, and there was very little data on it. We had only 10 or 11 flight hours on any command module up until that point, and we didn't know how it would last through eight revs, but the hybrid was there to protect us if it deteriorated over 10.8 days.

CUNNINGHAM — The SPS gauging is intolerably poor.

SCHIRRA — That's the worst thing I can imagine. The gauging is so poor that you can't even keep track on board. You've got to have the ground keep track. That's not the way to have a spacecraft. We've always said that onboard instrumentation is prime, and I kept asking Walt whether we knew anything about this, and Walt finally convinced me after we saw the gauges change that they were worthless.

CUNNINGHAM — The quality readings were grossly in error compared to the numbers we got from the ground.

SCHIRRA — Even the deltas we got off were...

CUNNINGHAM — I'd like not to carry the correction curves for the RCS because we carried the correction curves, and the best accuracy we got out of it was 11 percent towards the end.

SCHIRRA — That's a lousy feeling, Deke; I don't think you'd ever want to fly an airplane and have somebody tell you the fuel status.

CUNNINGHAM — I think it's interesting to note though, Wally, that the service module RCS fuel was the only thing that we really were concerned about. On everything else, we either had a good reading, or we didn't care. Hydrogen and oxygen you could sit there and read, and you could read deltas. The SPS gauging system didn't work very well either, but we weren't too much concerned because if you noticed, you got so many seconds of burn time on it. You shouldn't leave the impression that it wasn't working. It doesn't update for short burns.

SCHIRRA — The only thing that got to it was that they didn't want to lose sight of it. In Gemini, we all felt content. I didn't have it in Gemini VI, but I knew all about it because we helped work it up. The Volkswagen tank concept: here we had the secondary propellant, and we just went in on some unknown number that ground had ginned up. I'm sure it was a good number; I'm not trying to criticize the ground, but we didn't know what we were doing. We had no assurance that we were going into the secondary legitimately other than from ground data. The name Volkswagen comes up because when you run out of fuel in one, then you switch over.

CUNNINGHAM — A good way of testing that kind of thing, if we can get the test run, is to let the lines run dry. The thing we couldn't do was switch before the lines below the tanks were dry. I don't think it would hurt to have a few tests run where you flip the engines out by running those lines dry, pressurize the secondaries, turn the secondaries on the line, and see if there's any problem filling those lines back. You could run the tank until you were getting no more fuel out of that quad and then switch over, and you have a true Volkswagen.

SCHIRRA — There's supposed to be more Volkswagening down the road. The SPS fuel thing was very academic, and I guess all of our prep time, trajectory, and everything else, was academic. Some guy thought he was the most important man in ASPO. He had to get his pugs test done with the result of changing trajectories every time somebody sneezed. Right until launch date, I didn't really know for sure what kind of mode we were going to have in that darn SPS.

EISELE — Those burn times and schedules changed weekly; in fact, they changed in flight even. The whole business was keyed to this pugs test which had to be done when the fuel in the tank was down to a certain level in order to uncover the sensors.

CUNNINGHAM — It turns out that the burn we did make was longer than any we've ever made.

SCHIRRA — I'm afraid that that kind of thing gets highlighted to the point that the guy's objectives seem like the only thing that's going on. That's what was getting to us on some of these occasions. It's like anything else; you've got to stand in line. If the system isn't working too well for you, then let's get out of there.

10.4 Flight Plan Changes

I think flight plan changes are pretty fully documented; there is no sense hammering on that except to stress one point. If something comes up that's a departure from the flight plan, it's just a "gee whiz" change to make something better; it should be exercised and simulated on the ground before it's sent up, first to trim it down and make it come out right. You said earlier not to mess with the computer unless you've done it once before.

EISELE — Most of the flight changes we got were detailed things; for instance, the real time calling up of the fuel cell purges. Those were times when they expected an update for this event, also maneuvers and changing times to power up the computer, for instance - just little detailed things, and I thought it worked very smoothly. I used to get a lot of those flight plan updates on my watch. It was kind of interesting; you could pencil those in and look at your next day's schedule and then kind of put it all together.

SLAYTON — Those are updated times, and the basic plan was nearly identical to the flight. There was one day that we had to put some ETO's in there.

SCHIRRA — The only thing that did disappoint me was that we discovered our phenomena, the perigee torquing problem, and I gave them 48 hours notice to do something about it - it's in the log - and they didn't pay any attention to it.

EISELE — We had a couple of days that were rescheduled; I think it was around the third or fourth day when we were getting pretty bushed. We took it easy for one day, and the effect was that we lost a day or part of a day of landmark tracking which they subsequently sandwiched in later in the flight. I thought it all worked out very well. We still got our six good passes for landmarks.

SCHIRRA — We had a lot of time to regroup because we had someone on watch all the time. That guy could go ahead a little bit - which is what we all did on our quiet watches - and block out the next day. That's where we discovered that we ought to do a 51 about a rev or two earlier then we had planned doing it.

EISELE — Yes, I could see...

SCHIRRA — ...which helped us, Donn. You can really get in trouble on retro. The day we came down, I'd say we had about 5 minutes gravy there; and if we hadn't really made up just right, we would have gone another rev. Donn had already set us up about a rev early.

EISELE — One thing that enabled you to do that was that you could tell from the hydrogen usage early in flight that it appeared we were not hurting for consumables. I didn't mind at all about powering up an hour or so early once in a while to get started.

SCHIRRA — There is something we discussed which we haven't really talked about yet, and it's appropriate to catch it now. There's no reason why you can't bring the computer up for about 4 or 5 minutes and get something out of it and put it back down again, and the other crews ought to hear that.

EISELE — We did that a lot.

SCHIRRA — I know we did later. At first, we were very reluctant to do it, if you remember. That's just a decimal of the whole period of time you are powered down. It doesn't eat into your consumables, and it's a very easy procedure to just bring it up, get the information you want out of it, and plop it back down.

EISELE — I got a map update a couple of times that way. On one of these long pamphlets where it wouldn't go over a station, I'd want to update my map. At that time, I called up the computer and let it integrate forward in P00; I then called up program 21 and got a fix out of it.

SCHIRRA — I'm glad you said that, by the way. That's the other one that's fairly late in the game. That was the funny looking thing that came up late; it was integrating forward in P00, and it took about 40 seconds per hour.

EISELE — No, about a minute per hour.

SCHIRRA — Yes, that's right, a minute per hour - 40 seconds per hour... 20 seconds per state vector, and the computer would integrate forward. If you shut it down when it was not in P00 and then brought all this data back up to speed again, it took 20 seconds per hour per state vector. If you went into P00 from a dead computer, it would take 40 seconds for every hour you shut off.

EISELE — Yes, for a full day, it would take you about 20 minutes to get state vectors up. In other words, the COMP light would go out, and you could use it for something. MIT came up with some Mickey Mouse procedure of VERB's and NOUN's so that you can somehow bypass that integration, and this would permit you to load in a state vector from the ground over the uplink. Rather than fool with that, we just decided that we would go ahead and call it up deliberately every few hours and let it integrate forward so that we were never more than 5 or 6 minutes from having a usable computer. I think, if any of the other flights do intend to power down for extensive periods that they ought to consider doing things like that.

10.5 Real Time
Scheduling

SCHIRRA — I'd say for the first day or so, unless they are really going to try to make a point out of it, let the flight plan live as it is unless it is a safety device. That kicked us off the wrong way. There is no way to judge how well that crew is falling into the mission. The one guy that can judge, I feel, is the crew commander. We are all trained to sound casual even though we are just about coming apart at the seams. That's the way a pilot is. He knows he has had it; that's the way we've disciplined ourselves. I think you're best prepared on board to determine how well you're able to pick up new ideas or changes. We've got to have people respect that. I may have goofed by resisting it. You just don't know. What are you going to do? All of a sudden, you realize you can cut it. You don't know that before you get there, but no one else does either. I don't think you can judge us from the ground on how well we're doing. We were pushing hard at first. About the fifth or sixth day - we talked about this earlier - we could take these changes and swing with them, but not in the beginning. We adjusted to the environment immediately. I think we all liked that. Do you fellows have anything to say on the subject?

EISELE — I never really felt uncomfortable about the real time schedule.

SCHIRRA — Then you weren't aware of the problems?

11.0 TRAINING

CUNNINGHAM — Under training is a whole new section.

11.1 CMS

One of the things I said right from the beginning was "Thank God we've got a CMS." But watch your step as we go down the stream because it has been around waiting for the crew to come back for a year. I don't know how you are doing, but I assume that...

EISELE — I understand next week they are coming up for 104 on our simulator.

SCHIRRA — Yes. Those guys are doing a great job. I would like to make it clear, once and for all, that it is never 100 percent. That's never ever. The EMS never worked. If we had to work with the EMS in the spacecraft, I would have had go to back to Houston and get my EMS training.

CUNNINGHAM — Here is a very important point. Of the tasks that occupied me during the flight on the right side, almost none of them were on the simulator.

SCHIRRA — Our COMM never worked as a COMM system. I told you that very late in the game. We blew some runs with Houston on COMM; we just couldn't talk. We blew that run we had with real test conductors and our pad leader. Then we couldn't talk. We tried to do a last minute insertion with them.

CUNNINGHAM — The CMS is not a 100 percent representation of the real spacecraft, but it is pretty darn close. I still think that an hour in the simulator is worth 10 hours of book learning and...

SCHIRRA — In contrast, simulator time is worth a hell of a lot more than spacecraft time - free flight.

CUNNINGHAM — Yes.

SCHIRRA — I would say that it's probably on the basis of about 1 hour in the simulator being worth about 10 in the spacecraft.

EISELE — That is if the simulator is working. Actually, we did have pretty good luck.

CUNNINGHAM — I would like to add another opinion to this. I realize I was running down a slightly different path than you guys were on these systems because the simulator has a heck of a lot more benefit for trajectory and flying type things than simulations. Towards the end, during the last several weeks, I wasn't getting in the simulator too much, but I was getting more out of reviewing things that were paper work.

SCHIRRA — You were reviewing test data, too. More data was coming in.

CUNNINGHAM — That's right. I was also looking at the malfunction procedures. I feel that I could operate the malfunction procedures, not just read it and then throw the switches. I feel very strongly about being able to be involved in the procedures development on those systems malfunctions.

SCHIRRA — I think what Walt is trying to say is that the simulator let him down on systems training. It was way up on G&N training, SCS training,...

CUNNINGHAM — Yes it was. It was way up. It was excellent for some of those things.

SCHIRRA — As it turned out, it was even to the point that he and Mr. Bonhouse over there were like the real one. That still bugs me.

REP — We had two big blocks of systems malfunctions that we never did get in that one. We are probably not even going to get them in for 103. Many of these are based on your recommendations. It just takes time to get them in.

CUNNINGHAM — I understand. I never expected them to get in for us. I was thinking about downstream when I recommended them.

SCHIRRA — Well, don't misunderstand. We are trying to say that we never say all the good things.

EISELE — I had a good time in it. Some of the best time I got out of the simulator showed when I was doing alignments.

SCHIRRA — Let's make that point. We have said this to everybody, but I don't know if we ever recorded it. Simulator optics, but for the shaky star ball, is exactly like the world.

CUNNINGHAM — Yes, it sure is.

EISELE — If you can get out of the black hole through that telescope and find your way around, you have it made. We might suggest a little extra practice around Acamar and Achernar.

CUNNINGHAM — Before we left the CMS, we should have mentioned the fact that all three of us benefited by our Block I CMS training. I felt like I was a lot farther up when we started than we were at the beginning.

SCHIRRA — I don't think you should lose sight of the fact that we had quite a lot of time on Block I. It didn't show on our total bookkeeping. We felt we were ready. I think everybody else knew we were.

CUNNINGHAM — Numbers don't mean a darn thing.

SCHIRRA — LM crews are going to be in the LM. Pete Conrad told me he had something like 250 hours in the LM and less than 100 in the CMS. That is the exact answer I was searching for. He doesn't care about the CMS as much. That's the way they go. We are seeing that. I told Donn that the rendezvous was your baby all through the braking. Donn worked the thing out and spent many hours with that device in Houston and many hours down here. He even ran that thing for the last week or so. We are trying to prove that it is a one-man job, which it is supposed to be.

EISELE — With Colossus, it almost is if you just use it that way. Don't do anything else.

CUNNINGHAM — Yes, don't do any backup.

SCHIRRA — That brings in the CMPS.

11.2 The DCPS

The DCPS was a damned good machine, and I don't think you have to log hours on machines like the DCPS. If you can get good high fidelity training, you only need I hour of it. I keep using the example of that big balloon that Harold Johnson made for my Mercury flight. Remember, we went over and looked at it? That was enough. DCPS is by no means that simple to learn. Marshall was pushing for this darn angle-of-attack case, the max Q abort with the two engine out abort. Mike Wash and Dick Warren said to send them up the sample problem we were talking about with the entry board. We did it, but they could not conjure one up. It turned out that those people were just blowing smoke. They were worried, and they finally got down to trying to create a set of equations that would duplicate the problem. They couldn't get it within realism, so all that academic discussion was washed away. Maybe you knew that. I think that is a real example of what a device like the DCPS can do as a lever to knock out this trivia.

11.3 CMPS

We used it for EMS training. We probably would have used it a lot more if we didn't have the CMS. It was used independently of crews to evaluate the EMS. That was one of the few simulators where I was taught how to do something. I was taught how to use the EMS on the CMPS.

EISELE — I would just like to make a general comment, I think the amount that you use simulators other than the CMS depends on how much time you have. If you are tight (like I think we are going to be from here on in), these Apollo mission crews aren't going to have time for what I would consider auxiliary trainers. You do need some DCPS time if you are riding the left seat on launch because that is the only way you can learn the launch procedures and really get them pinned down. The CMS is limited in that it doesn't have very many resets or IC's for these various conditions. The same thing is true on rendezvous. The big advantage of the CMPS for rendezvous training was that you could get a complete spectrum of conditions, and so forth to play and work with. You always do that in the CMS; it's not that flexible.

CUNNINGHAM — It is also a place I can go and work by myself on the backup charts.

EISELE — As far as I am concerned, the heart of the whole training is that Command Module Simulator and the LMS.

SCHIRRA — Here is a point we discovered toward the end. I benefited more from the CMS for launch abort cases after staging.

EISELE — Yes. I used the DCPS for everything up to and including staging. I wouldn't use the DCPS for mode 2, 3, or 4 aborts. That was done with Houston and with the three-man crew here in the CMS. I think that might help the guys that have to go roaring back to Houston for DCPS.

CUNNINGHAM — The LMP needs a very brief familiarization on the DCPS. I don't think I have 4 to 6 hours with you in the DCPS. Anything that I have to do on aborts is more associated with what the CMS can give you.

11.4 North American Evaluator

SCHIRRA — I wanted all our burns validated because at first we weren't getting sextant star validation. Back in Block I days, we had I week to go before we got our final burn validation. Finally, the CMS started coming in. We had the evaluator available to cover us for a long time. I think it is still appropriate that when you make a change in a program like Colossus that you check it on the evaluator that has three little interface problems; then you finally live with the CMS. I don't think you will disagree with that.

11.4 NR Evaluator

EISELE — I was going to make a remark about that evaluator, to the effect that it is a good thing to take part in if you happen to be at Downey, but I think that future Apollo flight crews they should not make a special effort to go out and take part in the North American evaluation. It is nice to know that they are doing it. I think that the evaluator should be kept up out there to validate computer changes and even procedural matters and hardware problems as they come up, but I don't think that as a training device, it would be as useful at this point in time as it was a couple of years ago when we were just starting out.

SCHIRRA — You reminded me of something while you were talking about that, Donn; it is very significant. I was in a conversation with Pete Conrad the other day, and he and someone had to pack up and go all the way out to San Francisco just to look at some models of the dome of the S-IVB. They were looking at our movies in here and said, "My gosh, why did we mess around with that? All they have is black and white television." They went out to San Francisco to see something when, in fact, that's the kind of stuff you want to call up at DTO. We tried to take pictures of the S-IVB in all different attitudes so the sun would hit, knowing that it was going to be a problem to pluck the LM out of there. That's the kind of stuff you want data on. When you get into that kind of simulation or angle simulation for lunar landings, we should hope to get something from the next mission. That's the way the DTO should go. If you can worry about lighting, let's go ahead and work for that. We intuitively knew that was a problem so we tried to get lighting all the way around. I think the way out simulation, if I can call it that: leave the crew that is assigned off that; let somebody else do it; see if it's worth it. We had a lot of time at the plant because we were watching the spacecraft come back together again. We went through change periods so we could look at this evaluator.

11.5 Egress Training

SCHIRRA — The Cape was running awfully scared when we first came down here, and we had an overkill on egress training such that we started off with rather bad relations with the Cape. On the chamber run, they had us booked up for about 2 hours of dry run egress training with the real spacecraft in the chamber; on top of that, they wanted to lay on about 12 hours of altitude chamber, and that was a big mistake. They have learned a lesson, and we have too. I guess in a way, it is fortunate that we got it over and done with because we all grew up again. You know, you don't cover your numbers by putting the crew through their paces, and that's what they were doing. I think we have that pretty well straightened out now. You have to see all the different motives. We did that, and I think we were well prepared for any mode of egress from that spacecraft. They resisted us on very few things. I think Rocko's crew really turned around backwards to get things in there. The launch complex down there was exactly the way we wanted it when we left. We had the chemical fire extinguishers up there that we wanted. Wiring that was in the way when we were up there; that was out of the way. The egress training we have down here in our training building was a real stroke of fortune; that helped us a lot. That was used.

EISELE — In general, I'd say that you could knock off the shirt-sleeve dry-run egress training exercises; they don't prove a thing.

SCHIRRA — Yes, the people down here didn't realize that we knew what the entry interior was like.

EISELE — That's a good point.

SCHIRRA — One point on which we differed from our backup crew was in worrying about our suits maintaining their condition, and that point hasn't come up yet. The suits, in fact, haven't even come up in the debriefing. There were a limited number of cycles on the zippers on the suits. At the very end, Donn's suit was facing a zipper change, and we left it the way it was. The leak rate was marginal. It hadn't gone yet, but I think the zipper was about ready to be changed out. We bit the bullet on that and went with it because we didn't have anything to do with the suit to speak of. If we had had a hard cabin, I'm sure Donn would have had a little bit bigger lump in his throat than he had.

EISELE — Yes, it was a leak slightly over spec or something, but it really wasn't a bad leak.

SCHIRRA — The reason that I bring this up is that you don't want to abuse your suit practicing egress, but you better do it with a prime or backup suit, not a training suit. We used our backup suits on the slideware and they are and were very different from the training suits by bulk and stiffness or whatever.

CUNNINGHAM — I'd like to add one thing on this egress training. You're talking about pad and water. We had been through the water training in the tank and in the Gulf or spacecraft 14 and in spacecraft 101, and I feel that as a direct result of that, there was absolutely no consternation or concern or anything when we ended up in stable II.

SCHIRRA — That's right. I think the world was worried about it, but we were not.

EISELE — In fact, it is surprising, and it's hard for anybody to believe, but there was no concern. It was just - well, I'll be damned; here we are again.

SCHIRRA — The only thing was getting sick.

EISELE — But even that was practiced; I got out my barf bag just like I always do, and everything was normal.

CUNNINGHAM — I guess the main point is that I want to put a pat on the back for those guys. There may be some mild shortcomings in some of that training, or maybe we neglected a couple of things because of earlier seasick episodes, but the training was just damned good.

SCHIRRA — I've got a real big point I'd like to bring up, and that's right; it was that good. One of the big flaws - and I brought this up to the doctor, I told Bill Karpendea about it, and they understand this and I think it's just going to have to be a requirement: any time you do water egress training in the Gulf in the future, schedule in a flight surgeon like Bill Karpendea (who was there when we got in the chopper after the mission) to go down with the crew to the retriever.

When the choppers come by to pick them up out of the water - the chopper comes by the retriever to pick up their clothes, and then it goes over to pick up the crew - the chopper should come by and pick up the flight surgeon, and he should be in there just like he's on recovery bay. They go and pick up the crew and the guy sees a whole evolution. The reason I said it is because we were really pooped in no time at all, and that's the same way we were after the mission: we were pooped. The only thing that kept us up was that we were exultant about the fact that the damn 10.8 days were over at last. That's what was the variable.

SLAYTON — What you're saying is that the guy that's going to be in the recovery forces should be in the egress training exercise.

SCHIRRA — They were told this; they may have done it. Karpendea agreed with me completely, and it was a nice feeling to see someone you knew in that chopper, but he can see how we look if he goes through that exercise.

CUNNINGHAM — Yes, he was saying that he stayed awake the whole night before figuring out how he would handle a broken arm or broken back. He was really prepared to leap in and take care of things.

SCHIRRA — He was all rigged up with a wet suit, Deke, probably for the first time in years, and all sorts of stuff. The guy is very devoted, a real nice boy. One of the first ones I've seen in a long time that was really in there pushing. He saw the shortcomings of not covering the egress training. I think you just have to schedule that thing out, that's all. They've got to be there. That's one of the things I want to talk over with Chuck and make him understand this problem.

11.6 Planetarium

SCHIRRA — Walt and Donn, I guess what you're saying is probably right. When you first come to bat, you're familiarized with the planetarium, but you don't train.

CUNNINGHAM — You have general training, not specific mission training.

EISELE — I would not waste my time going into planetarium; you'd get better results using the star ball and the simulator.

CUNNINGHAM — You might leave it because we do have access to Griffin Observatory, and if there is ever a quiet time and you're in Los Angeles, it's available. But I wouldn't try to schedule it in the training schedule.

SCHIRRA — I'd cut down the time on that planetarium on the training plan.

11.7 MIT

EISELE — I would say for assigned flight crews in general that MIT training is a waste of time and a dead loss. You get next to nothing out of going up there because their simulation is not that good. It doesn't run most of the time. If it does run, it's not very realistic. It's a part-task trainer, at best. Their training discipline, I found, was always lax and just not up to speed. They look upon it as a laboratory exercise, such as flying a bodacious rate command. I just don't think it's worthwhile going up there. There's nothing unique about their hybrid. It's nice to know that they do or can verify certain programs or procedures on it, but as far as the flying crewmen having to go up there and actually taking part in that...

SLAYTON — That falls in exactly the same category as the MU trainer at North American. They have the tool for validating programs.

EISELE — After the first course, you don't need a week at MIT is what we're saying.

SLAYTON — How about the navigator and just the briefings up there?

CUNNINGHAM — He's mentioning specifically the hardware, and I personally felt that I had about 2 days worth of benefit to be gained during our training schedule from the briefings up there.

SCHIRRA — Whereas 6 days were invested.

CUNNINGHAM — There are some things I did get from listening to them, and I think we made a lot of criticism up there aimed at cutting it down.

EISELE — I think the briefings are worthwhile, but you don't need a whole week of it. There's something unique about going up there where all the people are who actually did the coding and did the detailed writing out of all that program; you can listen to them, and you can ask questions. You don't get that anywhere else, but it doesn't take a whole week of that.

SLAYTON — Couldn't you back off and do just as well if you had somebody like Frank Hughes spoon-feed you on the CMS?

CUNNINGHAM — Frank Hughes is a good simulator man, but frankly I think Donn and Frank saved time by sitting and listening to MIT as they did in that Donn is removing one layer of filtering out of the system. Personally I felt good that Donn got up there and talked to them himself instead of getting it all from a simulator.

SCHIRRA — Then again, that was developing. We were developing the program in a sense.

EISELE — I would say 2 or 3 days at the most are all you need at MIT for an assigned flight crew. Go up there, get that time block done, learn the details, and ask the questions. From then on, you don't have to go up there anymore. If you have any questions, you call them on the phone or have one of your support team call them.

SCHIRRA — What I'm trying to point out here to Walt and Donn is that we can face that. I think in part I can provide some help in some areas. For instance, what can we cut out of this thing that isn't worth devoting a lot of time to, since we're trying to abbreviate some of this.

CUNNINGHAM — I would say take the week at MIT and cut it in half; take only briefings, and don't bother with the simulators. I'll tell you one thing that you certainly don't need if it's not already cut out from the MIT briefings, and that is a briefing on the non-flight ropes, particularly the ones that are used for checking out the spacecraft. Our crew managed successfully to get around this every time we've been there, but they usually wanted a day or a day and a half to talk about the test ropes. However, we're just working in OCP, and I don't think it was necessary.

SCHIRRA — I think the point is that when you finally get to flight ropes, then you can start playing hard nose about seeing things that you expect to see. Until then, just assume the test engineers know more than you do about it. If you see anomalies, ask a question and put it in the hole. If they explain it as a flight rope thing, then say "okay" and keep your ghost book going; that's the thing to do. We had ghosts and they were coming up all the time. That's a good point.

SCHIRRA — Donn, do you think it is required (and I know what your answer is going to be) to go out to the desert to look through a sextant?

EISELE — No.

SCHIRRA — Or go up on the roof to look through the sextant, or should you just do it with the CMS?

EISELE — No, I'd do it in the CMS. The one thing you can do on the roof at MIT is put a star on a lunar landmark. Having done it on the roof and having done it in orbit, I can say that it's a very simple task, and there is no need to go up there and do it.

11.8 System Briefing   CUNNINGHAM — Systems briefing, I already covered that on that. Launch vehicle, S-IVB, S-II are going to be coming up. The review at Huntsville that I think is now worthwhile going to is the one day-long review. I knew more about certain things than a lot of people in that room did, for example, the lunar landing.

EISELE — That was the one subject that all three of us went for one day.

SCHIRRA — Yes, we covered it the whole day. That is the one briefing in which the crew should devote a day and leave them clear; that is all they should need.

SLAYTON — What about the spacecraft DCR? Would you say the same thing about that?

SCHIRRA — We're better prepared than anybody else down here to hit the spacecraft. I don't think it necessary that we should go to Downey for these big NASA reviews.

EISELE — Again, it's a question of priority and how much time you have.

CUNNINGHAM — That's right.

EISELE — I would say the DCR, particularly the ones at Downey, are probably pretty far down on the priority list.

SCHIRRA — Yes, you should know what your spacecraft is like by that time.

CUNNINGHAM — You've got to keep in mind that the crews coming along are not going to know it like we did, or how the spacecraft is at that time. I'm saying that my feeling would hold only if you felt very seriously on certain specific items.

SCHIRRA — I hope that isn't true, Walt; I hope that somewhere in their team someone does know; like Al Worden knows how that command module is going for that crew, and Fred Haise knew how a LM was doing because he lived with it. So the crew that's assigned to it individually, that's going to fly it may not, but they had representation. Those are the guys that go to the DCR's.

CUNNINGHAM — I agree on that.

SCHIRRA — That's what I'm trying to get at. I'm not saying to ignore the DCR's. I think one thing we can say on the spacecraft systems briefing is that the North American systems briefings were the best we can get. They're getting updated. I'm not sure how good they are now, but they were being left out of the loop as time went on. I suspect North American cut back in that area. They were always tempted to cut back in those auxiliary efforts because they're cutting back. The same point: the simulator kids are coming along pretty well. In Houston, particularly, they didn't come on too well here. There may be a way of looking at something we don't know enough about to discuss, but I'm predicting that North American's systems briefing experts are going to start being cut off the vine.

CUNNINGHAM — Well, there a shortage in both ends there. I feel as if they complement each other. The North American systems people know nit picking engineering details, but a lot of them also feed a company line, I think. On the other hand, I feel like the simulator people can tie in the operations, but they often don't know all the details. I guess I'm not that strong a fan of getting all my briefings from the simulator people at all.

SCHIRRA — No, but I'm saying the world has changed rapidly since we've flown.

CUNNINGHAM — I find I have to answer simulator people's questions more often than they answer my questions on systems.

SCHIRRA — Yes, we've go to move ahead. I do believe that North American's personnel are going to be cut back.

CUNNINGHAM — Well, they probably will.

SLAYTON — We always get whatever we need from them.

EISELE — The point is do you need a healthy major of systems briefings, particularly if this is your first go at a command module? Crews recycle; or whatever happens, maybe you can cut back on some of those. But I found that our sessions briefings were invaluable. We learned a tremendous amount during those periods. The subject is people that consult for special areas, and I'd like to register the fact that Bob Shane who works on the North American evaluator is probably the best one-man source of G&N information that you'll find any place because he either knows the answer right off, of if he doesn't, he can find it within an hour or so by digging through his data. I would just like to register that if any crews have any questions as long as Bob is out there in that capacity - now, of course, unless he gets transferred...

CUNNINGHAM — Part of the problem is that when people move up, they're not in that capacity any more.

EISELE — I'm sort of handing him a bouquet of roses.

CUNNINGHAM — He gets promoted out of there.

SCHIRRA — Interestingly enough, though, I notice what he's saying. He's not talking about anybody here with simulators or anybody in Houston or anybody at MIT; here's a guy with North American who has nothing to do with the damn thing like putting it in the spacecraft.

CUNNINGHAM — Yes, and I'd say the same thing on the systems. There are a couple of systems here like fuel cells ECS, DPS that when I really wanted information, I called North American or our FOD guys.

11.9 Experiments

SCHIRRA — We had a lot of time for a limited number of experiments. We did talk S005 and S006, that target of opportunity. It's always going to be, and I don't think we need to devote all that time to it. Initially, I asked for one man to come down here with a capsule digest, and a whole batch of people came down. It was nice to socialize, and we discussed all that stuff. But it ate us up; it took too much time. Clouds are clouds, and we know what they are.

CUNNINGHAM — Training equipment not really very applicable; we all have Hasselblads and shot them with 16mm film. I will say I did get something out of shooting the pictures that I did. I got a lot out of shooting the pictures I did.

SCHIRRA — I think, Deke, that the way to get guys to play with these Hasselblads in training is the real point. They are cutting back on budgets. You've got to give the guy the fun of realizing that he's going to get a picture back from it. Then he'll play with it some more.

CUNNINGHAM — I don't know how you're going to feed that because I tried religiously for a long time to take at least a roll a week on the weekends, and there was nothing slightly akin to the feeling I felt after I took the pictures in flight.

SCHIRRA — No, but your attention is brought to the camera if you can shoot a picture and expect to get it back, if it's your kids or your new car or a broken pipe in the house. You anticipate seeing that picture come back. And that's the reward for playing with the camera.

CUNNINGHAM — Incidentally, Dick Thompson down there did a nice job, I felt, on looking at each slide and critiquing each exposure, and I got something out of it. All you really have to do is keep that loop tight so that they get a priority; they get developed, and they get the feedback right away before you've taken a couple of other rolls of pictures and lose sight of it. What we really ought to push is everybody should be taking pictures with their light meter, as far as I'm concerned.

SCHIRRA — What we should push is to get more light in the CMS. We know what the numbers were in flight now. The lowest we got were sixes and sevens in that spot meter. Get that light level in the CMS and shoot some IVA movie in there, if we need to. Even that's not a requirement anymore.

CUNNINGHAM — On the movie camera, be familiar with the controls and be able to get it out. I'm hoping that the controls from the new camera - the new 16mm camera - are better than the ones that I had. I think, and I haven't logged this any place else, but when that camera was mounted in the window, I couldn't really see the index for the f stops, and I scratched another arbitrary index halfway around it and scratched some more marks around the lens for the f stops. I would hope that the new camera has that in clear position to see when it's mounted.

SCHIRRA — Okay. Let's make a capsule digest for future flights. The movie camera is only usable for photographing another object nearby. I don't think I would waste my time taking movies of the moon.

CUNNINGHAM — I agree with you, with your conclusion. It's just not that good a piece of equipment.

SCHIRRA — You really need a bigger lens, and you can't afford to have that 35mm movie camera.

**11.10 Spacecraft
Systems test**

SCHIRRA — On the spacecraft systems tests: at Downey, the philosophy was very good. They were a little worried about this; they had dry runs. They wanted the spacecraft to look good before we played with it. We had good support from the ATO research pilots. When we got to the Cape, they were not prepared to test the spacecraft well. They had a long, long arduous learning period, and they goofed many times. The reason for this is that they were completely and totally dependent upon the OCP because they never rehearsed. They sat down and worked paper, and that's what the Cape's problem is. They work paper; they don't work equipment. As a result, if the equipment doesn't follow the paper, they are completely bogged down. I think that's the difference between Downey and the Cape.

CUNNINGHAM — We did learn something here, too, as we tended to back off in participation in the OCP from what we had at one time thought we wanted to. I'm talking about prime crew or backup crew participation. I think that's very appropriate. The support crew did take part in some other tests which is appropriate also, but I think there is a tendency on the support crew to want to get the inside time, and there may be more emphasis than is necessary even on their part in some of those tests. But when the crew starts pulling out on some of those tests, we've got to have enough support from guys like the ATO pilots out at North American.

SCHIRRA — We've got it.

CUNNINGHAM — I think they're spread kind of thin right now. For instance, when they came down here, they had two people to cover 24-hour shifts.

SCHIRRA — Yes, but we've had only two people down here for some of these combined systems test.

EISELE — I don't know that you need that much coverage.

CUNNINGHAM — I guess I'm saying that when we're not there I like to have those guys with their nose on those critical tests.

SCHIRRA — I think the world has learned more about what to look for. You have to do that the first time around, but you don't need - in airplane words, you can use crew chiefs; you don't need a pilot in there to test the aircraft every time you test it because you know more about the aircraft. I think we know more about the command module now, and we can back off...

CUNNINGHAM — I agree. But the guy observing the test out there - you can have a critical anomaly not be noticed from the fact that you've got a COMM TECH sitting there instead of a better qualified person.

SCHIRRA — You're thinking back; I'm trying to think ahead. That's the difference. You're right. In those days, you had to have somebody.

CUNNINGHAM — An anomaly can come up and be discovered earlier by a more informed person. While I think the crews should be pulling out from some of those, I don't think we ought to change the intent of that memo that the ATO pilots still participate. I'm not asking them to go participate in more tests.

EISELE — True; I agree. I think we can keep essentially the same ground rules that you have right now, and maybe make a little more use of the ATO's.

SCHIRRA — The real point that I'm trying to get across is that the Cape has got to practice these OCP's more because they're changing all along. New equipment is coming down there, and we're moving faster. We had one session which paid off, and Skip thanked me for it. Skip went down to the simulator with us one day, and they got on the panel; and we went through another ingress together, and Skip said it really helped.

CUNNINGHAM — Prelaunch count, and we actually found things...

SCHIRRA — That was not a scheduled exercise. That was one we just copied. Both at Downey and the Cape too many components were running inordinately long during testing periods. Fans, cabin fans, suit fans, integral lighting, floodlighting, inverters, IMU, moving components that were just plain way out in the curb.

CUNNINGHAM — Inverters - I don't know, lots and lots of hours on inverters. If you ended up holding and going to a trouble shooting routine, they were always on for long periods of paper work and x number of hours for troubleshooting.

SCHIRRA — I made this plea at the FRR, and I just ask again that it be followed up; that somebody learn how to power down when there's a discussion going on, and we could power the spacecraft down. We had the drifting flight; we were powered down in about 2 minutes. We didn't have to route OCP for that. We followed the normal checklist, but it was a rapid power down. We were conserving the very same things we were talking about. That's how we stretched the flight. That's what Dave has to learn how to do. Trust the fact that the damn test connectors know how to power down, and we'll put the BMAGs in warm up; even that will

11.11 Launch
Simulations

help. Get the ID off the line, keep the heaters on, and this kind of stuff, and I think we can end up with even more highly reliable spacecraft than we have, which is very reliable.

11.12 Reentry
Simulations

11.13 Sim Net Sim

SCHIRRA — Launch SIMs, reentry SIMs, and Sim Net SIMs were all discussed very thoroughly, and they're the best part of the whole training program. That's when the CMS does become a mission simulator by name. Up until then, it's a part task trainer. I've said that for years, and if you recall, I came to you, Deke; I was a little worried about 180 hours, and I think we as a crew probably got a good 100 hours out of that.

SLAYTON — Excellent. You got more than that.

SCHIRRA — Yes, and it's the best thing that ever happened. That was really good.

SLAYTON — No doubt about it. I think my feeling about this is that you essentially have to be fully trained when you get to here.

SCHIRRA — You have to be, or you can't move with it. That's right. But then you really integrate. That's what I was trying to say in answer to your and Riley's suggestion that the three of us get together. That's when the three of us got together.

SLAYTON — Yes.

SCHIRRA — I think you're going to find that it's even more appropriate, because your two LM guys are going to be off in the LMS and your CMS guys are going to be in the CMS. You're going to be forced together on these simulations, and that's the time to bring them together. That's fine.

11.14 Mockups

SCHIRRA — I think we finally talked North American into what a mockup is for, and we learned a lot from it. We solved lots of problems with that mockup down here, and we saw lots of problems that North American made. You also have to have a full scale high fidelity mockup. When you make a change, you've got to see it from three dimensions. I guess the best example of that is that the GSE hatch counterbalance did not fit the real spacecraft. If they had done that properly in mockup, we would have discovered it there. As it was, we threw it away; that whole piece of hardware was thrown away because it wouldn't work.

EISELE — Yes, I think as far as training value rather than put a fixed number of hours - you could do that for planning, but mockup is something that you like to have available as things come up that you need to ring out or check in there. Just like we found out: we rehearsed in great detail our suiting and unstowing routine, and then at the other end of the flight the stowing and suiting up again for entry.

SCHIRRA — I don't know if you realize it but when we're in real time - in the simulator over here, both the mockup and the CMS, you can go through your time line to where we had things stowed, the gloves, the helmets, the suits, all of that. That helped us a lot; there were no surprises on that. The one thing I do recall when we gave up that mockup here because of the urgency, was that a lot of new things came down here all of a sudden that we needed to mockup, and we didn't have any place to do it but the real spacecraft. That's kind of awkward to go all the way down there to get your badges, put your little white suit on, climb up there, slip in there, and get inside each time. We did, but the mockup would have been the thing to solve it for us. The mockup followed behind us right at the end, way behind. I'm talking about the hatch, urine dump, waste water management change, the foot pan change that implemented unfortunately right in the command module because we have a high fidelity couch in there in the CMS. The mockups were falling way behind us toward the end there.

11.16 Sextant training equipment

SCHIRRA — One thing I would like to get on record here: I understand that you are finally going to do it; they are going to have a camera on the sextant.

CUNNINGHAM — Great.

SCHIRRA — Remember I asked for that up at MIT 3 years ago? Last year, they finally moved out and got one. We were really crying up there for something like that.

11.17 Planning of Training

CUNNINGHAM — I'd like to make a negative comment on planning and training. A lot of effort was put into trying to get us to go use the water tank for example for IVA.

SCHIRRA — It was turned off?

CUNNINGHAM — Yes, and I think appropriately so. I just think for the future crews coming on, they should have no concern at all about IVA.

SCHIRRA — What we're getting at - we have zero g airplanes? Forget it.

CUNNINGHAM — Right.

EISELE — Right.

SCHIRRA — Water tank, forget it. If somebody from the old EVA club thinks that water tanks are great, have him go play water tanks for EVA, but don't waste your time on IVA. We're here to say that IVA is no problem at all. We gave it every effort we could.

EISELE — There is no requirement for zero g aircraft or underwater training for IVA. I would say that includes going from the command module into the LM. It is going to be so easy in a shirt sleeve or suitcase if you have a reasonable cabin. It is a waste of time.

CUNNINGHAM — Absolutely correct.

EISELE — I don't understand what the problems are with EVA.

SCHIRRA — The suit, the suit is the basic problem.

CUNNINGHAM — That's a problem.

EISELE — If you have enough handholds, I think you should be in good shape for it. Incidentally, handholds do not have to be battleship type handholds.

SCHIRRA — That's right.

EISELE — You mentioned about going from the command module, to the LM. I know they are going to comment on the fact that you have to clear the docking tunnel. I don't think that's going to be a problem, either.

SCHIRRA — It can't be any worse than our putting a lid on that lithium hydroxide stowage box where I practically pushed the couch through the overhead.

EISELE — You are going to be able to do it just fine as long as you have a handle so you can apply the torque to unlock it, and as long as it will meet all the interfaces for stowage or what you're going to do with it when you remove it. I guess I'm saying that I don't think you need any zero g training on that either.

SCHIRRA — What we're saying is that all IVA is so easy that there's no sense doing underwater or zero g training.

SLAYTON — We have a lot of EVA.

SCHIRRA — EVA: That's where your bucking the suit. That's the only variable, and shouldn't be hard if you can get around. You don't need battleship hand holds. This idea of picking up 400 pounds or something like that: you don't have that load on you, suit or no suit. The whole thing is that you move slowly. All I can say is that the film didn't work out as well as we expected on this canister change. I had two canisters being held by me, two... held by me, two spacers held by me, and this grounding cord all at once, and I was still maintaining my position. That's a lot of things to hold on to. It didn't bother me one bit.

CUNNINGHAM — Even going into the LM from the command module should be no problem. As long as you can unfasten the tunnel, you can do it fine without water training.

SLAYTON — There are some things that you do want to train on.

CUNNINGHAM — We discussed this in flight, and we figured it would be hard to convince people how easy it is.

EISELE — I just wanted to mention that the first attempt at landmark tracking didn't work out too well, partly because there was no way to train for it adequately before the flight. There were some pieces of data that I thought I didn't need and found out that I did: mainly, how far north or south of track the target was; and also, the fact that I could run the trunnion angle out manually to around 35 degrees rather than wait for the computer drive to run it out there and the target came into view.

Once we got the procedural wrinkles ironed out and found that we did want to know how far north or south the target was, the next time we tried landmark tracking everything worked out fine. I think we got a whole series of good landmarks. Some of them turned out to be occluded by clouds, and when that happened, we went ahead and did unknown landmarks on a cloud bank or something. In fact, it was very curious that for the first set of good landmarks we did, the DELTA-R/ DELTA-V updates were zero, and yet the computer would always turn around and update the target. I thought this was kind of presumptuous of it, to think that the target must have moved from what the map coordinates were. I think that was a function of the W matrix they put in. The second day we did landmarks, we did get some DELTA-R/DELTA-V updates, small ones. I guess the main point is that it is a fairly simple and straightforward task to do. At least for earth landmarks, recognizing the target wasn't any problem at all.

CUNNINGHAM — I might add that it was essentially what you would call no training at all. I hadn't really been able to do any tracking at the simulator. After Donn had worked out the procedure the first day, I was able to track landmarks with no problem.

EISELE — Yes.

S68-49744

The NASA Mission Reports

The NASA Mission Report books come with a bonus Windows CDROM featuring related movies and pictures. Forthcoming books in the NASA Mission Reports Series:-

Apollo 8 - 1-896522-66-1 10" x 7" 232 pg (8 color) $16.95 AVAILABLE NOW!
Apollo 9 - 1-896522-51-3 10" x 7" 240 pg (8 color) $14.95 AVAILABLE NOW!
Friendship 7 - 1-896522-60-2 10" x 7" 216 pg (8 color) $14.95 AVAILABLE NOW!
Apollo 10 - 1-896522-52-1 10" x 7" 184 pg (8 color) $14.95 AVAILABLE NOW!
Apollo 11 Volume 1 - 1-896522-53-X 10" x 7" 248 pg (8 color) $16.95 AVAILABLE NOW!
Apollo 11 Volume 2 - 1-896522-49-1 10" x 7" 168 pg (8 color) $13.95 AVAILABLE NOW!
Apollo 12 - 1-896522-54-8 10" x 7" 248 pg (8 color) $16.95 AVAILABLE NOW!
Gemini 6 - 1-896522-61-0 10" x 7" 200 pg (8 color) $16.95 AVAILABLE NOW!
Apollo 13 1-896522-55-6 10" x 7" 256 pg (8 color) $16.95 AVAILABLE NOW!
Mars 1-896522-62-9 10" x 7" 424 pg (16 color) $21.95 AVAILABLE NOW!
Apollo 7 October 2000 1-896522-64-5 10" x 7" 272 pg (8 color) $16.95 AVAILABLE NOW!
X-15 December 2000 1-896522-65-3 10" x 7" TBA (w. color) (approx $16.95)
Apollo 14 February 2001 1-896522-56-4 10" x 7" TBA (w. color) (approx $16.95)
Apollo 15 June 2001 1-896522-57-2 10" x 7" TBA (w. color) (approx $16.95)

The series will continue on through Gemini, Mercury, Skylab, STS and unmanned missions. All prices are in US dollars

Available from Apogee Books, Box 62034, Burlington, Ontario, L7R 4K2, Canada.
http://www.cgpublishing.com

Also available on-line at all good booksellers.

"A unique reference providing details available heretofore only to researchers with access to the archives." . . .
Library Journal - Feb '99

"(the series) will serve as an invaluable reference tool for aficionados of human spaceflight." . . .
Astronomy - Jul '99

"The package is guaranteed to put space enthusiasts into orbit." . .
Today's Librarian - Jul '99

". . budding Tsiolkovskys, Goddards, and von Brauns will devour each title." . . .
Booklist - Jul '99

"Highly recommended for space buffs who want detailed information on these flights." . . . **Choice - Nov '99**

"This series is highly recommended . . . A bargain at twice the price!" . . .
Ad Astra - National Space Society - Jan '00

". . . the most ambitious look at our space program to date." . . .
Playboy - Mar '00

Apogee Books - An Imprint of Collector's Guide Publishing Inc.
C. G. Publishing Inc - 2289 Fairview Street, Suite # 318, Burlington, Ontario, L7R 2E3, Canada
Phone: 905 637 5737, Fax: 905 637 2631, e-mail: apogee@cgpublishing.com
http://www.cgpublishing.com

Mars
The NASA Mission Reports
ISBN 1-896522-62-9
424 pgs + 16 pgs of colour + CD-ROM
$21.95 USA, $29.95 CDN, £15.95 UK

Apollo 9
The NASA Mission Reports
ISBN 1-896522-51-3
232 pgs + 8 pgs of colour +CD-ROM
$14.95 USA, $20.95 CDN, £9.95 UK

Friendship 7
The NASA Mission Reports
ISBN 1-896522-60-2
208 pgs + 8 pgs of colour + CD-ROM
$14.95 USA, $20.95 CDN, £9.95 UK

Apollo 10
The NASA Mission Reports
ISBN 1-896522-52-1
176 pgs + 8 pgs of colour + CD-ROM
$14.95 USA, $20.95 CDN, £9.95 UK

Apollo 11
The NASA Mission Reports Vol. One
ISBN 1-896522-53-X
248 pgs + 8 pgs of colour + CD-ROM
$16.95 USA, $23.95 CDN, £13.95 UK

Apollo 11
The NASA Mission Reports Vol. Two
ISBN 1-896522-49-1
168 pgs + CD-ROM
$13.95 USA, $18.95 CDN, £10.95 UK

Apollo 12
The NASA Mission Reports
ISBN 1-896522-54-8
248 pgs + 8 pgs of colour + CD-ROM
$16.95 USA, $23.95 CDN, £13.95 UK

Gemini 6
The NASA Mission Reports
ISBN 1-896522-61-0
200 pgs + 8 pgs of colour + CD-ROM
$16.95 USA, $23.95 CDN, £13.95 UK

Apollo 13
The NASA Mission Reports
ISBN 1-896522-55-6
192 pgs + 8 pgs of colour + CD-ROM
$16.95 USA, $23.95 CDN, £13.95 UK

Apogee Books - An Imprint of Collector's Guide Publishing Inc.
C. G. Publishing Inc - 2289 Fairview Street, Suite # 318, Burlington, Ontario, L7R 2E3, Canada
Phone: 905 637 5737, Fax: 905 637 2631, e-mail: apogee@cgpublishing.com
http://www.cgpublishing.com

Apollo 7
The NASA Mission Reports
ISBN 1-896522-64-5
272 pgs + 8 pgs of colour + CD-ROM
$16.95 USA, $21.95 CDN, £13.95 UK

X-15
The NASA Mission Reports
ISBN 1-896522-65-3
with CD-ROM
Price TBA

Apollo 14
The NASA Mission Reports
ISBN 1-896522-56-4
with CD-ROM
Price TBA

CD-ROM

The accompanying CD-ROM is designed to use your World Wide Web browser to be viewed. It is programmed to not leave any footprint on your computer (i.e. no drivers, no installation, no updating your Windows registry etc.)

On inserting the disc in your CD-ROM drive you may be prompted to locate the file "Autorun.exe". This file is located in the root directory of your CD-ROM drive. (i.e. it is usually drive "D" but may be "E", "F" etc.) Most computers will find the Autorun program unassisted.

Autorun will open your default Web browser and you can then navigate the contents of the disc just like any web page.

Included on the disc are hundreds of images as well as hours of video. All of the video is in MPEG1 format and should automatically launch your default media player software (such as Windows Media Player).